FOUNDATIONS OF WIRELESS

M. G. SCROGGIE
B.Sc., M.I.E.E.

With 236 illustrations

Fifth Edition
(Entirely rewritten)

Published for

"WIRELESS WORLD"

by

ILIFFE & SONS, LTD : LONDON

First Edition (*by A. L. M. Sowerby, M.Sc.*) 1936
Second Edition 1938
    Second Impression March, 1940
    Third Impression June, 1940
    Fourth Impression (*Revised*) January, 1941
    Fifth Impression June, 1941
Third Edition (*Revised and enlarged by M. G. Scroggie, B.Sc., M.I.E.E.*)
    November, 1941
    Second Impression March, 1942
    Third Impression May, 1942
    Fourth Impression November, 1942
    Fifth Impression 1943
Fourth Edition February, 1944
    Second Impression July, 1944
    Third Impression (*Revised*) June, 1945
    Fourth Impression November, 1945
    Fifth Impression 1946
    Sixth Impression 1948
    Seventh Impression 1949
Fifth Edition (*Entirely rewritten*) 1951

Published for " *Wireless World* " by Iliffe & Sons,
Ltd., Dorset House, Stamford Street, London, S.E.1

Made and printed in Great Britain at The Chapel
River Press, Andover, Hants
(*Bks.* 917)

Contents

Page

PREFACE   9

INITIATION: INTO THE SHORTHAND OF WIRELESS

Algebraic Symbols. What Letter Symbols Really Mean. Some Other Uses of Symbols. Abbreviations. How Numbers are Used. *Graphs.* Scales. What a "Curve" Signifies. Three-Dimensional Graphs. Significance of Slope. Non-Uniform Scales. *Circuit Diagrams.* Alternative Methods. The Importance of Layout. Where Circuit Diagrams can Mislead   11

CHAPTER

1   A GENERAL VIEW

What Wireless Does. The Nature of Sound Waves. Characteristics of Sound Waves. Frequency. Wavelength. The Sender. The Receiver. Electrical Communication by Wire. Electric Waves. Why High Frequencies are Necessary. Wireless Telegraphy. Tuning. Wireless Telephony. Recapitulation   23

2   ELEMENTARY ELECTRICAL NOTIONS

Electrons. Electric Charges and Currents. Conductors and Insulators. Electromotive Force. Electrical Units. Ohm's Law. Larger and Smaller Units. Circuit Diagrams. Resistances in Series and in Parallel. Series-Parallel Combinations. Resistance Analysed. Conductance. Kirchhoff's Laws. P.D. and E.M.F. Electrical Effects. Instruments for Measuring Electricity. Electrical Power. A Broader View of Resistance   36

3   CAPACITANCE

Charging Currents. Capacitance—What It Is. Capacitance Analysed. Capacitors. Charge and Discharge of a Capacitor. Where the Power Goes   56

4   INDUCTANCE

Magnets and Electromagnets. Interacting Magnetic Fields. Induction. Self-Inductance. Inductance Analysed. Growth of Current in Inductive Circuit. Power During Growth. Mutual Inductance   65

5   ALTERNATING CURRENTS

Frequencies of Alternating Current. The Sine Wave. Circuit with Resistance Only. R.M.S. Values. A.C. Meters. Phase. Vector Diagrams. Adding Alternating Voltages   75

6   CAPACITANCE IN A.C. CIRCUITS

Current Flow in a Capacitive Circuit. Capacitive Current Waveform. The "Ohm's Law" for Capacitance. Capacitances in Parallel and in Series. Power in Capacitive Circuit. Capacitance and Resistance in Series. Impedance. Capacitance and Resistance in Parallel   84

CONTENTS

7 INDUCTANCE IN A.C. CIRCUITS   *Page*

Current Flow in an Inductive Circuit. Inductive Current Waveform. The " Ohm's Law " for Inductance. Inductances in Series and in Parallel. Power in Inductive Circuit. Inductance and Resistance in Series. Inductance and Resistance in Parallel. Transformers. The Primary Load Current. Transformer Losses. Impedance Transformation   93

8 THE TUNED CIRCUIT

Inductance and Capacitance in Series. L, C and R all in Series. The Series Tuned Circuit. Magnification. Resonance Curves. Selectivity. Frequency of Resonance. L and C in Parallel. The Effect of Resistance. Dynamic Resistance. Parallel Resonance. The Frequency of Parallel Resonance. Series and Parallel Resonance Compared. The Resistance of the Coil. Dielectric Losses. R.F. Resistance   101

9 VALVES: THE SIMPLER TYPES

Liberated Electrons. The Diode Valve. Anode A.C. Resistance. The Triode Valve. Amplification Factor. Mutual Conductance. Alternating Voltage at the Grid. The Load Line. Voltage Amplification. The " Valve Equivalent Generator." Calculating Amplification. The Effect of Load on Amplification. The Maximum-Power Law. Power in the Grid Circuit. Seven Important Points   117

10 OSCILLATION

Generating an Alternating Current. The Oscillatory Circuit. Frequency of Oscillation. Damping. The Valve-Maintained Oscillator. Valve Oscillator Circuits. Amplitude of Oscillation. Distortion of Oscillation. Stability of Frequency   131

11 THE SENDER

Essentials of a Sender. The R.F. Generator. High-Efficiency Oscillators: " Class B ". " Class C ". Constant Frequency. The Master-Oscillator Power-Amplifier System. Crystal Control. Telegraph Senders: Keying. Radio-telephony and Broadcasting: Modulation. Depth of Modulation. Methods of Modulation. Frequency Modulation. Microphones. Coupling to Aerial   141

12 RADIATION AND AERIALS

Bridging Space: Radiation. Electromagnetic Waves. The Inductor Radiator. The Capacitor Radiator. The Dipole. Aerial and Earth. Aerial Coupling and Tuning. Choice of Frequency. Influence of the Atmosphere. Beams and Reflectors. Radiation Resistance. Effective Height   155

13 DETECTION

The Need for Detection. The Detector. Rectifiers. Linearity of Rectification. The Diode Rectifier. Action of Reservoir Capacitor. Choice of Component Values. The Diode Detector in Action. Varieties of Diode Detector Circuit. The Grid Detector. Filters. A Typical Detector Circuit. Detector Characteristics. Detector Distortion. The Anode-Bend Detector   169

CONTENTS

14 THE SINGLE-VALVE RECEIVER: REACTION   *Page*

The Circuit. The Aerial Coupling. Effects of Primary Turns. Tuning Range. Miller Effect. The Anode By-Pass. Reaction. Over-Sharp Tuning. The Theory of Sidebands   188

15 RADIO-FREQUENCY AMPLIFICATION: SCREENED VALVES

Increasing Range. Simple Resistance Coupling. The Tuned-Anode Circuit. Grid-Anode Capacitance. Instability. The Theory of Screening. The Screened Valve. Characteristics of a Screened Valve. Secondary Emission. The Screened Pentode. Kinkless Tetrodes. Amplification Using Screened Valves. External Screening. Two Stages. Control of Gain and Volume. Distortion in the R.F. Amplifier. Cross-Modulation. Variable-Mu Valves. Automatic Gain Control   201

16 SELECTIVITY

Selectivity Comparison. Channel Separation. Selectivity Factor. The Generalized Resonance Curve. More Than One Tuned Circuit. Comparison on Equal-Gain Basis. Equal Selectivity. Equal Quality. Practical Coil Figures. Selectivity and Gain. Conclusions   220

17 THE SUPERHETERODYNE RECEIVER

A Difficult Problem Solved. Theory of the Frequency Changer. Types of Frequency Changer. Frequency-Changer Valves. Conversion Conductance. Ganging the Oscillator. Whistles. The Preselector. The Task of the I.F. Amplifier. Critically-Coupled Tuning Circuits. Effects of Varying the Coupling. A Typical I.F. Amplifier   230

18 AUDIO-FREQUENCY CIRCUITS

The Purpose of A.F. Stages. Distortion. Frequency Characteristics and Decibels. Effects of Frequency Distortion. Non-Linearity Distortion. Generation of Harmonics. Intermodulation. Allowable Limits of Non-Linearity. Phase Distortion. Distortion in Resistance-Coupled Amplifiers. Transformer Coupling. The Output Stage. Optimum Load Resistance. The Output Pentode. Harmonic Distortion in the Pentode. Negative Feedback. The Cathode Follower. Valves in Parallel and in Push-Pull. Phase Splitters. The Loudspeaker   248

19 POWER SUPPLIES

The Power Required. Batteries. Cathode Heating. Anode Current from A.C. Mains. Types of Rectifier. Rectifier Circuits. Filters. Decouplers. Grid Bias   279

20 CATHODE-RAY TUBES

Description of Cathode-Ray Tube. Electric Focusing. Deflection. Magnetic Focusing. Operation of Cathode-Ray Tube. Time Bases. Application to Television. Application to Radar. Noise   292

21 TRANSMISSION LINES

Feeders. Electrical Equivalent of a Line. Characteristic Resistance. Waves along a Line. Wave Reflection. Standing Waves. Line Impedance Variations. The Quarter-Wave Transformer. Fully Resonant Lines. Lines as Tuned Circuits   303

CONTENTS

APPENDIX | *Page*

1 ALTERNATIVE TECHNICAL TERMS 315
2 SYMBOLS AND ABBREVIATIONS 317
3 CIRCUIT SYMBOLS 319
4 DECIBEL TABLE 320

INDEX 321

Preface

WIRELESS—OR RADIO—has branched out and developed so tremendously that a much larger book than this would be needed to describe it all in detail. Besides broadcasting sound and vision, it is used for communication with and between ships, aircraft, trains and cars; for direction-finding and radar (radiolocation), photograph and "facsimile" transmission, telegraph and telephone links, meteorological probing of the upper atmosphere, and other things. All of these are based on the same foundational principles. The purpose of this book is to start at the beginning and lay these foundations, on which more detailed knowledge can then be built.

At the beginning. . . . If you had to tell somebody about a cricket match you had seen, your description would depend very much on whether or not your hearer was familiar with the jargon of the game. If he wasn't and you assumed he was, he would be puzzled. Vice versa, he would be irritated. There is the same dilemma with wireless. It takes much less time to explain it if the reader is familiar with methods of expression, such as symbols, that are taken for granted in scientific discussion but not in ordinary conversation. This book assumes hardly any special knowledge. But if the use of graphs and symbols had to be completely excluded, or else accompanied everywhere by digressions explaining them, it would be very boring for the initiated. So the methods of technical expression are explained separately in a preliminary Initiation. Those already initiated can of course skip it; but it might be as well just to make sure, because this is a most essential foundation.

Then there are the technical terms. They are explained one by one as they occur and their first occurrence is distinguished by printing in italics; but in case any are forgotten they can be looked up at the end of the book; and so can the symbols and abbreviations. These references are there to be used whenever the meaning of anything is not understood.

Most readers find purely abstract principles very dull; it is more stimulating to have in mind some application of those principles. As it would be confusing to have all the applications of radio in mind at once, broadcasting of sound programmes is mentioned most often because it directly affects the largest number of people. But the same principles apply to television and all the other things. The reader who is interested in the communicating of something other than sound has only to substitute the appropriate word.

May, 1951   M. G. SCROGGIE

Initiation : Into the Shorthand of Wireless

GLANCING THROUGH THIS BOOK, you can see numerous strange signs and symbols. Most of the diagrams consist of little else, while the occasional appearance of what looks like algebra may create a suspicion that this is a Mathematical Work and therefore quite beyond a beginner.

Yet these devices are not, as might be supposed, for the purpose of making wireless look more learned or difficult. Quite the contrary. Experience has shown them to be the simplest, clearest and most compact ways of conveying the sort of information needed.

The three devices used here are Graphs, Circuit Diagrams, and Algebraic Symbols. The following explanations are only for readers who are not quite used to them.

ALGEBRAIC SYMBOLS

If a car had travelled 90 miles in 3 hours, we would know that its average speed was 30 miles per hour. How? The mental arithmetic could be written down like this:

$$90 \div 3 = 30$$

That is all right if we are concerned only with that one particular journey. If the same car, or another one, did 7 miles in a quarter of an hour, the arithmetic would have to be:

$$7 \div \tfrac{1}{4} = 28$$

To let anyone know the speed of any car on any journey, it would be more than tedious to have to write out the figures for every possible case. All we need say is, " To find the average speed in miles per hour, divide the number of miles travelled by the number of hours taken."

What we actually would say would probably be briefer still— " To get the average speed, divide the distance by the time." Literally that is nonsense, because the only things that can be arithmetically divided or multiplied are numbers. But of course the words " the number of " are (or ought to be!) understood. The other words—" miles per hour ", " miles ", " hours "—the units of measurement, as they are called, may also perhaps be taken for granted in such an easy case. In others, missing them out might lead one badly astray. Suppose the second journey had been specified in the alternative form of 7 miles in 15 minutes. Dividing one by the other would not give the right answer in miles per hour. It would, however, give the right number of miles per minute.

In wireless, as in other branches of physics and engineering, this matter of units is often less obvious, and always has to be kept in mind.

11

Our instruction, even in its shorter form, could be abbreviated by using mathematical symbols as we did with the numbers:

Average speed = Distance travelled ÷ Time taken.

Here we have a concise statement of extremely general usefulness; note that it applies not only to cars but to railway trains, snails, bullets, the stars in their courses, and everything else in heaven or earth that moves.

Yet even this form of expression becomes tedious when many and complicated statements have to be presented. So for convenience we might write:

$$S = D \div T$$

or alternatively

$$S = \frac{D}{T}$$

or, to suit the printer,

$$S = D/T$$

What Letter Symbols Really Mean

This is the stage at which some people take fright, or become impatient. They say, " How *can* you divide D by T? Dividing one letter by another doesn't *mean* anything. You have just said yourself that the only things that can be divided are numbers! " Quite so. It would be absurd to try to divide D by T. Those letters are there just to show what to do with the numbers when you know them. D, for example, has been used to stand for the number of miles travelled.

The only reason why the letters S, D and T were picked for this duty is that they help to remind one of the things they stand for. Except for that there is no reason why the same information should not have been written:

$$x = y/z$$

or even:

$$\alpha = \beta/\gamma$$

so long as we know what these symbols mean. As there are only 26 letters in our alphabet, and fewer still in the Greek, it may not be feasible to allocate any one of them permanently, be it S or x or α, to mean " average speed in miles per hour ". x, in particular, is notoriously capable of meaning absolutely anything. Yet to write out the exact meaning every time would defeat the whole purpose of using the letters. How, then, does one know the meaning?

Well, some meanings have been fixed by international agreement. There is one symbol that means the same thing every time, not only in wireless but in all the sciences—the Greek letter π (read as " pie "). It is a particularly good example of abbreviation because it stands for a number that would take eternity to write out in full—the ratio of the circumference of a circle to its diameter, which begins: 3·1415926535 . . . . . (The first three or four decimal places give enough accuracy for most purposes).

Then there is a much larger group of symbols which have been given meanings that hold good throughout a limited field such as electrical engineering, or one of its subdivisions such as wireless, but are liable to mean something different in, say, astronomy or hydraulics. These have to be learnt by anyone going in for the subject seriously. A list of those that concern us appears on pages 317–8 of this book; but do not try to learn them there. It is much easier to wait till they turn up one by one in the body of the book.

Lastly, there are symbols that one uses for all the things that are not in a standard list. Here we are free to choose our own; but there are some rules it is wise to observe. It is common sense to steer clear as far as possible from symbols that already have established meanings. The important thing is to state the meaning when first using the symbol. It can be assumed to bear this meaning to the end of the particular occasion for which it was attached; after that, the label is taken off and the symbol thrown back into the common stock, ready for use on another occasion, perhaps with a different label—provided it is not likely to be confused with the first.

Sometimes a single symbol might have any of several different meanings, and one has to decide which it bears in that particular connection. The Greek letter μ (pronounced "mew") is an example that occurs in this book. When the subject is a radio valve, it can be assumed to mean *amplification factor*. But if iron cores for transformers are being discussed, μ should be read as *permeability*. And if it comes before another letter it may be an abbreviation for *micro-*, meaning " one millionth of ".

Some Other Uses of Symbols

The last of these three meanings of μ is a different kind of meaning altogether from those we have been discussing. Until then we had been considering symbols as abbreviations for quantities of certain specified things, such as speed in miles per hour. But there are several other uses to which they are put.

Instead of looking on " $S = D/T$ " as an instruction for calculating the speed, we can regard it as a statement showing the relationship to one another of the three quantities, speed, time and distance. Such a statement, always employing the " equals " sign, is called by mathematicians an *equation*. From this point of view S is no more important than T or D, and it is merely incidental that the equation was written in such a form as to give instructions for finding S rather than for finding either of the other two. We are entitled to apply the usual rules of arithmetic in order to put the statement into whatever form may be most convenient when we come to put in the numbers for which the letters stand.

For example, we might want to be able to calculate the time taken on a journey, knowing the distance and average speed. We can divide or multiply both " sides " of an equation by any number

13

(known, or temporarily represented by a letter) without upsetting their equality. If we multiply both sides of S = D/T by T we get ST = D (ST being the recognized abbreviation for S × T). Dividing both sides of this new form of the equation by S we get T = D/S. Our equation is now in the form of an instruction to divide the number of miles by the speed in miles per hour (e.g., 120 miles at 24 m.p.h. takes 5 hours).

When you see books on wireless (or any other technical subject) with pages covered almost entirely with mathematical symbols, you can take it that instead of explaining in words how their conclusions are reached, the authors are doing it more compactly in symbols. It is because such pages are concentrated essence, rather than that the meanings of the symbols themselves are hard to learn, that makes them difficult. The procedure is to express the known or assumed facts in the form of equations, and then to combine or manipulate these equations according to the recognized rules in order to draw some useful or interesting conclusions from those facts.

This book, being an elementary one, explains everything in words, and only uses symbols for expressing the important facts or conclusions in concise form.

Abbreviations

Another use of symbols is for abbreviation pure and simple. We have already used one without explanation—m.p.h.—because it is well known that this means " miles per hour ". The mile-per-hour is a unit of speed. " Lb " is a familiar abbreviation for a unit of weight. The unit of electrical pressure is the volt, denoted by the abbreviation V. Sometimes it is necessary to specify very small voltages, such as 5 millionths of a volt. That could be written 0·000005 V. But a more convenient abbreviation is 5 μV, read as " 5 microvolts ". The list on pages 317–8 gives all the abbreviations commonly used in wireless.

Still another use for letters is to point out details on a diagram. R stands for electrical *resistance*, but one has to guess whether it is intended to mean resistance in general, as a property of conductors, or the numerical value of resistance in an equation, or the particular resistance marked R in a diagram. Often it may combine these meanings, being understood to mean " the numerical value of the resistance marked R in Fig. So-and-so ".

Attaching the right meanings to symbols probably sounds dreadfully difficult and confusing. So do the rules of a new game. The only way to defeat the difficulties is to start playing the game.

But before starting to read the book, here are a few more hints about symbols.

How Numbers are Used

One way of making the limited stock of letters go farther is to number them. To prevent the numbers from being treated as

14

separate things they are written small near the foot of the letter (" subscript "). For example, if we want to refer to several different resistances we can mark them R_1, R_2, R_3, etc. Sometimes a modification of a thing denoted by one symbol is distinguished by a tick or dash; A might stand for the amplification of a receiver when used normally, and A' when modified in some way.

But on no account must numbers be used " superscript " for this purpose, because that already has a standard meaning. 5^2 (read as " 5 squared ") means 5×5; 5^3 (" 5 cubed ") means $5 \times 5 \times 5$; 5^4 (" 5 to the 4th power ") means $5 \times 5 \times 5 \times 5$; x^2 means the number represented by x multiplied by the same number.

x^{-2} seems nonsensical according to the rule just illustrated. It has been agreed, however, to make it mean $1/x^2$ (called the *reciprocal* of x squared). The point of this appears most clearly when these superscripts, called *indices*, are applied to the number 10. $10^4 = 10,000$, $10^3 = 1,000$, $10^2 = 100$, $10^1 = 10$, $10^0 = 1$, $10^{-1} = 0.1$, $10^{-2} = 0.01$, and so on. The rule is that the power of 10 indicates the number of places the decimal point has to be away from 1; with a positive index it is on the right; negative, on the left. Advantage is taken of this to abbreviate very large or very small numbers. It is easier to see that 0.0000000026 is 2.6 thousand-millionths if it is written 2.6×10^{-9}. Likewise 2.6×10^{12} is briefer and clearer than $2,600,000,000,000$.

$x^{\frac{1}{2}}$ also needs explanation. It is read as " the square root of x ", and is often denoted by $\sqrt{x}$. It signifies the number which, when multiplied by the same number, gives x. In symbols $(\sqrt{x})^2 = x$.

Note that $10^6 \times 10^6 = 10^{12}$, and that $10^{12} \times 10^{-3} = 10^{12}/10^3 = 10^9$. In short, multiply by adding indices, and divide by subtracting them. This idea is very important in connection with decibels (p. 250).

GRAPHS

Most of us when we were in the growing stage used to stand bolt upright against the edge of a door to have our height marked up. The succession of marks did not convey very much when reviewed afterwards unless the dates were marked too. Even then one had to look closely to read the dates, and the progress of growth was difficult to visualize. Nor would it have been a great help to have presented the information in the form of a table with two columns— Height and Date.

But, disregarding certain technical difficulties, imagine that the growing boy had been attached to a conveyor belt which moved him horizontally along a wall at a steady rate of, say, one foot per year, and that a pencil fixed to the top of his head had been tracing a line on the wall (Fig. 1). If he had not been growing at all, this line would, of course, be straight and horizontal. If he had been growing at a uniform rate, it would be straight but sloping upwards. A variable rate of growth would be shown by a line of varying slope.

15

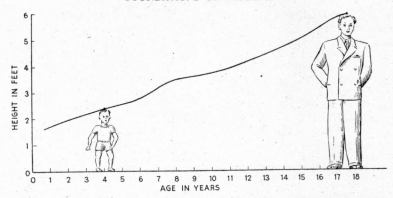

Fig. 1—Simple (but inconvenient) system for automatic graph plotting of human growth. The equipment consists of a conveyor belt moving at the rate of one foot per year, a pencil, and a white wall

In this way the progress over a period of years could be visualized by a glance at the wall.

Scales

To make the information more definite, a mark could have been made along a horizontal line each New Year's Day and the number of the year written against it. In more technical terms this would be a time scale. The advantage of making the belt move at uniform speed is that times intermediate between those actually marked can be identified by measuring off a proportionate *distance*. If one foot represented one year, the height at, say, the end of May in any year could be found by noting the height of the pencil line 5 inches beyond the mark indicating the start of that year.

Similarly a scale of height could be marked anywhere in a vertical direction. It happens in this case that height would be represented by an equal height. But if the graph were to be reproduced in a book, although height would still represent height it would have to do so on a reduced scale, say half an inch to a foot.

To guide the eye from any point on the information line to the two scales, it is usual to plot graphs on paper printed with horizontal and vertical lines so close together that a pair of them is sure to come near enough to the selected point for any little less or more to be judged. The position of the scales is not a vital matter, but unless there is a reason for doing otherwise they are marked along the lines where the other quantity is zero. For instance, the time scale would be placed where height is nil; i.e., along the foot of the wall. If, however, the height scale were erected at the start of the year 1 A.D. there would be nearly half a mile of blank wall between it and the pencil line. To avoid such inconvenience we can use a " false zero ", making the scale start at or slightly below the first figure in which we are interested. A sensible way of doing it in this

16

example would be to reckon from the time the boy was born, as in Fig. 1. The point that is zero on both scales is called the *origin*. False zeros are sometimes used in a slightly shady manner to give a wrong impression. Fig. 2*a* shows the sort of graph that might appear in a company-promoting prospectus. The word " Profit " would, of course, be in big type, and the figures indistinctly, so that the curve would seem to indicate a sensational growth in profits. Plotted without a false zero, as in Fig. 2*b*, it looks much less impressive. Provided that it is clearly admitted, however, a false zero is useful for enabling the significant part of the scale to be expanded and so read more precisely.

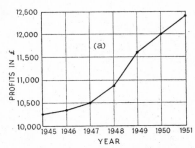 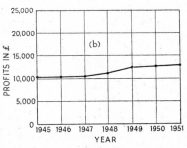

Fig. 2—(a) Typical financial graph arranged to make the maximum impression consistent with strict truthfulness. (b) The same information presented in a slightly different manner

Fig. 2, by the way, is not a true graph of the sort a mathematician would have anything to do with. Profits are declared annually in lumps, and the lines joining the dots that mark each year's result have no meaning whatever but are there merely to guide the eye from one to another. In a true graph a continuous variation is shown, and the dots are so close together as to form a line. This line is technically a *curve*, whether it is what is commonly understood as a curve or is as straight as the proverbial bee-line.

What a " Curve " Signifies

Every point on the curve in Fig. 1 represents the height of the boy at a certain definite time (or, put in another way, the time at which the boy reached a certain height). Since it is possible to distinguish a great number of points along even a small graph, and each point is equivalent to saying " When the time was T years, the height was M feet ", a graph is not only a very clear way of presenting information, but a very economical one.

Here we have our old friend T again, meaning time, but now in years instead of hours. It is being used to stand for the number of years, as measured along the time scale, represented by *any* point on the curve. Since no particular point is specified, we cannot tell how many feet the corresponding height may be, so have to denote it by H. But directly T is specified by a definite number,

17

the number or *value* of H can be found from the curve. And vice versa.

In its earlier role (p. 12) T took part in an equation with two other quantities, denoted by S and D. The equation expressed the relationship between these three quantities. We now see that a graph is a method of showing the relationship between two quantities. It is particularly useful for quantities whose relation-ship is too complicated or irregular to express as an equation—the height and age of a boy, for instance.

Three-Dimensional Graphs

Can a graph deal with three quantities? There are two ways in which it can, neither of them entirely satisfactory.

One method is to make a three-dimensional graph by drawing a third scale at right angles to the other two. Looking at the corner of a room, one can imagine one scale along the foot of one wall,

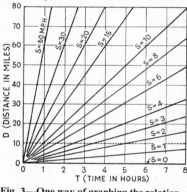

Fig. 3—One way of graphing the relation-ship between speed, time and distance of a journey

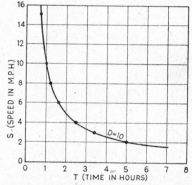

Fig. 4—A graph of speed against time for any given distance can be derived from Fig. 3

another at the foot of the other wall, and the third upwards along the intersection between the two walls. The "curve" would take the form of a surface in the space inside—and generally also outside—the room. Quite apart from the inconvenience of this form of presenting information, even brilliant brains have admitted the difficulty of visualizing three-dimensional graphs.

The other method is to draw a number of cross-sections of the three-dimensional graph on a two-dimensional graph. In other words, the three variable quantities are reduced to two by assuming some numerical value for the third. We can then draw a curve showing the relationship between the two. A different numerical value is then assumed for the third, giving (in general) a different graph. And so on.

Let us take again as an example D = ST. If any numerical value is assigned to the speed, S, we can easily plot a graph connecting

18

D and T, as in Fig. 3. When the speed is zero, the distance remains zero for all time, so the " S = 0 " curve is a straight line coinciding with the time scale. When S is fixed at 1 m.p.h., D and T are always numerically equal, giving a line (" S = 1 ") sloping up with a 1-in-1 gradient (measured by the T and D scales). The " S = 2 " line slopes twice as steeply, the " S = 3 " line three times as steeply, etc.

If a fair number of S curves are available, it is possible to replot the graph to show, say, S against T for fixed values of D. A horizontal line drawn from any selected value on the D scale in Fig. 3 (such as D = 10) cuts each S curve at one point, from which the T corresponding to that S can be read off and plotted, as in Fig. 4. Each point plotted in Fig. 4 corresponds to an S curve in Fig. 3, and when joined up they give a new curve (really curved this time!). This process has been demonstrated for only one value of D, but of course it could be repeated to show the time/speed relationship for other distances. Fig. 4 gives numerical expression to the well-known fact that the greater the speed the shorter is the time to travel a specified distance.

Graphs of this triple kind are important in many branches of wireless, and particularly with valves, because their relationships cannot be accurately expressed as equations.

Significance of Slope

Even from simple two-dimensional graphs like Fig. 1 it may be possible to extract information that is worth replotting separately. It is clear that a third quantity is involved—rate of *growth*. This is not an independent variable; it is determined by the other two. For it is nothing else than rate-of-change-of-height. As we saw at the start, when the curve slopes upward steeply, growth is rapid; when the curve flattens out, it means that growth has ceased; and if the curve started to slope downwards—a negative gradient—it would indicate negative growth. So it would be possible to plot growth in, say, inches per year, against age in years. This idea of rate-of-change, indicated on a graph by slope, is the essence of no less a subject than the differential calculus, which is much easier than it is often made out to be. If you are anxious to get a clearer view of any electrical subject it would be well worth while to read at least the first few chapters of an elementary book on the differential calculus, such as S. P. Thompson's " Calculus Made Easy ".

Non-Uniform Scales

Finally, although uniform scales for graphs are much the easiest to read, there may quite often be reasons which justify some other sort of scale. The most important, and the only one we need consider here, is the *logarithmic* scale. In this, the numbers are so spaced out that a given distance measured anywhere along the scale represents, not a certain *addition*, but a certain *ratio* or *multiplication*,

19

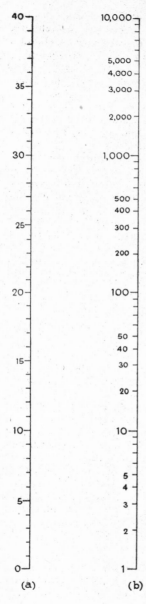

Musicians use such a scale (whether they know it or not); their intervals correspond to ratios. For example, raising a musical note by an octave means doubling the frequency of vibration, no matter whereabouts on the scale it occurs. Users of slide-rules are familiar with the same sort of scale. Readers who are neither musicians nor slide-rule pushers can see the difference by looking at Fig. 5, where *a* is an ordinary uniform (or *linear*) scale and *b* is logarithmic. If we start with *a* and note any two scale readings $1\frac{1}{2}$ inches apart we find that they always *differ* by 10. Applying the same test to *b* we find that the difference may be large or small, depending on whether the inch and a half is near the top or bottom. But the larger reading is always 10 times the smaller.

One advantage of this is that it enables very large and very small readings to be shown clearly on the same graph. Another is that with some quantities (such as musical pitch) the ratio is more significant than the numerical interval. Fig. 141 is an example of logarithmic scales.

CIRCUIT DIAGRAMS

It is easier to identify the politicians depicted in our daily papers in the cartoons than in the news photos. There is a sense in which the distorted versions of those gentlemen presented by the caricaturist are more like them than they are themselves. The distinguishing features are picked out and reduced to conventional forms that can be recognized at a glance.

A photograph of a complicated machine shows just a maze of wheels and levers, from which even an experienced engineer might derive little information. But a set of blue-prints, having little relation to the original in appearance, would enable him, if necessary, to reproduce such a machine.

Fig. 5—Comparison between uniform or " linear " scale (*a*), and logarithmic scale (*b*)

20

There should be no further need to argue why circuit diagrams are more useful than pictures of radio sets.

In a circuit diagram each component or item that has a significant electrical effect is represented by a conventional symbol, and the wires connecting them up are shown as lines. Fortunately, except for a few minor differences or variations, these symbols are recognizably the same all over the world. Most of them indicate their functions so clearly that one could guess what they mean. However, they are introduced as required in this book, and the whole lot are lined up for reference on page 319.

Alternative Methods

The only matter about which there is a sharp difference of opinion is the way in which crossing wires should be distinguished from connected wires. Fig. 6a shows the method preferred by the author; an unconnected crossing wire is indicated by a little half-loop. In an alternative method b, which is general in America, crossing wires are assumed to be unconnected unless marked by a blob. There is obviously a risk that either the blob may be omitted where needed or may form unintentionally (especially when the lines are drawn in ink) where not wanted. Even when correctly drawn the difference is harder to see. A third method c is sometimes used; it is neater and

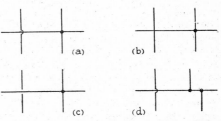

Fig. 6—Alternative methods of distinguishing crossing from connected wires in circuit diagrams

easier to draw than a and clearer than b. The blob is not essential in a but it makes the distinction doubly sure. To make triply sure it is recommended that connecting crossings should always be staggered, as at d. Of all the methods, b is by far the worst. It is only shown here because unfortunately it is often used.

Another variation that may be worth mentioning is that some people omit to draw a ring round the symbols that represent the " innards " of a valve. In this book they are drawn thicker than the connecting wires, and make the valves (which are usually key components) stand out distinctly. See Fig. 169, for example.

The Importance of Layout

But there is a good deal more in the drawing of circuit diagrams than just showing all the right symbols and connections. If the letters composing a message were written at random all over the paper, nobody would bother to read it even if the correct sequence were shown by a maze of connecting lines—unless it was a clue to valuable buried treasure. And a circuit diagram, though perfectly

21

accurate, makes little sense even to a radio engineer if it is laid out in an unfamiliar manner. The layout has by now become largely standardized, though again there are some national differences. It is too soon in the book to deal with layout in detail, but here are some general principles for later reference.

The first is that the diagram should be arranged for reading from left to right. In a receiver, for example, the aerial should be on the left and the final item, the loudspeaker, on the right.

Next, there is generally an "earthed" or "low-potential" connection. This should be drawn as a thicker line along the foot of the diagram. The highest potential connections should be at the top. This helps one to visualize the potential distribution.

Long runs of closely parallel wires are difficult to follow and should be avoided.

But, as with written symbols, it is easier to get accustomed to circuit diagrams with practice. An effort has been made in this book to exemplify sound practice in diagram drawing.

Where Circuit Diagrams can Mislead

There is one warning which it is prudent to sound in connection with circuit diagrams, especially when going on to more advanced work. They are an amazingly convenient and well-conceived aid to thought, but it is possible to allow one's thoughts to be moulded too rigidly by them. The diagram takes for granted that all electrical properties are available in separate lumps, like chemicals in bottles, and that one can make up a circuit like a prescription. Instead of which they are more like the smells from the said chemicals when the stoppers have been left open—each one strongest near its own bottle, but pervading the surrounding space and mixing inextricably with the others. This is particularly true at very high frequencies, so that the diagram must not always be taken as showing the whole of the picture. Experience tells how far a circuit diagram can be trusted.

CHAPTER 1

A General View

WHAT WIRELESS DOES

PEOPLE WHO REMARK on the wonders of wireless seldom seem to consider the fact that all normal persons can broadcast speech and song merely by using their voices. We can instantly communicate our thoughts to others, without wires or any other visible lines of communication and without even any sending or receiving apparatus outside of ourselves. If anything is wonderful, that is. Wireless is merely a device for increasing the range.

There is a fable about a dispute among the birds as to which could fly the highest. The claims of the wren were derided until, when the great competition took place and the eagle was proudly outflying the rest, the wren took off from his back and established a new altitude record.

It has been known for centuries that communication over vast distances of space is *possible*—it happens every time we look at the stars and detect light coming from them. If there were intelligent beings on the moon they could send messages to us by means of searchlights. We know, then, that a long-range medium of communication exists. Wireless simply uses this medium for the carrying of sound.

Simply?

Well, there actually is quite a lot to learn about it. Before getting to grips with the several kinds of subject matter that must be included in even an elementary book it will be helpful to take a general look at the whole to see why each is necessary and where it fits in.

THE NATURE OF SOUND WAVES

Wireless, as we have just observed, is essentially a means of extending natural communication beyond its limits of range. It plays the part of the swift eagle in carrying the wren of human speech to unaccustomed distances. So first of all let us see what is required for " natural " communication.

There are three essential parts: the *speaker*, who generates sound; the *hearer* who receives it; and the *medium*, which connects one with the other.

The last of these is the key to the other two. By suspending a source of sound in a container and extracting the air (Fig. 7) one can demonstrate that sound cannot travel without air (or some other physical substance) all the way between sender and receiver.

Anyone who has watched a cricket match will recall that the smack of bat against ball is heard a moment after they are seen to

23

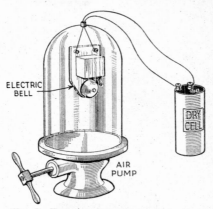

Fig. 7—Experiment to demonstrate that sound waves cannot cross empty space. As the air is removed from the glass vessel, the sound of the bell fades away

ELECTRIC BELL

AIR PUMP

meet; the sound of the impact has taken an appreciable time to travel from the pitch to the viewpoint. If the pitch were 1,100 feet away, the time delay would be one second. The same speed of travel is found to hold good over longer or shorter distances. Knowing the damage that air does when it travels at even one-tenth of that speed (hurricane force) we conclude that sound does not consist in the air itself leaping out in all directions.

When a stone is thrown into a pond it produces ripples, but the ripples do not consist of the water which was directly struck by the stone travelling outwards until it reaches the banks. If the ripples pass a cork floating on the surface they make it bob up and down; they do not carry it along with them.

What does travel, visibly across the surface of the pond, and invisibly through the air, is a *wave*, or more often a succession of waves. While ripples or waves on the surface of water do have much in common with waves in general, they are not of quite the same type as sound waves *through* air or any other medium (including water). So let us forget about the ripples now they have served their purpose, and consider a number of men standing in a queue. If the man at the rear is given a sharp push he will bump into the man in front of him, and he into the next man; and so the push may be passed on right to the front. The push has travelled along the line although the men—representing the medium of communication—have all been standing still except for a small temporary displacement.

In a similar manner the cricket ball gives the bat a sudden push; the bat pushes the air next to it; that air gives the air around it a push; and so a wave of compression travels outwards in all directions like an expanding bubble. Yet all that any particular bit of air does is to move a small fraction of an inch away from the cause of the disturbance and back again. As the original impulse is spread over an ever-expanding wave-front the extent of this tiny air movement becomes less and less and the sound fainter and fainter.

CHARACTERISTICS OF SOUND WAVES

The generation of sound is only incidental to the functioning of cricket bats, but the human vocal organs make up a generator capable of emitting a great variety of sounds at will. What surprises

24

most people, when the nature of sound waves is explained to them, is how such a variety of sound can be communicated by anything so simple as to-and-fro tremors in the air. Is it really possible that the subtle inflexions of the voice by which an individual can be identified, and all the endless variety of music, can be represented by nothing more than that?

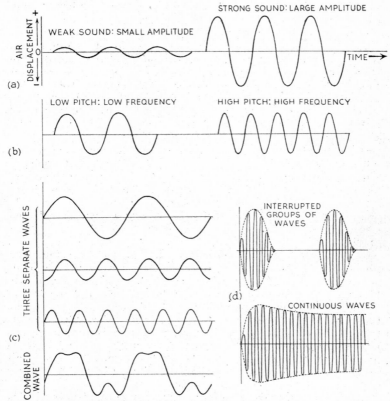

Fig. 8—Graphical representation of the four basic ways in which sound (or any other) waves can differ. (a) amplitude; (b) pitch or frequency; (c) waveform; and (d) envelope

Examining the matter more closely we find that this infinite variety of sounds is due to four basic characteristics, which can all be illustrated on a piano. They are:

(a) LOUDNESS. A single key can be struck either gently or hard, giving a soft or loud sound. The harder it is struck, the more violently the piano string vibrates and the greater the tremor in the air, or, to use technical terms, the greater the amplitude of the sound wave. Difference in loudness is shown graphically in

25

Fig. 8a. (Note that to-and-fro displacement of the air is represented here by up-and-down displacement of the curve, because horizontal displacement is usually used for time.)

(b) PITCH. Now strike a key nearer the right-hand end of the piano. The resulting sound is distinguishable from the previous one by its higher pitch. The piano string is tighter and lighter, so vibrates more rapidly and generates a greater number of sound waves per second. In other words, the waves have a higher *frequency*, which is represented in Fig. 8b.

(c) WAVEFORM. If now several keys are struck simultaneously to give a chord, they blend into one sound which is richer than any of the single notes. The first three waves in Fig. 8c represent three such notes singly; when the displacements due to these separate notes are added together they give the more complicated waveform shown on the last line. Actually any one piano note itself has a complex waveform, which enables it to be distinguished from notes of the same pitch played by other instruments.

(d) ENVELOPE. A fourth difference* in sound character can be illustrated by first " pecking " at a key, getting brief (staccato) notes, and then pressing it firmly down and keeping it there, producing a sustained (legato) note. This can be shown as in Fig. 8d. The dotted lines, called envelopes, drawn around the wave peaks, have different shapes. Another example of this type of difference is the contrast between the flicker of conversational sound and the steadiness of a long organ note.

Every voice or musical instrument, and in fact everything that can be heard, is something that moves; its movements cause the air to vibrate and radiate waves; and all the possible differences in the sounds are due to combinations of the four basic differences.

The details of human and other sound generators are outside the scope of this book, but the sound waves themselves are the things that have to be carried by long-range communication systems such as wireless. Even if something other than sound is to be carried (pictures, for instance) the study of sound waves is not wasted, because the basic characteristics illustrated in Fig. 8 apply to all waves—including wireless waves.

The first (amplitude) is simple and easy to understand. The third and fourth (waveform and envelope) lead us into complications that are too involved for this preliminary survey, and will have to be gone into later. The second (frequency) is very important indeed and not too involved to take at this stage.

FREQUENCY

Let us consider the matter as exemplified by the vibrating string or wire shown in Fig. 9. The upper and lower limits of its vibration are indicated (rather exaggeratedly, perhaps) by the dotted lines.

* Mathematically it is covered by Waveform, so may not always be listed separately.

26

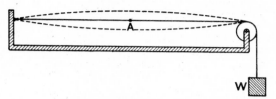

Fig. 9—A simple sound generator, consisting of a string
held taut by a weight. When plucked it vibrates as
indicated by the dotted lines

If a point on the string, such as A, were arranged to record its
movements on a sheet of paper moving rapidly from one end of the
string to the other, it would trace out a wavy line which would be its
displacement/time graph, like those in Fig. 8. Each complete
up-and-down-and-back-again movement is called a *cycle*. In
Fig. 10, where several cycles are shown, one has been picked out in
heavy line. The time it takes, marked T, is known as its *period*.

We have already noted that the rate at which the vibrations take
place is called the *frequency*, and determines the pitch of the sound
produced. It is generally reckoned in cycles per second (abbreviated
c/s) and its symbol is f. Middle C in music has a frequency of
261 c/s. The full range* of a piano is 27 to 3,516 c/s. People with
good hearing can hear sounds from about 20
to 16,000 c/s.

You may have noticed in passing that T
and f are closely related. If the period of
each cycle is one-hundredth of a second, then
the frequency is obviously one hundred cycles

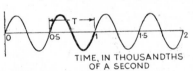

TIME, IN THOUSANDTHS
OF A SECOND

Fig. 10—The extent of one cycle in a series
of waves is shown in heavy line. The time
occupied by its generation, or by its passing
a given point, is marked T

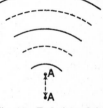

Fig. 11—End view of the
vibrating string at A in
Fig. 9. As it moves up
and down over the dis-
tance AA it sends out air
waves which carry some
of its energy of vibration
to the listener's ear

per second. Putting it in general terms, $f = 1/T$. So if the time
scale of a waveform graph is given, it is quite easy to work out the
frequency. In Fig. 10 the time scale shows that T is 0·0005 sec, so
the frequency must be 2,000 c/s.

WAVELENGTH

Next, consider the air waves set up by the vibrating string. Fig. 11
shows an end view, with point A vibrating up and down. It pushes

* In wireless the word " range " means distance that can be covered, so to avoid
confusion a range of frequencies is more often referred to as a *band*.

27

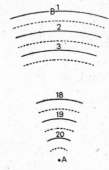

Fig. 12—Twenty successive waves from the string shown in Figs. 9 and 11. If the string is vibrating 20 times per second, the 1st wave has been travelling for one second by the time it reaches B, and the 20th has just left the string at A. As sound travels 1,100 feet in one second, AB = 1,100 feet, and the distance occupied by one wave (the wavelength) is 1/20th of 1,100 feet, or 55 feet

the air alternately up and down, and these displacements travel outwards from A. Places where the air has been temporarily moved a little farther from A than usual are indicated by full lines, and places where it is nearer by dotted lines; these lines should be imagined as expanding outwards at a speed of about 1,100 feet per second. So if, for example, the string is vibrating at a frequency of 20 c/s, at one second from the start the first air wave will be 1,100 feet away, and there will be 20 complete waves spread over that distance (Fig. 12). The length of each wave is therefore one-twentieth of 1,100 feet, which is 55 feet.

Now it is a fact that sound waves of practically all frequencies and amplitudes travel through the air at the same speed, so the higher the frequency the shorter the wavelength. This relationship can be expressed by the equation:

$$\lambda = \frac{v}{f}$$

where the Greek letter λ (pronounced " lambda ") stands for wavelength, v for the velocity of the waves, and f for the frequency. If v is given in feet per second and f in cycles per second, then λ will be in feet. The letter v has been put here instead of 1,100, because the exact velocity of sound waves in air depends on its pressure and temperature; moreover the equation applies to waves in water, wood, rock, or any other substance, if the v appropriate to the substance is filled in.

It should be noted that it is the frequency of the wave which determines the pitch, and that the wavelength is a secondary matter depending on the speed of the wave. That this is so can be shown by sending a sound of the same frequency through water, in which the velocity is 4,700 feet per second; the wavelength is therefore more than four times as great as in air, but the pitch, as judged by the ear, remains the same as that of the shorter air wave.

THE SENDER

The device shown in Fig. 9 is a very simple sound transmitter or sender. Its function is to generate sound waves by vibrating and stirring up the surrounding air. In some instruments, such as violins, the stirring-up part of the business is made more effectual by attaching the vibrating parts to surfaces which increase the amount of air disturbed.

The pitch of the note can be controlled in two ways. One is to vary the weight of the string, which is conveniently done by varying the length that is free to vibrate, as a violinist does with his fingers. The other is to vary its tightness, as a violinist does when tuning, or can be done in Fig. 9 by altering the weight W. To lower the pitch, the string is made heavier or slacker. As this is not a book on sound there is no need to go into this further, but we shall have a lot to say (especially in Chapter 8) on the electrical equivalents of these two things, which control the frequency of wireless waves.

THE RECEIVER

What happens at the receiving end? Reviving our memory of the stone in the pond, we recall that the ripples made corks and other small flotsam bob up and down. Similarly, air waves when they strike an object try to make it vibrate with the same characteristics as their own. That is how we can hear sounds through a door or partition; the door is made to vibrate, and its vibrations set up a new lot of air waves on our side of it. When they reach our ears they strike the ear-drums; these vibrate and stimulate a very remarkable piece of receiving mechanism, which sorts out the sounds and conveys its findings via a multiple nerve to the brain.

ELECTRICAL COMMUNICATION BY WIRE

To extend the very limited range of sound-wave communication it was necessary to find a carrier. Nothing served this purpose very well until the discovery of electricity. At first electricity could only be controlled rather crudely, by switching the current on and off; so spoken messages had to be translated into a code of signals before they could be sent, and then translated back into words at the receiving end. A simple electric telegraph consisted of a switch or " key " at the sending end, some device for detecting the current at the receiving end, and a wire between to carry the current.

Most of the current detectors made use of the discovery that when some of the electric wire was coiled round a piece of iron the iron became a magnet so long as the current flowed, and would attract other pieces of iron placed near it. If the neighbouring iron was in the form of a flexible diaphragm held close to the ear, its movements towards and away from the iron-cored coil when current was switched on and off caused audible clicks even when the current was very weak.

To transmit speech and music, however, it was necessary to make the diaphragm vibrate in the same complicated way as the sound waves at the sending end. Since the amount of attraction varied with the strength of current, this could be done if the current could be made to vary in the same way as the distant sound waves. In the end this problem was solved by quite a simple device—the carbon microphone, which, with only details improved, is still the type used in modern telephones.

In its simplest form, then, a telephone consists of the equipment shown in Fig. 13. Although this invention extended the range of speech from yards to miles, every mile of line weakened the electric currents and set a limit to clear communication. So it was not

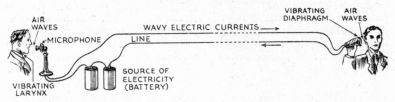

Fig. 13—A very simple form of one-way electric telephone, showing how the characteristics of the original air waves are duplicated in electric currents, which travel farther and quicker, and which are then transformed back into air waves to make them perceptible by the listener

until the invention of the electronic valve, making it possible to amplify the complicated current variations, that telephoning could be done over hundreds and even thousands of miles.

ELECTRIC WAVES

Wire or line telephones and telegraphs were and still are a tremendous aid to communication. But something else was needed for speaking to ships and aeroplanes. And even where the intervening wire is practicable it is sometimes very inconvenient.

At this stage we can profitably think again of the process of unaided voice communication. When you talk to another person you do not have to transfer the vibrations of your vocal organs directly to the ear-drum of your hearer by means of a rod or other " line ". What you do is to stir up waves in the air, and these spread out in all directions, shaking anything they strike, including ear-drums.

" Is it possible ", experimenters might have asked, " to stir up *electric* waves by any means, and if so would they travel over greater distances than sound waves ? " Gradually scientists supplied the answer. Clerk Maxwell showed mathematically that electric waves were theoretically possible, and indeed that in all probability light, which could easily be detected after travelling vast distances, was an example of such waves. But they were waves of unimaginably high frequency, about 5×10^{14} c/s. A few years later Hertz actually produced and detected electric waves of much lower (but still very high) frequency, and found that they shared with sound the useful ability to pass through partitions opaque to light.

Unlike sound, however, they are not carried by the air. They travel equally well (if anything, better) where there is no air or any other material substance present. If the experiment of Fig. 7 is repeated with a source of electric waves instead of sound waves, extracting the air makes no appreciable difference. We know, of course, that light and heat waves travel to us from the sun across

93,000,000 miles of empty space. What does carry them is a debatable question. It was named ether (or aether, to avoid confusion with the anaesthetic liquid ether), but experiments which ought to have given results if there had been any such thing just didn't. So scientists deny its existence. But it is very hard for lesser minds to visualize how electric waves, whose behaviour corresponds in so many respects with waves through a material medium, can be propagated by nothingness.

There is no doubt about their speed, however. Light waves travel through space at about 186,282 miles, or nearly 300,000,000 metres, per second. Other sorts of electric waves, such as X-rays, ultra-violet and wireless waves, travel at the same speed, and differ only in frequency. Their length is generally measured in metres; so filling in the appropriate value of v in the formula on page 28 we have:

$$\lambda = \frac{300,000,000}{f}$$

If, for example, the frequency is 1,000,000 c/s, the wavelength is 300 metres.

WHY HIGH FREQUENCIES ARE NECESSARY

Gradually it was discovered that electric waves are capable of travelling almost any distance, even round the curvature of the earth to the antipodes.

Their enormous speed was another qualification for the duty of carrying messages; the longest journey in the world takes less than a tenth of a second. But attempts to stir up electric waves of the same frequencies as sound waves were not very successful. To see why this is so we may find it helpful to consider again how sound waves are stirred up.

If you try to radiate air waves by waving your hand you will fail, because the highest frequency you can manage is only a few c/s, and at that slow rate the air has time to rush round from side to side of your hand instead of piling up and giving the surrounding air a push. If you could wave your hand at the speed of an insect's (or even a humming bird's) wing, then the air would have insufficient time to equalize the pressure and would be alternately compressed and rarefied on each side of your hand and so would generate sound waves. Alternatively, if your hand were as big as the side of a house, it could stir up air waves even if waved only a few times per second, because the air would have too far to go from one side to the other every time. The frequency of these air waves would be too low to be heard, it is true; but they could be detected by the rattling of windows and doors all over the neighbourhood.

The same principle applies to electric waves. But because of the vastly greater speed with which they can rush round, it is necessary for the aerial—which corresponds to the waving hand— to be correspondingly vaster. To radiate electric waves at the lower

31

audible frequencies the aerial would have to be miles high, so one might just as well (and more conveniently) use it on the ground level as a telephone line.

Even if there had not been this difficulty, another would have arisen directly large numbers of senders had started to radiate waves in the audible frequency band. There would have been no way of picking out the one wanted; it would have been like a babel of giants.

That might have looked like the end of any prospects of wireless telephony, but fortunately human ingenuity was not to be beaten. The solution arose by way of the simpler problem of wireless telegraphy, so let us follow that way.

WIRELESS TELEGRAPHY

Hertz discovered how to stir up electric waves; we will not bother about exactly how, because his method is obsolete. Their frequency was what we would now call ultra-high; in the region of hundreds of millions of c/s, so their length was only a few centimetres. Such frequencies are used nowadays for radar. He also found a method of detecting them over distances of a few yards.

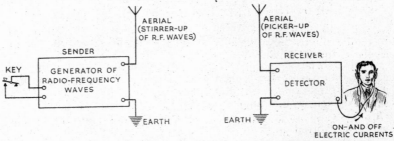

Fig. 14—Elementary wireless telegraph. Currents flow in the receiving headphones and cause sound whenever the sender is radiating waves

With the more powerful senders and more sensitive receivers developed later, ranges rapidly increased, until in 1901 Marconi actually signalled across the Atlantic. The various sorts of detectors that were invented from time to time worked by causing an electric current to flow in a local receiving circuit when electric waves impinged on the receiving aerial. Human senses are unable to respond to these " wireless " waves directly—their frequency is far too high for the ear and far too low for the eye—but the electric currents resulting from their detection can be used to produce audible or visible effects.

At this stage we have the wireless counterpart of the simple telegraph. Its diagram, Fig. 14, more or less explains itself. The sending key turns on the sender, which generates a rapid succession of electric waves, radiated by an aerial. When these reach the receiver they operate the detector and cause an electric current to

32

flow, which can make a noise in a telephone earpiece. By working the sending key according to the Morse code, messages can be transmitted. That is roughly the basis of wireless telegraphs to this day, though some installations have been elaborated almost out of recognition, and print the messages on paper as fast as the most expert typist.

TUNING

One important point to note is that the current coming from the detector does not depend on the frequency of the waves, within wide limits. (The frequency of the current is actually the frequency with which the waves are turned on and off at the sender.) So there is a wide choice of wave frequency. In Chapter 12 we shall consider how the choice is made; but in the meantime it will be sufficient to remember that if the frequency is low, approaching audibility, the aerials have to be immense; while if the frequency is much higher than those used by Hertz it is difficult to generate them powerfully, and they are easily obstructed, like light waves.

The importance of having many frequencies to choose from was soon apparent, when it was found to be possible—and highly advantageous—to make the receiver respond to the frequency of the sender and reject all others. This invention of *tuning* was essential to effective wireless communication, and is the subject of a large part of this book. So it may be enough just now to point out that it has its analogy in sound. We can adjust the frequency of a sound wave by means of the length and tightness of the sender. A piano contains nearly a hundred strings of various fixed lengths and tightnesses, which we can select by means of the keys. If there is a second piano in the room, with its sustaining pedal held down so that all the strings are free to vibrate, and we strike a loud note on the first piano, the string tuned to the same note in the second can be heard to vibrate. If we had a single adjustable string, we could tune it to respond in this way to any one note of the piano and ignore those of substantially different frequency. In a corresponding manner the electrical equivalents of length (or weight) and tightness are adjusted by the tuning controls of a wireless receiver to select the desired sending station.

WIRELESS TELEPHONY

The second important point is that (as one would expect) the strength of the current from the detector increases with the strength of the wireless waves transmitted. So, with Fig. 13 in mind, we need no further hint to help us to convert the wireless telegraph of Fig. 14 into a wireless telephone, or a broadcasting system, by substituting for the Morse key a device for varying the strength of the waves, just as the microphone varied the strength of the line current in Fig. 13. Such devices are called *modulators*, and will be referred to in more detail in Chapter 11. The microphone is still needed, because the output of the wireless sender is not controlled directly by the impinging sound waves but by the wavily-varying currents from the microphone.

A practical system needs amplifiers in various places, firstly to amplify the feeble sound-controlled currents from the microphone until they are strong enough to modulate a powerful wave sender; then to amplify the feeble high-frequency currents stirred up in a distant receiving aerial by the far flung waves; then another to amplify the sound-frequency currents from the detector so that they

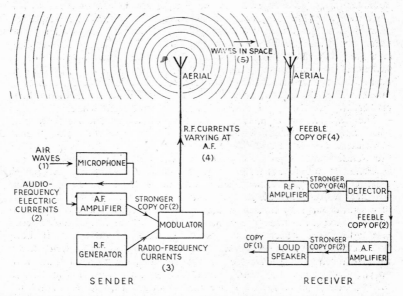

Fig. 15—The wireless telegraph of Fig. 14 converted into a wireless telephone by controlling the output of the sender by sound waves instead of just turning it on and off. In practice it is also generally necessary to use amplifiers where shown

are strong enough to work a loudspeaker instead of the less convenient head-phones. This somewhat elaborated system is indicated —but still only in broadest outline—by the block diagram, Fig. 15.

RECAPITULATION

At this stage it may be as well to review the results of our survey. We realize that in all systems of communication the signals must, in the end, be detectable by the human senses. Of these, hearing and seeing are the only ones that matter. Both are wave-operated. Our ears respond to air waves between frequency limits of about 20 and 16,000 c/s; our eyes respond to waves within a narrow band of frequency centred on 5×10^{14} c/s—waves not carried by air but by space, and which have been proved to be electrical in nature.

Although our ears are remarkably sensitive, air-wave (i.e., sound) communication is very restricted in range. Eyes, it is true, can see over vast distances, but communication is cut off by the slightest wisp of cloud. If, however, we can devise means for " translating " audible or visible waves into and out of other kinds of waves, we have a far wider choice, and can select those that travel best. It has been found that these are electric waves of far lower frequencies than the visible ones, but higher than audible (or " audio ") frequencies. The useful limits of these *radio frequencies* are about 20,000 to 20,000,000,000 c/s; the lowest frequencies require excessively large aerials to radiate them, and the highest are impeded by the air. All travel through space at the same speed of nearly 300,000,000 metres per second, so the wavelength in metres can be calculated by dividing that figure by the frequency in c/s.

The frequency of the sender is arranged by a suitable choice and adjustment of the electrical equivalents of weight and tightness (or, more strictly, slackness) in the tuning of sound generators. In the same way the receiver can be made to respond to one frequency and reject others. There are so many applicants for frequencies— broadcasting authorities, telegraph and telephone authorities, naval, army, and air forces, police, the merchant navies, airlines, and others—that even with such a wide band to choose from it is difficult to find enough for all, especially as only a small part of the whole band is generally suitable for any particular kind of service.

The change-over from the original sound waves to electric waves of higher frequency is done in two stages: first by a microphone into electric currents having the same frequencies as the sound waves; these currents are then used in a modulator to control the radio-frequency waves in such a way that the original sound characteristics can be extracted at the receiver. Here the change-back is done in the same two stages reversed: first by a detector, which yields electric currents having the original sound frequencies; then by ear-phones or loud speakers which use these currents to generate sound waves.

Since the whole thing is an application of electricity, our detailed study must obviously begin with the general principles of electricity. And it will soon be necessary to pay special attention to electricity varying in a wavelike manner at both audio and radio frequencies. This will involve the electrical characteristics that form the basis of tuning. To generate the radio-frequency currents in the sender, as well as to amplify and perform many other services, use is made of various types of electronic valves, so it is necessary to study them in some detail. The process of causing the r.f. currents to stir up waves, and the reverse process at the receiver, demands some knowledge of aerials and radiation. Other essential matters that need elucidation are modulation and detection. Armed with this knowledge we can then see how they are applied in typical senders and receivers. Lastly the special requirements of television and radar will be briefly noted.

CHAPTER 2

Elementary Electrical Notions

ELECTRONS

THE EXACT NATURE of electricity is a mystery that may never be fully cleared up, but from what is known it is possible to form a sort of working model or picture which helps us to understand how it produces the results it does, and even to think out how to produce new results. The reason why the very existence of electricity went unnoticed until comparatively recent history was that there are two opposite kinds which exist in equal quantities and (unless separated in some way) cancel one another out. This behaviour reminded the investigating scientists of the use of positive ($+$) and negative ($-$) signs in arithmetic—the introduction of either $+1$ or -1 has a definite effect, but $+1-1$ equals just nothing. So, although at that time hardly anything was known about the composition of the two kinds of electricity, they were called positive and negative. Both positive and negative electricity produce very remarkable effects when they are separate, but a combination of equal quantities shows no signs of electrification.

Further research led to the startling conclusion that all matter consists largely of electricity. All the thousands of different kinds of matter, whether solid, liquid, or gaseous, consist of atoms which contain only a very few different basic components. Of these we need take note of only one kind—particles of negative electricity, called *electrons*. Each atom can be imagined as a sort of ultra-microscopic solar system in which a number of electrons revolve round a central nucleus, rather as our earth and the other planets revolve round the sun (Fig. 16).

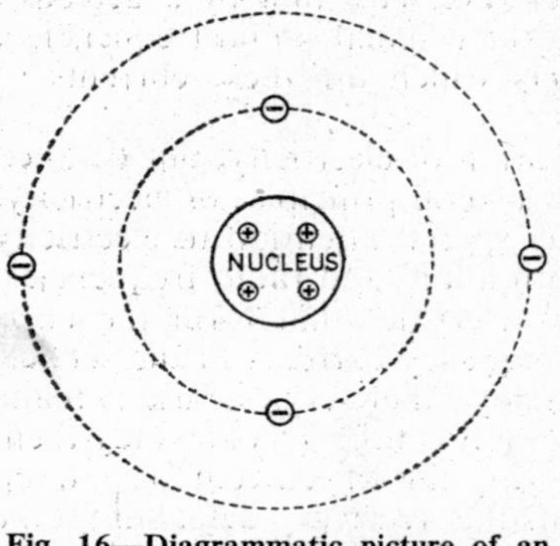

The nucleus is generally a more or less composite structure ; it makes up nearly all the weight of the atom, and the number and type of particles it contains determine which element it is—oxygen, carbon, iron, etc. Recent research has shown how to change some elements into others by breaking up the nucleus under very intense laboratory treatment. For our present purpose, however, the only things we need remember

Fig. 16—Diagrammatic picture of an atom. Most of the weight is concentrated in the nucleus, which by itself is electrically positive; around it circles a number of electrons, normally just sufficient to neutralize the nuclear electricity

about the nucleus are that it is far heavier than the electrons, and that it has a surplus of positive electricity.

In the normal or unelectrified state of the atom this positive surplus is exactly neutralized by the planetary electrons. But it is a comparatively easy matter to dislodge one or more of these electrons from each atom. One method is by rubbing; for example, if a glass rod is rubbed vigorously with silk some of the electrons belonging to the glass are transferred to the silk. Doing this produces no change in the material itself—the glass is still glass and the silk remains silk. As separate articles they show no obvious evidence of the transfer. But if they are brought close together it is found that they attract one another. And the glass rod can pick up small scraps of paper. It is even possible, in a dry atmosphere, to produce sparks. These curious phenomena gradually fade away, and the materials become normal again.

ELECTRIC CHARGES AND CURRENTS

The silk with its surplus of electrons is said to be negatively charged. The glass has a corresponding deficiency of electrons, so its positive nuclear electricity is incompletely neutralized, and the result is called a positive charge. It is a pity that the people who decided which to call positive did not know anything about electrons, because if they had they would certainly have called electrons positive and so spared us a great deal of confusion. As it is, however, one just has to remember that a *surplus* of electrons is called a *negative* charge.

Any unequal distribution of electrons is a condition of stress. Forcible treatment of some kind is necessary to create a surplus or deficiency anywhere, and if the electrons get a chance they move back to restore the balance; i.e., from negatively to positively charged bodies. This tendency shows itself as an attraction between the bodies themselves. That is what is meant by saying that opposite charges attract.

The space between opposite charges, across which this attraction is exerted, is said to be subject to an *electric field*. The greater the charges, the more intense is the field and the greater the attractive force.

If a number of people are forcibly transferred from town A to town B, the pressure of overcrowding and the intensity of desire to leave B depend, not only on the number of displaced persons, but also on the size of B and possibly on whether there is a town C close by with plenty of accommodation. The electrical pressure also depends on other things than the charge, reckoned in displaced electrons; so it is more convenient to refer to it by another term, namely *difference of potential*, often abbreviated to p.d. We shall consider the exact relationship between charge and p.d. in the next chapter. The thing to remember now is that wherever there is a difference of potential between two points there is a tendency for electrons to move from the point of lower (or negative) potential

37

to that of higher (or positive) potential in order to equalize the distribution.* If they are free to move they will do so; and their movement is what we call an *electric current*.

This is where we find it so unfortunate that the names " positive " and " negative " were allocated before anybody knew about electrons. For it amounted to a guess that the direction of current flow was the opposite to that in which we now know electrons flow. By the time the truth was known this bad guess had become so firmly established that reversing it would have caused worse confusion. Moreover, when the positively charged atoms (or positive *ions*) resulting from the removal of electrons are free to do so they also move, in the direction + to —, though much more slowly owing to their greater mass. So this book follows the usual custom of talking about current flowing from + to — or high to low potential, but it must be remembered that nearly every time this means electrons moving from — to +.

CONDUCTORS AND INSULATORS

Electrons are not always free to move. Except in special circumstances (such as high temperature, which we shall consider in connection with valves) atoms do not allow their electrons to fly off completely on their own, even when they are surplus. The atoms of some substances go so far as to allow frequent exchanges, however, like dancers in a Paul Jones, and in fact such exchanges go on all the time, even in the normal unelectrified state. The directions in which the electrons flit from one atom to another are then completely random, because there is nothing to influence them one way or another.

But suppose the whole piece of substance is pervaded by an electric field. The electrons feel an attraction towards the positive end; so between partnerships they tend to drift that way. The drift is what is known as an electric current, and substances that allow this sort of thing to go on are called *conductors* of electricity. All the metals are more or less good conductors, hence the extensive use of metal wire. Carbon and some liquids are fairly good conductors.

Note that although electrons start to go in at the negative end and electrons start to arrive at the positive end the moment the p.d. is set up, this does not mean that these are the same electrons, which have instantaneously travelled the whole length of the conductor. An electron drift starts almost instantaneously throughout miles of wire, but the speed at which they drift is seldom much more than an inch a minute.

Other substances keep their electrons, as it were, on an elastic leash which allows them a little freedom of movement, but never " out of sight " of the atom. If such a substance occupies the

---

* Note that + 1 is positive with respect to — 1 or even to 0, but it is negative with respect to + 2; — 1 or 0 are both positive with respect to — 2. There is nothing inconsistent in talking about two oppositely charged bodies one minute, and in the next referring to them both as positive (relative to something else).

space between two places of different potential, the electrons strain at the leash in response to the positive attraction, but a continuous steady drift is impossible. Materials of this kind, called *insulators*, can be used to prevent charges from leaking away, or to form boundaries restricting currents to the desired routes. Dry air, glass, ebonite, rubber, and silk are among the best insulating materials. None is absolutely perfect, however; electrified glass rods, etc., lose their charge sooner or later.

ELECTROMOTIVE FORCE

If electrons invariably moved from − to +, as described, they would in time neutralize all the positive charges in the world, and that, for all practical purposes, would be the end of electricity. But fortunately there are certain appliances, such as batteries and dynamos (or generators) which can force electrons to go from + to −, contrary to their natural inclination. In this way they can continuously replenish a surplus of electrons. Suppose A and B in Fig. 17 are two insulated metal terminals, and a number of electrons have been transferred from A to B, so that A is at a higher potential than B. If now they are joined by a wire, electrons will drift along it, and, if that were all, the surplus would soon be used up, and the potential difference would disappear. But A and B happen to be the terminals of a battery, and as soon as electrons leave B the battery provides more, while at the same time it withdraws electrons arriving at A. So while electrons are moving from B to A through the wire, the battery keeps them moving from A to B through itself. The battery is, of course, a conductor; but if it were only that it would be an additional path for electrons to go from B to A and dissipate the charge all the quicker. It is remarkable, then, for being able to make electrons move against a p.d. This ability is called *electromotive force* (usually abbreviated to e.m.f.).

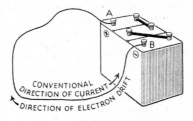

Fig. 17—A very simple electrical circuit, round which a current of electrons is made to flow continuously by the electromotive force of a battery

Fig. 17 shows what is called a *closed circuit*, there being a continuous endless path for the current. This is invariably necessary for a continuous current, because if the circuit were opened anywhere, say by disconnecting the wire from one of the terminals, continuation of the current would cause electrons to pile up at the break, and the potential would increase without limit; which is impossible.

ELECTRICAL UNITS

The amount or strength of an electric current might reasonably be reckoned as the number of electrons passing any point in the circuit each second, but the electron is so extremely small that such a unit would lead to inconveniently large numbers. For practical purposes it has been agreed to base the unit on the metric system. It is called the *ampere* (or more colloquially the amp), and happens to be rather more than 6,000,000,000,000,000,000 (or 6×10^{18}) electrons per second.

As one would expect, the number of amps caused to flow in a given circuit depends on the strength of the electromotive force operating in it. The practical unit of e.m.f. is the *volt*.

Obviously the strength of current depends also on the circuit—whether it is made up of good or bad conductors. This fact is expressed by saying that circuits differ in their electrical *resistance*. The resistance of a circuit or of any part of it can be reckoned in terms of the e.m.f. required to drive a given current through it. For convenience the unit of resistance is made numerically equal to the number of volts required to cause one amp to flow, and to avoid the cumbersome expression "volts per amp" this unit of resistance has been named the *ohm*.

By international agreement the following letter symbols have been allocated to denote these electrical quantities and their units, and will be used from now on:

Quantity	Symbol for Quantity	Unit of Quantity	Symbol for Unit
E.M.F.	E	Volt	V
Current	I	Ampere	A
Resistance	R	Ohm	Ω

(Ω is a Greek capital letter, "Omega".)

These three important quantities are not all independent, for we have just defined resistance in terms of e.m.f. and current. Expressing it in symbols:

$$R = \frac{E}{I}$$

Ohm's Law

The question immediately arises: Does R depend only on the conductor, or does it depend also on the current or voltage? This was one of the first and most important investigations into electric currents. We can investigate it for ourselves if we have an instrument for measuring current, called an *ammeter*, a battery of identical cells, and a length of wire or other resistive conductor. A closed circuit is formed of the wire, the ammeter, and a varying number of the cells; and the ammeter reading corresponding to each number of cells is noted. The results can then be plotted in the form of a graph (Fig. 18). If the voltage of a cell is known, the current can be plotted against voltage instead of merely against number of cells.

When all the points are joined up by a line it will probably be found that the line is straight and inclined at an angle and passes through the origin (O). If a different resistance is tried, its line will slope at a different angle. Fig. 18 shows two possible samples resulting from such an experiment. In this case each cell gave 2 volts, so points were plotted at 2, 4, 6, 8, etc., volts. The points at −2, −4, etc., volts were obtained by reversing the battery. A current of −2 amps means a current of the same strength as +2 amps, but in the opposite direction.

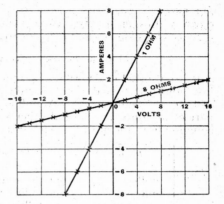

Fig. 18—Graph showing the results of an experiment on the relationship between current in amps and e.m.f. in volts, for two different circuits

Referring to the steep line, we see that an e.m.f. of 2 V caused a current of 2 A, 4 V caused 4 A, and so on. The result of dividing the number of volts by the number of amps is always 1. And this, according to our definition, is the resistance in ohms. So there is no need to specify the current at which the resistance must be measured, or to make a graph; it is only necessary to measure the voltage required to cause any one known current (or the current caused by any one voltage). The amount (or, as one says in technical language, the *value*) of resistance so obtained can be used to find the current at any other voltage. For this purpose it is more convenient to write the relationship R = E/I in the form

$$I = \frac{E}{R} \quad \text{or} \quad E = IR$$

Thus if any two of these quantities are known, the third can be found.

Conductors whose resistance does not vary with the amount of current flowing through them are described as *linear*, because the line representing them on a graph of the Fig. 18 type (called their *current/voltage characteristic*) is straight. Although the relationship I = E/R is true for any resistance, its greatest usefulness lies in the fact, discovered by Dr. Ohm, that ordinary conductors are linear.* With this assumption it is known as Ohm's Law.

As an example of the use of Ohm's Law, we might find, in investigating the value of an unknown resistance, that when it was connected to the terminals of a 100 V battery a current of 0·01 A was driven through it. Using Ohm's Law in the form R = E/I, we get for the value of the resistance 100/0·01 = 10,000 Ω. Alternatively, we might know the value of the resistance and find that an

* We shall come across some exceptions, such as valves and rectifiers, from Chapter 9 onwards.

41

old battery, nominally of 120 V, could only drive a current of
0·007 A through it. We could deduce, since $E = I \times R$, that the
voltage of the battery had fallen to $10,000 \times 0·007 = 70$ V.

LARGER AND SMALLER UNITS

It is not usual to describe a current as 0·007 ampere, as was done
just now; one speaks of " 7 milliamperes ", or, more familiarly
still, of " 7 milliamps ". A milliampere is thus one-thousandth
part of an ampere. Several other such convenient prefixes are in
common use; the most frequent are:

Prefix	Meaning	Symbol
milli-	one thousandth of	m
micro-	one millionth of	μ
micromicro- or pico-	one billionth of (million millionth)	$\mu\mu$ or p
kilo-	one thousand	k
mega-	one million	M

(μ is the Greek letter " mu ".)

These prefixes can be put in front of any unit; one speaks
commonly of milliamps, microamps, megohms, and so on. " Half
a megohm " comes much more trippingly off the tongue than
" Five hundred thousand ohms ", just as $\frac{1}{2}$ MΩ is quicker to write
than 500,000 Ω.

It must be remembered, however, that Ohm's Law in the forms
given above refers to volts, ohms, and amps. If a current of 5 mA
is flowing through 15,000 Ω, the voltage across that resistance will
not be 75,000 V. But seeing that most of the currents we shall be
concerned with are of the milliamp order, it is worth noting that
there is no need to convert them to amps if R is expressed in
thousands of ohms (kΩ). So in the example just given one can get
the correct answer, 75 V, by multiplying 5 by 15.

CIRCUIT DIAGRAMS

At this stage it would be as well to start getting used to circuit
diagrams. In a book like this, concerned with general principles
rather than with constructional details, what matters about (say) a
battery is not its shape or the design of its label, but its voltage and
how it is connected in the circuit. So it is a waste of time drawing
a picture as in Fig. 17. All one needs is the symbol shown as
Fig. 19a, which represents one cell. An accumulator cell gives
2 V, and a dry cell about 1·4 V. The longer stroke represents
the + terminal. To get higher voltages, several cells are connected
one after the other, as in Fig. 19b, and if so many are needed that it
is tiresome to draw them all one can represent all but the end ones
by a dotted line, as in Fig. 19c, which also shows how to indicate the

voltage between two points. Other symbols in Fig. 19 are (*d*) a circuit element called a *resistor*, because resistance is its significant feature, (*e*) a switch shown " open " or " off ", and (*f*) a measuring instrument, the type of which can be shown by " mA " for milliammeter, " V " for voltmeter, etc., and the range of measurement marked as here. A simple line represents an electrical connection of negligible resistance, often called a *lead* (rhyming with " feed ").

The circuit diagram for the Ohm's Law experiment can therefore be shown as in Fig. 20. The arrow denotes a movable connection, used here for including anything from one to eight cells in circuit.

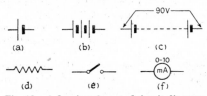

(a)   (b)   (c)

(d)   (e)   (f)

Fig. 19—A first instalment of circuit-diagram symbols, representing (*a*) a cell, (*b*) a battery of three cells, (*c*) a battery of many cells, (*d*) a resistor, (*e*) a switch, and (*f*) a milli-ammeter

Fig. 20—Circuit diagram of the apparatus used for obtaining Fig. 18

Fig. 20 is a simple example of a *series* circuit. Two elements are said to be connected in series when, in tracing out the path of the current, we encounter them one after the other. With steadily flowing currents the electrons do not start piling up locally, so it is clear that the same current flows through both elements. In Fig. 20, for instance, the current flowing through the ammeter is the same as that through the resistor and the part of the battery " in circuit ".

Two elements are said to be in *parallel* if they are connected so as to form alternative paths for the current, for example the resistors in Fig. 23a. Since a point cannot be at two different potentials at once, it is obvious that the same potential difference exists across both of them (i.e., between their ends or terminals). One element in parallel with another is often described as *shunting* the other.

It is important to realize that the same method of connection can sometimes be regarded as either series or parallel, according to circumstances. In Fig. 21, R_1 and R_2 are in series as regards battery B_1, and in parallel as regards B_2.

Looking at the circuit diagrams of wireless sets one often sees quite complicated networks of resistors. Fortunately Ohm's Law can be applied to every part of a complicated system of e.m.fs and resistances as well as to the whole. Beginners often seem reluctant to make use of this fact, being scared by the apparent difficulty of the problem. So it may be as well to see how it works out with more elaborate circuits.

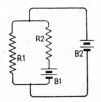

Fig. 21—R_1 is in series with R_2 as regards B_1, but in parallel with it as regards B_2

43

RESISTANCES IN SERIES AND IN PARALLEL

Complex circuit networks can be tackled by successive stages of finding a single element that is equivalent (as regards the quantity to be found) to two or more. Consider first two resistances R_1 and R_2, in series with one another and with a source of e.m.f. E (Fig. 22a). To bring this circuit as a whole within the scope of calculation by Ohm's Law we need to find the single resistance R (Fig. 22b) equivalent to R_1 and R_2 together.

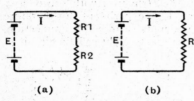

(a)   (b)

Fig. 22—Resistances in series. The circuit *b* is equivalent to the circuit *a*, in the sense that both take the same current from the battery E, if $R = R_1 + R_2$

We know that the current in the circuit is everywhere the same; call it I. Then, by Ohm's Law, the voltage across R_1 is I R_1, and that across R_2 is I R_2. The total voltage across both must therefore be I R_1 + I R_2, or I ($R_1 + R_2$), which must be equal to the voltage E.

In the equivalent circuit, E is equal to IR, and since, to make the circuits truly equivalent, the currents must be the same in both for the same battery-voltage, we see that $R = R_1 + R_2$. Generalizing from this result, we conclude that: *The total resistance of several resistances in series is equal to the sum of their individual resistances.*

Turning to the parallel-connected resistances of Fig. 23a, we see that they have the same voltage across them; in this case the e.m.f. of the battery. Each of these resistances will take a current depending on its own resistance and on the e.m.f.—the simplest case of Ohm's Law. Calling the currents respectively I_1 and I_2, we therefore know that $I_1 = E/R_1$ and $I_2 = E/R_2$. The total current drawn is the sum of the two: it is $I = E/R_1 + E/R_2 = E (1/R_1 + 1/R_2)$. In the equivalent circuit of Fig. 23b the current is E/R, which may also be written E (1/R). Since, for equivalence between the circuits, the current must be the same for the same battery voltage, we see that $1/R = 1/R_1 + 1/R_2$. Generalizing from this result, we may conclude that: *If several re-*

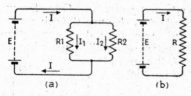

(a)   (b)

Fig. 23—Resistances in parallel. The circuit *b* is equivalent to the circuit *a* in the sense that both take the current from the battery E, if $1/R = 1/R_1 + 1/R_2$

sistances are connected in parallel, the sum of the reciprocals of their individual resistances is equal to the reciprocal of their total resistance.

If the resistances of Fig. 23a were 100 Ω and 200 Ω, the single resistance R that, connected in their place, would draw the same current is given by $1/R = 1/100 + 1/200 = 0.01 + 0.005 = 0.015$.

Hence, $R = 1/0 \cdot 015 = 66 \cdot 67 \; \Omega$. This could be checked by adding together the individual currents through $100 \; \Omega$ and $200 \; \Omega$, and comparing the total with the current taken from the same voltage-source by $66 \cdot 67 \; \Omega$. In both cases the result is $0 \cdot 015$ A per volt of battery.

We can summarize the two rules in symbols:

1. Series Connection: $R = R_1 + R_2 + R_3 + R_4 + \cdots$
2. Parallel Connection: $1/R = 1/R_1 + 1/R_2 + 1/R_3 + \cdots$

For two resistances in parallel, a more easily calculated form of the same rule is $R = R_1 R_2 / (R_1 + R_2)$.

SERIES-PARALLEL COMBINATIONS

How the foregoing rules, derived directly from Ohm's Law, can be applied to the calculation of more complex circuits can perhaps best be illustrated by a thorough working-out of one fairly elaborate network, Fig. 24. We will find the total current flowing, the equivalent resistance of the whole circuit, and the voltage and current of every resistor individually.

The policy is to look for any resistors that are in simple series or parallel. The only two in this example are R_2 and R_3. Writing R_{23} to symbolize the combined resistance of R_2 and R_3 taken together, we know that $R_{23} = R_2 R_3 / (R_2 + R_3) = 200 \times 500/700 = 142 \cdot 8 \; \Omega$. This gives us the simplified circuit of Fig. 25a. If R_{23} and R_4 were one resistance, they and R_5 in parallel would make another simple case, so we proceed to combine R_{23} and R_4 to make R_{234}. $R_{234} = R_{23} + R_4 = 142 \cdot 8 + 150 = 292 \cdot 8 \; \Omega$. Now we have the circuit of Fig. 25b. Combining R_{234} and R_5, $R_{2345} =$

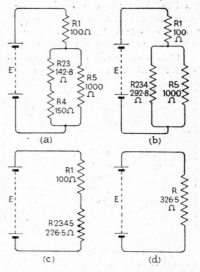

(a)   (b)

(c)   (d)

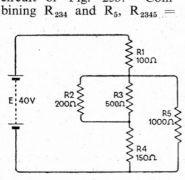

Fig. 24—The current through and voltage across each resistor in this complicated network can be calculated by applying the two simple rules derived from Figs. 22 and 23

Fig. 25—Successive stages in simplifying the circuit of Fig. 24. R_{23} stands for the single resistances equivalent to R_1 and R_2; R_{234} to that equivalent to R_2, R_3 and R_4; and so on. R represents the whole system

45

$292 \cdot 8 \times 1000/1292 \cdot 8 = 226 \cdot 5 \ \Omega$. This brings us within sight of the end; Fig. 25c shows us that the total resistance of the network now is simply the sum of the two remaining resistances; that is, R of Fig. 25d is $R_{2345} + R_1 = 226 \cdot 5 + 100 = 326 \cdot 5 \ \Omega$.

From the point of view of current drawn from the 40-V source the whole system of Fig. 24 is equivalent to a single resistor of this value. The current taken from the battery will therefore be $40/326 \cdot 5 = 0 \cdot 1225$ A $= 122 \cdot 5$ mA.

To find the current through each resistor individually now merely means the application of Ohm's Law to some of our previous results. Since R_1 carries the whole current of $122 \cdot 5$ mA, the potential difference across it will be $100 \times 0 \cdot 1225 = 12 \cdot 25$ V. R_{2345} also carries the whole current (25c); the p.d. across it will again be the product of resistance and current, in this case $226 \cdot 5 \times 0 \cdot 1225 = 27 \cdot 75$ V. This same voltage also exists, as comparison of the various diagrams will show, across the whole complex system $R_2 R_3 R_4 R_5$ in Fig. 24. Across R_5 there lies the whole of this voltage; the current through this resistor will therefore be $27 \cdot 75/1000$ A $= 27 \cdot 75$ mA.

The same p.d. across R_{234} of Fig. 25b, or across the system $R_2 R_3 R_4$ of Fig. 24, will drive a current of $27 \cdot 75/292 \cdot 8 = 94 \cdot 75$ mA through this branch. The whole of this flows through R_4 (25a), the voltage across which will accordingly be $150 \times 0 \cdot 09475 = 14 \cdot 21$ V. Similarly, the p.d. across R_{23} in Fig. 25a, or across both R_2 and R_3 in Fig. 24, will be $0 \cdot 09475 \times 142 \cdot 8 = 13 \cdot 54$ V, from which we find that the currents through R_2 and R_3 will be respectively $13 \cdot 54/200$ and $13 \cdot 54/500$ A, or $67 \cdot 68$ and $27 \cdot 07$ mA, making up the required total of $94 \cdot 75$ mA for this branch.

This completes an analysis of the entire circuit; we can now collect our scattered results in the form of the table below.

Resistance (ohms)		Current (milliamps)	Voltage (volts)
R_1	100	122·5	12·25
R_2	200	67·68	13·54
R_3	500	27·07	13·54
R_4	150	94·75	14·21
R_5	1000	27·75	27·75
R	326·5	122·5	40

It should be noted that by using suitable resistors any potential intermediate between those given by the terminals of the battery can be obtained. For instance, if the lower and upper ends of the battery in Fig. 24 are regarded as 0 and $+ 40$ (they could equally be reckoned as $- 40$ and 0, or $- 10$ and $+ 30$, with respect to any selected level of voltage), the potential of the junction between

R_3 and R_4 is 14·21 V. The arrangement is therefore called a *potential divider*, and is often employed for obtaining a desired potential not given directly by the terminals of the source. If a sliding connection is provided on a resistor, to give a continuously variable potential, it is generally known—though not always quite justifiably—as a *potentiometer*.

RESISTANCE ANALYSED

So far we have assumed the possibility of almost any value of resistance without inquiring very closely into what determines the resistance of any particular resistor or part of a circuit. We understand that different materials vary widely in the resistance they offer to the flow of electricity, and can guess that with any given material a long piece will offer more resistance than a short piece, and a thin piece than a thick. We have indeed actually proved as much and more; by the rule for resistances in series the resistance of a wire is exactly proportional to its length—doubling the length is equivalent to adding another equal resistance in series, and so on (Fig. 26a). Similarly, putting two equal pieces in parallel, which halves the resistance, is equivalent to doubling the thickness; so resistance is proportional to the reciprocal of thickness. Or, in more precise language, to the cross-section area (Fig. 26b). Altering the shape of the cross-section has no effect on the resistance—with steady currents, at least. Fig. 26c shows how doubling the *diameter* of a piece of wire divides the resistance by *four*.

To compare the resistances of different materials it is necessary to bring them all to the same standard length and cross-section area, which is one metre long by one square metre. This comparative resistance for any material is called its *resistivity* (symbol: ρ, pronounced " roe "). Knowing the resistivity (and it can be found in almost any electrical reference book) one can easily calculate the resistance of any wire or piece having uniform section by multiplying by the length in metres (l) and dividing by the cross-section area in square metres (A). In symbols:

$$R = \frac{\rho\, l}{A}$$

It is seldom necessary to make such calculations, because there are tables showing the resistance per metre or per yard of all the different gauges of wire, both for copper (usually used for parts of the circuit where resistance should be as low as possible), and for the special alloys intended to have a high resistance.

Resistance varies to some extent with temperature, so the tables show the temperature at which

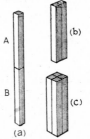

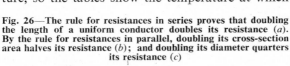

Fig. 26—The rule for resistances in series proves that doubling the length of a uniform conductor doubles its resistance (*a*). By the rule for resistances in parallel, doubling its cross-section area halves its resistance (*b*); and doubling its diameter quarters its resistance (*c*)

47

they apply, and also the proportion by which the resistance rises or falls with rise of temperature.

CONDUCTANCE

It is often more convenient to work in terms of the *ease* with which a current can be made to flow, rather than the difficulty; in other words, in *conductance* rather than resistance. The symbol for conductance is G, and its unit is equal to the number of amps caused to flow by one volt. So $I = EG$ is an alternative form of $I = E/R$; and $G = I/R$. As conductance is thus the opposite of resistance, its unit is called the mho. It has no special symbol, but $\mho$ has been suggested.

KIRCHHOFF'S LAWS

We have already taken it as obvious that no one point can be at more than one potential at the same time. (If it is not obvious, try to imagine a point with a difference of potential between itself; then electrons will flow from itself to itself, i.e., a journey of no distance and therefore non-existent.) So if you start at any point on a closed circuit and go right round it, adding up all the voltages on the way, with due regard for $+$ and $-$, the total is bound to be zero. If it isn't, a mistake has been made somewhere; just as a surveyor must have made a mistake if he started from a certain spot, measuring his ascents as positive and his descents as negative, and his figures told him that when he returned to his starting-point he had made a net ascent or descent.

This simple principle is one of what are known as Kirchhoff's Laws, and is a great help in tackling networks where the methods already described fail because there are no two elements that can be simply combined. One writes down an equation for each closed loop, by adding together all the voltages and equating the total to zero, and one then solves the resulting simultaneous equations. That can be left for more advanced study, but the same Law is a valuable check on any circuit calculations. Try applying it to the several closed loops in Fig. 24, such as that formed by E, R_1, and R_5. If we take the route clockwise we go " uphill " through the battery, becoming more positive by 40 V. Coming down through R_1 we move from positive to negative so add $- 12\cdot25$ V, and, through R_5, $-27\cdot75$ V, reaching the starting point again. Check: $40 - 12\cdot25 - 27\cdot75 = 0$.

Taking another clockwise route via R_3, R_5, and R_4, we get $13\cdot54 - 27\cdot75 + 14\cdot21 = 0$. And so on for any closed loop.

The other Kirchhoff Law is equally obvious; it states that if you count all currents arriving at any point in a circuit as positive, and those leaving as negative, the total is zero. This can be used as an additional check, or as the basis of an alternative method of solving circuit problems.

P.D. AND E.M.F.

The fact that both e.m.f. and p.d. are measured in volts may sometimes make it seem difficult to distinguish between them.

E.m.f. is a cause; p.d. an effect. An e.m.f. can only come from something active, such as a battery or generator. It has the ability to set up a p.d. But a p.d. can exist across a passive element such as a resistor, or even in empty space. The p.d. across a resistor (or, as it is sometimes called, the voltage drop, or just " drop ") is, as we know, equal to its resistance multiplied by the current through it; and the positive end is that at which the current enters (or electrons leave). The positive end of a source of e.m.f., on the other hand, is that at which current would leave if its terminals were joined by a passive conductor. That is because an e.m.f. has the unique ability of being able to drive a current against a p.d.

Note that the positive terminal of a source of e.m.f. is not always the one at which current actually *does* leave; there may be a greater e.m.f. opposing it in the circuit.

It will be worth while to make quite sure that these questions of direction of e.m.f., p.d. and current are clearly understood, or

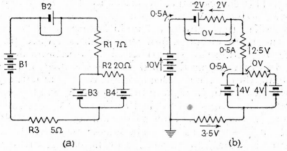

Fig. 27—(*a*) is an imaginary circuit for illustrating the meanings of e.m.f. and p.d. The voltages and currents in different parts of it are marked in (*b*). Arrows alongside voltages show the direction of *rise* of potential

there will be endless difficulty later on. So let us consider the imaginary circuit shown in Fig. 27a. Assume each cell has an e.m.f. of 2 V.

All five cells in the battery B_1 are connected in series and all tend to drive current clockwise, so the total clockwise e.m.f. of B_1 is $5 \times 2 = 10$ V, and we can show this as in Fig. 27b.

B_2 seems to be a flat contradiction of Kirchhoff's Law. Here we have an e.m.f. of 2 V between two points which must be at the same potential because they are joined by a wire of negligible resistance! The cell is, as we say, *short-circuited*, or " dead-shorted ". Part of the answer to this apparent impossibility is that no real source of e.m.f. can be entirely devoid of resistance. Often it is not enough to matter, so is not shown in diagrams. But where the source is short-circuited it is vital, because it is the only thing to limit the current. To represent a source of e.m.f. completely, then, we must include between its terminals not only a symbol for e.m.f. but also one for resistance. When a source of

49

e.m.f. is open-circuited, so that no current flows, there is no voltage drop in its internal resistance, so the terminal voltage is equal to the e.m.f. When current is drawn the terminal voltage falls, and if the source is dead-shorted the internal drop must be equal to the e.m.f., as shown in Fig. 27b. The other part of the answer is that when the source has a very low resistance (e.g., a large accumulator or generator) such an enormous current flows that even a wire of normally negligible resistance does not reduce the terminal voltage to zero, and the wire is burnt out, and perhaps the source too.

In our example we shall assume that all the resistance is internal, so the external effect of B_2 is nil.

If the loop containing B_3, B_4, and R_2 is considered on its own as a series circuit, we see two e.m.fs each of 4 V in opposition, so the net e.m.f. is zero, and no current due to them flows through R_2. As regards the main circuit, B_3 and B_4 are in parallel, and contribute an e.m.f. of $-$ 4 V (because in opposition to B_1, which we considered positive). This can be indicated either by " $-$ 4 V " and a clockwise arrow, or by " 4 V " and an anticlockwise arrow as shown.

We see, then, that putting a second battery in parallel does not increase the main circuit e.m.f., but it does reduce the internal resistance by putting two in parallel, so is sometimes done for that reason. In our example the 20 Ω in series with B_4 is probably far greater than the internal resistance of B_3, so practically all the current will flow through B_3, and the effect of B_4 will be negligible.

We have, then (ignoring B_2), $10 - 4 = 6$ V net e.m.f. in the circuit, and (neglecting the internal resistances of B_1 and B_3) a total resistance of $7 + 5 = 12$ Ω. The current round the circuit is therefore $6/12 = 0.5$ A, as marked, and the voltage drops across R_1 and R_3 are $0.5 \times 7 = 3.5$ V and $0.5 \times 5 = 2.5$ V respectively.

To help maintain the distinction between e.m.f. and p.d. it is usual to reserve the symbol E for e.m.f., and to use V to mean p.d.

Note that the potential difference between two points is something quite definite, but the potential of a point (like the height of a hill) is relative, depending on what one takes as the reference level. Heights are usually assumed to be relative to sea level, unless it is obvious that some other " zero " is used (such as street level for the height of a building). The potential of the earth is the corresponding zero for electrical potentials, where no other is implied. To ensure definiteness of potential, apparatus is often connected to earth, as indicated by the symbol at the negative end of B_1 in Fig. 27b.

ELECTRICAL EFFECTS

It is time now to consider what electricity can *do*. One of the most familiar effects of an electric current is heat. It is as if the jostling of the electrons in the conductor caused a certain amount of friction. But whereas it makes the wire in an electric fire red hot, and in an electric light bulb white hot, it seems to have no appreciable effect on the flex and other parts of the circuit—in a reputable installation, anyway. Experiments show that the rate at which heat is generated in a conductor containing no e.m.fs is proportional to the product of the current flowing through it and the voltage across it; in symbols, EI. Since both E and I are related to the resistance of the conductor, we can substitute IR for E or E/A for I, getting I^2R or E^2/R as alternative measures of the heating effect. Thus for a given current the heating is proportional to the resistance. Electric lamps and heaters are designed so that their resistance is far higher than that of the wires connecting them to the generator. I^2R shows that the heating increases very rapidly as the current rises. Advantage is taken of this in fuses, which are short pieces of wire that melt (or " blow ") and cut off the current if, owing to a short-circuit somewhere, it rises dangerously above normal.

Another effect of an electric current is to magnetize the space around it. This effect is particularly marked when the wire is coiled round a piece of iron. As we shall see, it is of far more significance than merely being a handy way of making magnets.

An effect that need not concern us much is the production of chemical changes, especially when the current is passed through watery liquids. A practical example is the charging of accumulators. The use of the word " charging " for this process is unfortunate, for no surplus or deficiency of electrons is accumulated by it.

All these three effects are reversible; that is to say, they can be turned into causes, the effect in each case being an e.m.f. The production of an e.m.f. by heating the junction of two different metals is of only minor importance, but magnetism is the basis of all electrical generating machinery, and chemical changes are very useful on a smaller scale in batteries.

INSTRUMENTS FOR MEASURING ELECTRICITY

All three effects can be used for indicating the strength of currents; but although hot-wire ammeters are occasionally used in radio senders, the vast majority of current meters are based on the magnetic effect. There are two main kinds—the moving-iron instrument, in which the current coil is fixed, and a small piece of iron with a pointer attached moves to an extent depending on the amperage; and the moving-coil (generally preferred) in which the coil is deflected by a fixed permanent magnet.

Besides these current effects there is the potential effect—the attraction between two bodies at different potential. The force of attraction is seldom enough to be noticeable, but if the p.d. is not too small it can be measured by a delicate instrument. This is the principle of what is called the electrostatic voltmeter, in which a rotatable set of small metal vanes is held apart from an interleaving fixed set by a hairspring. When a voltage is applied between the two sets the resulting attraction turns the moving set through an angle depending on the voltage. This type of instrument, which is a true voltmeter because it depends directly on potential and

51

draws no current, is practical and convenient for full-scale readings from about 1,000 V to 10,000 V, but not for low voltages. (" Full-scale reading " means the reading when the pointer is deflected to the far end of the scale.)

Since $E = IR$, voltage can be measured indirectly by measuring the current passed through a known resistance. If this additional conducting path were to draw a substantial current from the source of voltage to be measured, it might give misleading results by lowering that voltage appreciably; so R is made relatively large. The current meter (usually of the moving-coil type) is therefore a milliammeter, or better still a microammeter. For example, a voltmeter for measuring up to 1 V could be made from a milli-ammeter reading up to 1 mA by adding sufficient resistance to that of the moving coil to bring the total up to 1,000 Ω. The same instrument could be adapted to read up to 10 V (all the scale readings being multiplied by 10) by adding another resistance, called a *multiplier*, of 9,000 Ω, bringing the total to 10,000 Ω. Such an arrangement, shown in Fig. 28a, can obviously be extended.

The same milliammeter can of course be used for measuring currents up to 1 mA by connecting it in series in the current path;

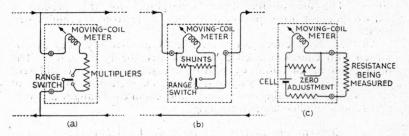

Fig. 28—Showing how a single moving-coil indicating instrument can be used for measuring (*a*) voltage, (*b*) current, (*c*) resistance. The moving coil and pointer attached are shown diagrammatically

but to avoid increasing the resistance of the circuit more than can be helped the voltage resistances would have to be short-circuited or otherwise cut out. Care must be taken never to connect a current meter directly across a voltage source, for its low resistance might pass sufficient current to destroy it. Higher currents can be measured by diverting all but a known fraction of the current through a by-pass resistance called a *shunt*. If, for example, the resistance of the 0–1 milliammeter is 75 Ω, shunting it with $75/9 = 8 \cdot 33 \, \Omega$ would cause nine times as much current to flow through the shunt as passes through the meter, so multiplying the range by 10 (Fig. 28b).

Thus a single moving-coil instrument can be made to cover many ranges of current and voltage measurement, simply by connecting appropriate shunts and multipliers. These are, in effect, known resistances used to reduce the current through the instrument to any desired fraction. But the operation can be reversed by incorporating a battery sufficient to give full-scale deflection; then, when an *unknown* resistance is connected, either as a shunt or multiplier, according to whether it is small or large, the extent to which the reading is reduced depends on the value of that resistance. It is therefore possible to graduate the instrument in ohms and we have an *ohmmeter* (Fig. 28c).

ELECTRICAL POWER

When everyday words have been adapted for scientific purposes by giving them precise and restricted meanings, they are more likely to be misunderstood than words that were specially invented for use as scientific terms—" electron ", for example. *Power* is a word of the first kind. It is commonly used to mean force, or ability, or authority. In technical language it has only one meaning—rate of doing work. *Work* here is also a technical term, confined to purely physical activity such as lifting weights or forcing things to move against pressure or friction—or potential difference. If by exerting muscular force you lift a 10 lb weight 3 ft against the opposing force of gravity you do 30 foot-pounds of work. And if you take a second to do it, your rate of doing work—your power output—is 30 ft-lbs per second, which is rather more than 1/200th of a horse-power. Correspondingly, if the electromotive force of a battery raises the potential of 10 electrons by 3 volts (i.e., causes them to flow against an opposing p.d. of 3 V) it does 30 electron-volts of work; and if it takes one second to do it the output of power is 30 volt-electrons per second. The electron per second is, as we saw, an extremely small unit of electric current, and it is customary to use one about 6×10^{18} times larger—the ampere. So the natural choice for the electrical unit of power might be called the volt-ampere. Actually, for brevity (and another reason), it has been given the name *watt*.

We now have the following to add to the table which was given on page 40:

Quantity	Symbol for Quantity	Unit of Quantity	Symbol for Unit
Electrical power	P	Watt	W

We also have the equation $P = EI$. So when your 3 V torch battery is lighting a 0·2 A bulb it is working at the rate of $0·2 \times 3 = 0·6$ W. In this case the battery e.m.f. is occupied in forcing the current through the resistance of the filament in the bulb, and the resulting heat is visible. We have already noted the experimental fact that the rate at which heat is produced in a resistance is proportional to EI—the product of the e.m.f. applied and the current flowing—

53

and now we know this to be a measure of the power expended. So alternate forms of the power relationship are:

$$P = I^2R \text{ and } P = \frac{E^2}{R}.$$

Thus if any two of the four quantities E, I, R, and P are given, all are known. For example, if a 1,000 Ω resistor is to be used in a circuit where 50 V will be maintained across it, the power dissipated as heat will be $50^2/1{,}000 = 2{\cdot}5$ W. In choosing such a resistor one must take care not only that the resistance is correct but also that it is large enough to get rid of heat at the rate equivalent to $2{\cdot}5$ W without reaching such a high temperature as to damage itself or things near it.

To familiarize oneself with power calculations it would be a good exercise to add another column to the table on page 46, headed " Power (watts) ", working out the figures for each resistor, and checking that they are the same, whether derived from EI, I^2R, or E^2/R. A further check is to add up all the wattages for R_1 to R_5 and see that the total is the same as that for R.

A Broader View of Resistance

It will be found later on in this book that there are other ways in which electrical power can be " lost " than by heating up the circuit through which the current flows. This leads to a rather broader view of resistance; instead of defining it as E/R, resulting from an experiment such as that connected with Fig. 18, one defines it as P/I^2 (derived from $P = I^2R$), P being the expenditure of power in the part of the circuit concerned, and I the current through it. The snag is that P is often difficult to measure. But as a definition to cover the various sorts of " resistance " encountered in radio it is very useful.

A feature of electrical power expended in resistance—however defined—is that it leaves the circuit for good. Except by some indirect method it is not possible to recover any of it in the form of electrical power. But there are ways in which electrical power can be employed to create a store of energy that can be released again as electrical power. *Energy* here is yet another technical term, meaning the amount of work that such a store can do. To return to our mechanical analogy, 30 ft-lbs expended by exerting a force of 10 lbs to push a box 3 ft across the floor is all dissipated as heat caused by friction.* But 30 ft-lbs of work used in raising a 10 lb weight 3 ft is stored as what is called potential energy. If the weight is allowed to descend, it delivers up the 30 ft-lbs of work, which could be used to drive a grandfather clock for a week. Another

---

* It has been found by experiment that if work at the rate of 550 ft-lbs per second (which is called 1 horse power) is devoted entirely to overcoming frictional resistance, heat is generated at the same rate as when 746 watts are dissipated in electrical resistance. By relating both mechanical and electrical power to a common product—heat—it has been possible to find the fixed " rate of exchange " between mechanical and electrical power, namely, 746 W ($=0{\cdot}746$ kW) is equivalent to 1 HP.

way of storing the work would be to push a heavy truck mounted on ball bearings along rails. In this case very little of the pressure would be needed to overcome the small amount of friction; most of it would have the effect of giving it momentum which would keep it going long after the 3 ft push had finished. A heavy truck in motion is capable of doing work because the force setting it in motion has been used to store energy in it; this kind is called kinetic energy.

In the next chapter we shall begin the story of how electrical power can be stored and released in two ways, corresponding to potential and kinetic energy, and how this makes it possible to tune in to different stations on the radio.

CHAPTER 3

Capacitance

CHARGING CURRENTS

ALTHOUGH MOST of the last chapter was about steady e.m.fs driving currents through resistances, you may remember that the whole thing began with the formation of an electric charge. We likened it to the deportation of unwilling citizens from town A to town B. Transferring a quantity of electrons from one place to another and leaving them there sets up a stress between the two places, which is only relieved when the same quantity of electrons has been allowed to flow back. The total amount of the stress is the p.d., measured in volts. And the place with the surplus of electrons is said to be negatively charged. The original method of charging—by friction—is inconvenient for most purposes and has been generally superseded by the use of e.m.f. If an e.m.f. of, say, 100 V is used, electrons will flow until the p.d. builds up to 100 V; then the flow will cease because the charging and discharging forces are exactly equal.

It was at this stage that we provided a conductive path between the negatively and positively charged bodies, allowing the electrons

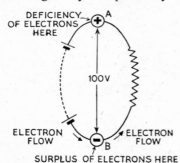

Fig. 29—Before a p.d. can be established between any two parts of a circuit (such as A and B) they must be charged, and when the p.d. is rapidly varied the charging current may be important

to flow back just as fast as the constant e.m.f. drove them, so that a continuous steady current was set up. This state of affairs could be represented as in Fig. 29. Our attention then became attached to this continuous current and the circuit through which it flowed; the electron surplus at the negative end—and the deficit at the positive end—seemed to have no bearing on this, and dropped out of the picture. So long as e.m.f. and current are quite steady, the charges can be ignored.

But not during the process of charging. While that is going on there must be more electrons entering B than are leaving it; and vice versa during discharging. Assuming that there are parts of a circuit requiring a substantial number of electrons to charge them to a potential equal to the applied e.m.f., then it is clear that the ordinary circuit principles we have been studying become more complicated whenever the e.m.f. varies. For one thing, it seems that the current is no longer the same in all parts of a series circuit.

The moment the e.m.f. is applied, a charging current starts to flow, over and above any current through conducting paths. If the e.m.f. is increased at any time, a further charging current flows to raise the p.d. correspondingly. Reducing the e.m.f. causes a discharging current. Seeing that both wire and wireless communication involve e.m.fs that are continually varying, it is evidently important to know how far the charging and discharging currents affect matters.

CAPACITANCE—WHAT IT IS

The first thing is to find what decides the number of electrons needed to charge any part of a circuit. The number of people that could be transferred to another town would probably depend on (a) the pressure brought to bear on them, (b) the size of the town, and (c) its remoteness. The number of electrons that are transferred as a charge certainly depends on the electrical pressure applied— the e.m.f. As one would expect, it is proportional to it. If the battery in Fig. 29 gave 200 V instead of 100, the surplus of electrons forced into B would be just twice as great. The quantity of electrons required to charge any part of a circuit to 1 V is called its *capacitance*.

We have already found that as a practical unit of electric current one electron-per-second would be ridiculously small, and the number that fits the metric system is rather more than 6×10^{18} electrons per second ($=1$ A). So it is natural to take the same number as the unit of electric charge or *quantity* of electricity (symbol: Q). It is therefore equal to the number that passes a given point every second when a current of 1 A is flowing, and the name for it is the *coulomb*. So the obvious unit of capacitance is that which requires 1 coulomb to charge it to 1 volt. It is named the *farad* (abbreviation: F) in honour of Michael Faraday, who contributed so much to electrical science. In symbols, the relationship between electric charge, voltage, and capacitance is:

$$Q = VC$$

which may be compared with the relationship between electric current, voltage, and conductance (p. 48). V is used instead of E because fundamentally it is the p.d. that is involved rather than the charging e.m.f. If the conducting path and e.m.f. in Fig. 29 were both removed, leaving A and B well insulated, their charge and the p.d. would remain.

As capacitance is equal to the charge required to set up a given potential *difference* between two parts of a circuit or other objects, one has to speak of the capacitance *between* those objects, or of one to another.

CAPACITANCE ANALYSED

We saw that when any object is being charged the current going into it is greater than that coming out. So if Kirchhoff's Law about currents is true in all circumstances, the object must be more than just a point; i.e., it must have some size. We would expect

57

the capacitance of objects to one another to depend in some way on their size; the question is, what way?

When analysing resistance (p. 47) we found that it depended on the dimensions of the conductor and what it was made of. So, of course, does conductance, though in inverse ratio. Capacitance, however, has to do with the space between the conductors—it results from the force of attraction that can be set up in that space, or from what is called the electric field. Suppose A and B in

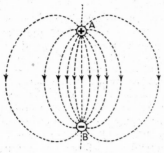

Fig. 30 are our oppositely-charged terminals. The directions along which the force is felt are indicated by dotted lines, called *lines of electric force*. These show the paths electrons would take if they were free to move under the force of attraction to +. (But to agree with the convention for direction of electric currents the arrows point in the opposite direction.) To represent a more intense field, lines are drawn more closely together. Each can be imagined to start from a unit of positive charge and end on a unit of negative charge. It must be understood that it is a matter of

Fig. 30—The dotted lines indicate the direction and distribution of electric field between two oppositely-charged terminals, A and B

convenience what size of unit is taken for this purpose; and that the lines are not meant to convey the idea that the field itself is in the form of lines, with no field in the spaces between.

The fact that the space between two small widely-separate objects such as these is not confined to a uniform path makes the capacitance between them a more difficult thing to calculate than the resistance of a wire. But consider two large flat parallel plates, shown edge-on in Fig. 31a. Except for a slight leakage round the edges, the field is confined to the space directly between the plates, and this space, where the field is uniformly distributed, is a rectangular chunk.

Suppose, for the sake of example, the plates are charged to a p.d. of 100 V. Since the field is uniform, the potential changes at a uniform rate as one moves from one plate to the other. Reckoning the potential of the lower plate as zero, the potential half way

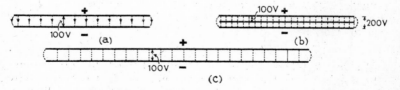

Fig. 31—Consideration of the electric field between closely-spaced parallel plates leads to the relationship between dimensions and capacitance

between the plates is therefore $+ 50$ V. A third plate could be inserted here, and we would then have two capacitances in series, each with a p.d. of 50 V. Provided that the thickness of the third plate was negligible, its presence would make no difference to the amount of the charge required to maintain 100 V across the outer plates. Each of the two capacitances in series would therefore have the same charge but only half the voltage. To raise their p.d. to 100 V each, the amount of charge would have to be doubled (Fig. 31b). In other words (remembering that $C = Q/V$) halving the spacing doubles the capacitance. In general, C is inversely proportional to the distance between the plates (which we can denote by t).

Next, imagine a second pair of plates, exactly the same as those in Fig. 31a. Obviously they would require the same quantity of electricity to charge them to 100 V. If the two pairs were joined together as in Fig. 31c, they would form one unit having twice the cross-section area and requiring twice the charge to set up a given p.d.—in other words, twice the capacitance. In general, C is directly proportional to the cross-section area of the space between the plates (which we can denote by A).

What about the material in the space? The remarkable thing is that an electric field does not depend on there being any material; its stress exists even in a vacuum. Filling the space with air makes hardly any difference; but if you use solid or liquid materials such as glass, paper, plastics or oil, the capacitance is increased. You may remember that a feature of insulators (p. 38) is that their electrons are unable to drift through the material in large numbers but that they " strain at the leash " under the influence of an electric field. When the field is set up—by applying an e.m.f.—this small shift of the electrons all in one direction is equivalent to a momentary current, just like a charging current. Similarly their return to normal position in the atoms is equivalent to a discharging current. The total charging and discharging currents are therefore greater than when the space is unoccupied. The amount by which the capacitance is multiplied in this way by filling the whole of the space with such a material is called the *relative permittivity* of the material, or often just *permittivity* (symbol: κ, pronounced " kappa "). Insulating materials themselves are called *dielectrics*, and another name for relative permittivity is *dielectric constant*. For most solids and liquids it lies between 2 and 10, but for special materials it may be as much as several thousands.

Just as the embodiment of resistance is a resistor, a circuit element designed for its capacitance is called a *capacitor*; the older and misleading name *condenser* is also used. Usually it consists of two or more parallel plates spaced so closely that most of the field is directly between them.

The capacitance of a capacitor thus depends on three factors: area and thickness of the space between the plates, and permittivity of any material there. If suitable units are used it is possible for us to express the capacitance as:

$$C = \frac{\kappa A}{t}$$

in which C is in farads, t in metres, A in square metres, and κ is what is called the *absolute* permittivity; but with κ relative to vacuum a numerical factor must be included:

$$C = \frac{8 \cdot 854 \; \kappa \; A}{t} \times 10^{-12}$$

Supposing, for example, the dielectric had a permittivity of 5 and was 0·1 cm thick, the area needed to provide a capacitance of 1 F would be about 9 square miles. In practice the farad is far too large a unit, so is divided by a million into microfarads (μF), or even by 10^{12} into picofarads (pF), sometimes called micro-microfarads ($\mu\mu$F). Adapting the above formula to the most convenient units for practical purposes, we have:

$$C = \frac{\kappa A}{11 \cdot 3t} \text{ picofarads,}$$

the dimensions being in *centimetres*.

CAPACITORS

The general symbol for a capacitor in circuit diagrams is Fig. 32a. The capacitors themselves appear in great variety in radio circuits, according to the required capacitance and other circumstances.

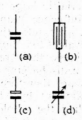

Fig. 32—Standard symbols for (a) fixed capacitor, (c) the same (electrolytic), in which the white plate is positive, and (d) variable capacitor. The symbol (b) denoting one of large capacitance is generally obsolete

Some actually do consist of a single sheet of insulating material such as mica sandwiched between a pair of metal plates, but sometimes there are a number of plates on each side as indicated in Fig. 32b. The effective area of one dielectric is of course multiplied by their number—in this case four. Fig. 32b was at one time used in circuit diagrams to indicate a large capacitance.

A very common form of capacitor consists of two long strips of tinfoil separated by waxed paper and rolled up into a compact block. Above one or two microfarads it is often more economical to use aluminium plates in a chemical solution or paste which causes an extremely thin insulating film to form on one of them. Apart from this film-forming, the solution also acts as a conductor between the film and the other plate. These *electrolytic* capacitors

must always be connected and used so that the terminal marked +
never becomes negative relative to the other. Even when correctly
used there is always a small leakage current. To help the wireman,
the symbol Fig. 32c, in which the + plate is distinguished by an
outline stroke, is often used for electrolytic types.

Air is seldom used as the dielectric for fixed capacitors, but is
almost universal in variable capacitors. These, indicated in
diagrams as Fig. 32d, consist of two sets of metal vanes which can
be progressively interleaved with one another, so increasing the
effective area, to obtain any desired capacitance up to the maximum
available, commonly about 500 pF.

Besides the capacitance, an important thing to know about a
capacitor is its maximum working voltage. If the intensity of
electric field in a dielectric is increased beyond a certain limit the
elastic leashes tethering the electrons snap under the strain, and the
freed electrons rush uncontrollably to the positive plate, just as if
the dielectric were a good conductor. It has, in fact, been broken
down or punctured by the excessive voltage. For a given thickness,
mica stands an exceptionally high voltage, or, as one says, has a
relatively high dielectric strength. Air is less good, but has the
advantage that the sparking across resulting from breakdown does
it no permanent harm.

The highest voltage that could be safely applied to a variable
capacitor would not cause nearly enough attraction between the
fixed and moving vanes to make them turn into the maximum
capacitance position; but an electrostatic voltmeter (p. 51) can
be looked upon as a very small variable capacitor with its moving
vanes so delicately suspended that they do move under the attractive
force and indicate the voltage.

In our concentration on intentional capacitance between plates,
we should not forget that, whether we like it or not, every part of a
circuit has capacitance to surrounding parts. When the circuit
e.m.fs are varying rapidly, these stray capacitances may be very
important.

Charge and Discharge of a Capacitor

It is instructive to consider the charging process in greater detail.
In Fig. 33 the capacitor C can be charged by moving the switch to A,
connecting it across a battery; and
discharged by switching to B. R
might represent the resistance of the
wires and capacitor plates, but as
that is generally very small it will be
easier to discuss the matter if we
assume we have added some resistance, enough to bring the total up
to, say, 200 Ω. Suppose the
capacitor is 5 μF and the battery
e.m.f. 100 V.

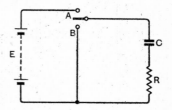

Fig. 33—Circuit used for obtaining the charge and discharge
curves shown in Fig. 34

At the exact moment of switching to A the capacitor is as yet uncharged, so there can be no voltage across it; the whole of the 100 V e.m.f. of the battery must therefore be occupied in driving current through R, and by Ohm's Law that current is found to be 0·5 A (extreme left of Fig. 34a). Reckoning the potential of the

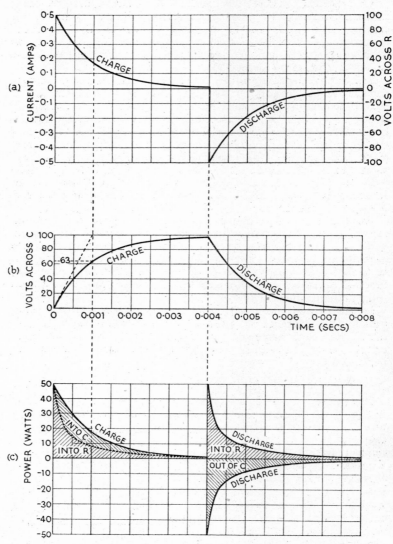

Fig. 34—These curves show the current, voltage and power in the circuit of Fig. 33 during charge and discharge

negative end of the battery as zero, we have at this stage the positive end of the battery, the switch, the upper plate of the capacitor, and (because the capacitor has no p.d. across it) the lower plate also, all at + 100 V. The lower end of the resistor is zero, so we have 100 V drop across the resistor, as already stated. Note that *immediately* the switch is closed the potential of the lower plate of the capacitor as well as that of the upper plate jumps from zero to + 100. The use of a capacitor to transfer a sudden change of potential to another point, without a conducting path, is very common.

We have already seen that the number of coulombs required to charge a capacitor of C farads to V volts is VC. In this case, it is $100 \times 5 \times 10^{-6}$, which is 0·0005. As a coulomb is an ampere-second, the present charging rate of 0·5 A, *if maintained*, would fully charge the capacitor in 0·001 sec. The capacitor voltage would rise steadily as shown by the sloping dotted line in Fig. 34b. Directly it starts to do so, however, there are fewer volts available for driving current through R, and so the current becomes less and the capacitor charges more slowly. When it is charged to 50 V, 50 V are left for the resistor, and the charging rate is 0·25 A. When C is charged to 80 V, 20 are left for R, and the current is 0·1 A. And so on, as shown by the curves in Fig. 34.

Curves of this type are known as *exponential*, and are characteristic of many growth and decay phenomena. Note that the current curve's downward slope, showing the rate at which the current is decreasing, is at every point proportional to the current itself. It can be shown mathematically that in the time a capacitor would take to charge at the starting rate it actually reaches 63 per cent of its full charge. By using the principles we already know we have calculated that this time in the present example is 0·001 sec. Try working it out with letter symbols instead of numbers, so that it covers all charging circuits, and you should find that it is CR secs, regardless of the voltage E. CR—equal to the time taken to reach 63 per cent of final charge—is of course a characteristic of the circuit, and is called its *time constant*.

Theoretically, the capacitor is never completely charged, because the charging depends on there being a difference between the applied e.m.f. and the capacitor voltage, to drive current through the resistance. If the current scale is multiplied by 200 (the value of R), the upper curve is a graph of this voltage across R. Note that the voltages across C and R at all times up to 0·004 sec add up to 100, just as Kirchhoff says they ought (p. 48).

For practical purposes the capacitor may be as good as fully charged in a very short time. Having allowed 0·004 sec for this to happen in the present case, we move the switch to B. Here the applied voltage is zero, so the voltages across C and R must now add up to zero. We know that the capacitor voltage is practically 100, so the voltage across R must be − 100, and the current −0·5 A; that is to say, it is flowing in the opposite direction, discharging the capacitor. And so we get the curves in Fig. 34 from 0·004 sec onwards.

63

WHERE THE POWER GOES

The height of the charging curve above the zero line in Fig. 34a represents the current supplied by the battery. Multiplied by its e.m.f. (100 V) it represents the power (Fig. 34c). When first switched on, the battery is working at the rate of $0.5 \times 100 = 50$ watts, but at the end of 0.004 sec this has fallen off almost to nothing. Since horizontal distance represents time, the shaded area below the power curve represents the total work done by the battery (p. 53).

At first the whole 50 watts goes into the resistance and is lost as heat. But the effort of the e.m.f. immediately becomes divided, part being required to drive the current through R and the rest to charge C. Fig. 34b shows how it is shared, the vertical distance below the " CHARGE " curve representing the voltage across C, and the distance above it, as far as the 100 V level, the resistor's share. The shaded area in c can therefore be divided at every instant in the same proportion by a dotted line, the lower portion representing the energy lost in R as heat, and the upper portion the energy stored in C. These areas are always found to be equal, showing that half the battery energy is lost and half stored.

When we come to the discharge we find that the voltage across R and the current through R follow exactly the same curves as during the charge, except that they are both reversed. But multiplying two negatives together gives a positive, so the curve of power put into R is the same as before (Fig. 34c). The capacitor voltage is still positive during discharge, so with a negative current the power is negative—in other words, it is coming out of the capacitor. The shaded areas above and below the zero line during the discharge are obviously identical except for $+$ and $-$ signs, and in fact represent the same energy from two opposite points of view—those of the capacitor and the resistor. Obviously, too, the " INTO R " shaded areas during charge and discharge are the same; and remembering that the " INTO C " and " INTO R " areas are equal we can check that the " INTO C " and " OUT OF C " energies are also equal.

Summing up: During the charging period half the energy supplied by the battery is stored as an electric field in the capacitor and half is dissipated as heat in the resistor; during discharge the half that was stored is given back at the expense of the collapsing field and is dissipated in the resistor.

It may be as well to repeat the warning that the " charging " and " discharging " of accumulator batteries is an entirely different process, accompanied by only minor variations in voltage. The electricity put into the battery is not stored as an electric charge; it causes a reversible chemical change in the plates.

A point to remember is that the p.ds set up across R at the instants of switching to A and B were short-lived; some idea of their duration in any particular case can be found by multiplying C by R (in farads and ohms respectively, giving the answer in seconds).

CHAPTER 4

Inductance

MAGNETS AND ELECTROMAGNETS

IF A PIECE of paper is laid on a straight " bar " magnet, and iron filings are sprinkled on the paper, they are seen to arrange themselves in a pattern something like Fig. 35*a*. The lines show the paths along which the attraction of the magnet exerts itself. (Compare the lines of electric force in Fig. 30.) As a whole, they map out the *magnetic field*, which is the " sphere of influence ", as it were, of the magnet. The field is most concentrated around two regions, called *poles*, at the ends of the bar. The lines may be supposed to continue right through the magnet, emerging at the end marked N and returning at S. This direction, indicated by the arrows, is (like the direction of an electron current) purely conventional, and the lines themselves are an imaginary representation of a condition occupying the whole space around the magnet.

The same result can be obtained with a previously quite ordinary and unmagnetized piece of iron by passing an electric current through a wire coiled round the iron—an arrangement known as an electromagnet. It is not even necessary to have the iron; the coil alone, so long as it is carrying current, is interlinked with a magnetic field having the same general pattern as that due to a bar magnet, as can be seen by comparing Fig. 35*a* and *b*. Without the iron core, however, it is considerably weaker. Finally, if the wire is unwrapped, every inch of it is still found to be surrounded by a magnetic field. Though very much less concentrated than in the coil, it can be demonstrated with filings as in Fig. 36, if the current is strong enough.

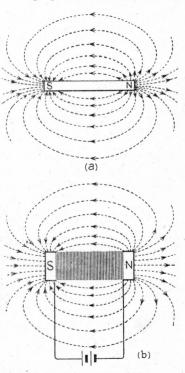

Fig. 35—The dotted lines indicate the direction and distribution of magnetic field around (a) a permanent bar magnet, and (b) a coil of wire carrying current

The results of these and other experiments in electromagnetism are expressed by saying that wherever an electric current flows it surrounds itself with a field which sets up magnetic *flux* (symbol: Φ, pronounced " fie "). If this flux is imagined to be concentrated into a single path instead of occupying the whole space around an electric circuit, then the circuit and the flux link one another like

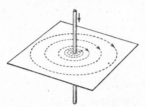

Fig. 36—Direction of magnetic field around a straight wire carrying current

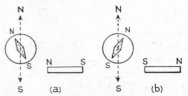

Fig. 37—Deflection of a compass needle by a magnet, proving that like poles repel and unlike poles attract. The N and S poles of the bar magnet can be found by suspending it like a compass needle and marking as N that pole which turns to the north

two adjoining links in a chain. By winding the circuit into a compact coil, the field due to each turn of wire is made to operate in the same space, producing a concentrated magnetic flux (Fig. 35b). Finally, certain materials, chiefly iron and its alloys, are found to have a very large multiplying effect on the flux, this effect being called the *relative permeability* of the material, denoted by the symbol μ. The permeabilities of most things, such as air, water, wood, brass, etc., are all practically the same and are therefore generally reckoned as 1. Certain iron alloys have permeabilities running into thousands. Unlike resistivity and permittivity, however, the permeability of " magnetic " metals is not even approximately constant but varies greatly according to the magnetizing force.

INTERACTING MAGNETIC FIELDS

The " N " and " S " in Fig. 35 stand for North-seeking and South-seeking respectively. Everybody knows that a compass needle points to the north. The needle is a magnet, and turns because its own field interacts with the field of the earth, which is another magnet. Put differently, the north magnetic pole of the earth attracts the north-seeking pole of the needle, while the earth's south pole attracts its south-seeking pole. The poles of a magnet are often called, for brevity, just north and south, but strictly, except in referring to the earth itself, this is incorrect. By bringing the two poles of a bar magnet—previously identified by suspending it as a compass—in turn towards a compass needle it is very easy to demonstrate that, as in Fig. 37, unlike poles attract one another. This reminds one of the way electric charges behave.

Now suppose we hang a coil in such a way that it is free to turn, as suggested in Fig. 38. So long as no current is passing through the coil it will show no tendency to set itself in any particular direction, but if a battery is connected to it the flow of current will transform the coil into a magnet. Like the compass needle, it will then indicate the north, turning itself so that the plane in which the turns of the coil lie is east and west, the axis of the coil pointing north. If now the current is reversed the coil will turn through 180 degrees, showing that what was the N pole of the coil is now, with the current flowing the opposite way, the S.

The earth's field is weak, so the force operating to turn the coil is small. When it is desired to make mechanical use of the magnetic effect of the current in a coil it is better to provide an artificial field of the greatest possible intensity by placing a powerful magnet as close to the coil as possible. This is the basis of all electric motors. In radio, however, we are more interested in other

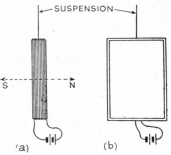

Fig. 38—A coil carrying current, and free to rotate, sets itself with its axis pointing N and S. *a* is a side view and *b* an end view

applications of the same principle, such as the moving-coil measuring instruments described very briefly on page 51.

The coil is shaped somewhat as in Fig. 38, and is suspended in the intense field of a permanent magnet. Hairsprings at each end of the coil serve the double purpose of conducting the current to the coil and keeping the coil normally in the position where the pointer attached to it indicates zero. When current flows through it the coil tends to rotate against the restraint of the springs, and the angle through which it moves is proportional to the magnetic interaction, which in turn is proportional to the value of the current.

INDUCTION

If two moving-coil meters, A and B, are connected together, so that there is a complete circuit through the two coils, then taking hold of the pointer of A and turning the coil round with it will make the pointer of B indicate a current. This current lasts as long as A's coil is being moved, and stops when the coil stops. Allowing the coil of A to spring back causes B to deflect in the opposite direction. The strength of current is proportional to the rate at which the coil is moved.

The current is driven by an e.m.f. generated by the movement of the coil in a magnetic field. It need not be a coil; any conductor moved in a magnetic field has an e.m.f. generated in it, so long as it is not being moved *along* the lines of flux. It has to be moved *across* them. The e.m.f. is, in fact, proportional to the number of lines (or rather the flux represented by those lines) that the conductor cuts across per second.

To generate an e.m.f. all that is necessary is some device for moving wires across a magnetic field. It is equally effective if the field is moved across the wires. All the dynamos or generators in power stations do either one or other.

It is not absolutely necessary for either to move. If the magnetic field is produced by an electromagnet, varying the current that energizes the magnet varies the amount of flux linked with any conductor in the field, even though it be stationary. Thus suppose a number of wires are lying alongside one another. If a current is passed through one of them a magnetic field is set up, and most of its flux will embrace the other wires also. So long as the current is steady, nothing will happen. But if the current is varied, e.m.fs will be generated in *all* the wires, including the one or more responsible for the varying magnetic field. These e.m.fs are said to be *induced* by the varying or moving magnetic flux.

SELF-INDUCTANCE

As every circuit carrying current has some magnetic flux it follows that an e.m.f. is induced in *any* circuit in which the current is varied. The amount of e.m.f. induced in a circuit (or part of a circuit) when the current is varied at some standard rate is called its *self-inductance*, or often just " inductance " (symbol: L). To line up with the units we already know, the unit of self-inductance, called the *henry* (abbreviation: H) was made equal to the number of volts induced in a circuit when the current in that circuit is changing at the rate of 1 ampere per second.

Actually it is the change of *flux* that induces the e.m.f., but since information about the flux is less likely to be available than that about the current, inductance is specified in terms of current. What it depends on, then, is the amount of flux produced by a given current, say 1 A. The more flux, the greater the e.m.f. induced when that current takes one second to grow or die, and so the greater the inductance. The flux produced by a given current depends, as we have seen, on the dimensions and arrangement of the circuit or part of circuit, and on the permeability.

We had no great difficulty in finding a formula expressing resistance in terms of resistivity and the dimensions of the circuit element concerned, because currents are usually confined to wires or other conductors of uniform cross-sections. Capacitance was more difficult because it depends on the dimensions of space between conductors, and the distribution of the electric field therein is likely to be anything but uniform; but for the particular and practically-important case of a thin space between parallel plates we found a formula for capacitance in terms of permittivity and the dimensions of the space. The only form of circuit producing a magnetic field confined mainly to an easily calculable shape, however, is the toroid—a long cylindrical coil bent round into a ring so that the ends meet—and one rarely comes across that particular type. Formulae have been worked out for the inductance of straight wires and coils of various shapes, however, and can be looked up in radio reference books. All we need do just now is to get a general idea.

INDUCTANCE ANALYSED

Currents flowing in opposite directions tend to cancel out so far as magnetic effects are concerned. But if the wire is wound into a coil, each added turn makes the current flow again in the same direction. If two turns are very close together, nearly all the flux due to each links with the other, so that it is nearly true to say that the total flux linking each is twice that due to one separate turn. So long as the turns of a coil are wound very closely together, then, the total flux linking each is nearly proportional to the number of turns. With a coil such as that in Fig. 35b, however, much of the flux due to a turn at one end fails to link those at the other; so the flux linking a single turn is multiplied by something considerably less than the number of turns.

Next, the e.m.f. generated in two turns when the current is changing at a given rate is twice that in one turn linked with the same flux per amp. But since two closely spaced turns are each linked with nearly twice the flux of one, the e.m.f.—and hence the inductance—is nearly four times that of one turn. Inductance is therefore proportional to the square of the number of turns, reduced by a factor to allow for the spacing of the turns.

It can be calculated by theory and is confirmed by experiment that the flux density (the amount passing through a given area at right angles to its direction) is the same whether a turn is large or small; so it follows that the inductance is proportional to the area embraced by the turn, or to the square of its diameter.

Lastly, the permeability. If the whole space surrounding the wire is filled with iron having a μ of, say, 500, the flux for a given current, and therefore the inductance, is 500 times what it would be without the iron. Unfortunately one cannot look up the permeabilities of materials in a list, as with resistivity and permittivity, because permeability varies with the magnetizing force. The information is obtained by experiment and supplied in the form of a graph for each material, with either μ or flux density plotted against magnetizing force. The latter depends on current and number of turns. So although the inductance of an iron-cored coil (as it is called) is generally many times greater than that of the same coil with an air core, it varies with the amount of current, and that leads to complications.

Because the permeability of iron is so high, nearly all the flux tends to pass through it in preference to air and other non-magnetic materials, so a closed iron link as in Fig. 39 is very nearly as effective as the impracticable ideal of filling the whole surrounding space with iron. And very nearly all the flux links all the turns (the little that misses them by straying from the core is called *leakage* flux), so—except for the permeability—it is much easier to calculate the inductance of an iron-cored coil. But a very small gap in the iron " circuit " is equivalent to an iron path μ times as great, so has an inductance-reducing effect out of all proportion to its size.

From all the foregoing it will be clear that between a short length of wire and an iron-cored coil with thousands of turns there is an enormously large range of inductance. The iron-cored coil might have an inductance of many henries; the short wire a small fraction of a microhenry. Yet the latter is not necessarily unimportant.

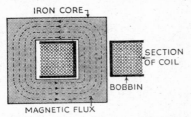

Fig. 39—Showing how a closed iron core links with the turns of the coil and carries nearly all the flux set up by the coil

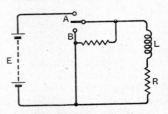

Fig. 40—Circuit used for studying the rise and fall of current in an inductive circuit

The maximum current may be much less than 1 A, but if it comes and goes a thousand million times a second its rate of change may well be millions of amps per second and the induced voltage quite large.

It is, of course, this induced voltage that makes inductance significant. Just how significant will appear in later chapters, but we can make a start now by comparing and contrasting it with the voltage that builds up across a capacitance while it is being charged.

GROWTH OF CURRENT IN INDUCTIVE CIRCUIT

Firstly, what is the direction of the induced voltage? There are two possibilities: it might be in such a direction as to assist or to oppose the change of current that caused it. If it were to assist, the current would change more rapidly, inducing a greater voltage, increasing the change of current still more, and there would be no limit to the thing. In fact, however, the induced voltage always tends to *oppose* the change of current responsible for it.

What happens when current is switched on in an inductive circuit can be studied with the arrangement shown in Fig. 40, which should be compared with Fig. 33. To make the comparison easy, let us assume that the inductance, for which the curliness marked L is the standard symbol, is 0·2 H, and that R (which includes the resistance of the coil) is 200 Ω, and E is 100 V as before. By the way, the name for a component designed to provide inductance is, as one would expect, an *inductor*.

With the switch as shown, no current is flowing through L and there is no magnetic field. At the instant of switching to A, the full 100 V is applied across L and R. The current cannot instantly

70

leap to 0·5 A, the amount predicted by Ohm's Law, for that would mean increasing the current at an infinite rate, which would induce an infinite voltage opposing it. So the current must rise gradually, and at the exact moment of closing the circuit it is zero. There is therefore no voltage drop across R, and the battery e.m.f. is opposed

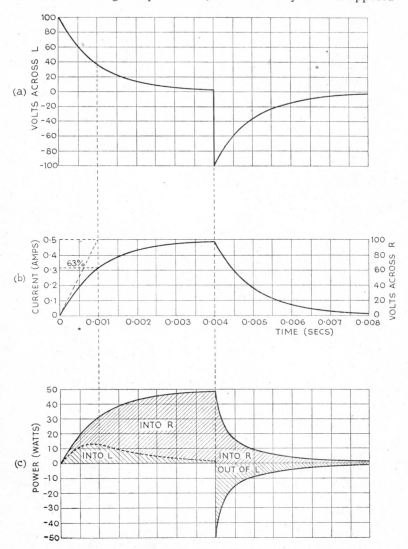

Fig. 41—Curves showing the current, voltage and power in the circuit of Fig. 40 when the switch is moved first to A and then to B

71

solely by the inductive e.m.f., which must be 100 V (Fig. 41a). That enables us to work out the rate at which the current will grow. If L were 1 H, it would have to grow at 100 A per sec to induce 100 V. As it is only 0·2 H it must grow at 500 A per sec.

In the graph (Fig. 41b) corresponding to Fig. 34b for the capacitive circuit, the dotted line represents a steady current growth of 500 A per sec. If it kept this up, it would reach the full 0·5 A in 0·001 sec. But directly the current starts to flow it causes a voltage drop across R. And as the applied voltage remains 100, the induced voltage must diminish. The only way this can happen is for the current to grow less rapidly. By the time it has reached 0·25 A there are 50 V across R, therefore only 50 across L, so the current must be growing at half the rate. The full line shows how it grows; here is another exponential curve and, as in the capacitive circuit, it theoretically never quite finishes. In the time that the current would take to reach its full Ohm's Law value if it kept up its starting pace, it actually reaches 63 per cent of it. This time is, as before, called the time constant. A little elementary algebra based on the foregoing shows it to be L/R seconds.

The voltage across L is also shown. Compared with Fig. 34, current and voltage have changed places. The voltage across R is of course proportional to the current and therefore its curve is the same shape as Fig. 41b. Added to the upper, it must equal 100 V as long as that is the voltage applied.

But when the current has reached practically its full value, we flick the switch instantaneously across to B. The low resistance across the contacts is merely to prevent the circuit from being completely interrupted in this process. At the moment the switch touches B, the magnetic field is still in existence; it can only be abolished by cutting off the current, and that cannot be done without inducing an e.m.f. that tends to prevent it from dying out. Before the current has had time to change, the voltage drop across R remains at 100, so the current must diminish at such a rate as to induce 100 V, that is to say, at 500 A per sec. As the current wanes, so does the voltage across R, and so must the induced voltage, and therefore the current dies away more slowly, as shown in the continuation of Fig. 41. In L/R (= 0·001) secs it has been reduced by the inevitable 63 per cent.

POWER DURING GROWTH

In reckoning how the power in the circuit varies during these operations, we note firstly that the input from the battery (calculated by multiplying the current at each instant by its 100 V) instead of starting off at 50 W and then tailing off almost to nothing, as in the capacitive example, starts at nothing and works up to nearly 50 W (Fig. 41c). The shaded area up to 0·004 sec therefore represents the total energy supplied by the battery. Of this, part is expended against the resistance of R and part against the inductive e.m.f. of L, in the proportions indicated by graphs b and a respectively.

72

Dividing the shaded area in these proportions by the dotted line, we see how much of the battery energy is dissipated in R as heat and how much goes into L. Evidently the energy put into L is stored (actually in the magnetic field), because during the second phase an equal amount of energy comes out of L and goes into R, as shown by the power graphs from 0·004 sec onwards, derived in the same manner as for Fig. 34.

In this case the energy dissipated in R during the first phase is obviously much greater than during the second, so there is no question of the battery energy being shared equally between R and L. But the close analogy between this experiment and the one with the capacitor can be preserved by looking at the first half of the power diagram from a different point of view. If there were no L, the current would jump immediately to 0·5 A, so the power would start at 50 W and remain at that figure indefinitely, the whole of it being dissipated in R. To bring out more closely the activity of L, therefore, we may regard 50 W as being the normal or reference level during the first 0·004 sec, and concentrate attention on the area lying between this and the actual power curve. This area represents battery energy *held back* by the inductive e.m.f. It is the same shape—upside down—as the shaded area in Fig. 34c, and since the voltage and current curve shapes are also identical the area divides up in the same way into two equal parts, one representing energy held back from R, and the other representing energy put into L, equal to that coming out of L during the second phase.

Mutual Inductance

If a coil with the same number of turns as that in Fig. 40 were wound so closely around it that practically all the magnetic flux due to the original *primary winding* embraced also this *secondary winding*, then an equal voltage would at all times be induced in the secondary. Generally it is impracticable to wind so closely that the whole flux links or couples with both coils, and the secondary voltage is less, according to the looseness of magnetic coupling. But by giving the secondary more turns than the primary, it is possible to obtain a greater voltage in the secondary than in the primary.

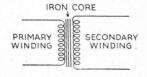

Fig. 42—How a transformer is represented in circuit diagrams

Remember that this voltage depends on the *varying* of the primary current. A device of this kind, for stepping voltages up or down, or for inducing voltages into circuits without any direct connection, is named (rather inappropriately) a *transformer*. It is represented in circuit diagrams by two or more coils drawn closely together. An iron core is shown by one or more straight lines drawn between them (Fig. 42).

The effect that one coil can exert, through its magnetic field, on another, is called *mutual* inductance (symbol : M), and like self-

73

inductance is measured in henries. The definition is similar too: the mutual inductance in henries between two coils is equal to the number of volts induced in one of them when the current in the other is changing at the rate of 1 A per second.

Transformers are an immensely useful application of the inductive effect, and in fact are the main reason why alternating current (a.c.) has almost superseded direct current (d.c.) for electricity supply. So we shall now proceed to study a.c.

CHAPTER 5

Alternating Currents

Frequencies of Alternating Current

In our first chapter we saw that speaking and music are conveyed from one person to another by sound waves, which consist of rapid vibrations or alternations of air pressure. And that to transmit them over longer distances by telephone it is necessary for electric currents to copy these alternations. And further, that for transmitting them across space, by wireless, it is necessary to use electric currents alternating still more rapidly. We have now just noted the fact that the great advantage of being able to step voltages up and down as required is obtainable only when the electricity supply is continually varying, which is most conveniently done by arranging for it to be alternating. Public electricity supplies which light and heat our houses and provide the power that works our wireless sets (instead of the more expensive and troublesome batteries) are therefore mostly of the alternating-current kind.

The only essential difference between all these alternating currents is the number of double-reversals they make per second; in a word, the frequency. We have already gone fairly fully into the matter of frequency (p. 26), so there is no need to repeat it; but it may be worth noting what frequencies are used for different purposes.

There is no hard-and-fast division between one lot of frequencies and another; but those below 100 cycles per second are used for power (the standard in this country is 50 c/s); those from 25 to 15,000 or so are audible, and therefore are classed as audio frequencies (a.f.), while those above about 20,000 are more or less suitable for carrying signals across space, and are known as radio frequencies (r.f.). Certain of these, notably 525,000 to 1,605,000, are allocated for broadcasting.

The useful band of r.f. is subdivided as shown in the table below.

Class	Abbreviation	Frequencies	Wavelengths
Very low	v.l.f.	Below 30 kc/s	Over 10,000 metres
Low	l.f.	30–300 kc/s	1,000–10,000 metres
Medium	m.f.	300–3,000 kc/s	100–1,000 metres
High	h.f.	3–30 Mc/s	10–100 metres
Very high	v.h.f.	30–300 Mc/s	1–10 metres
Ultra high	u.h.f.	300–3,000 Mc/s	10–100 cm
Super high	s.h.f.	3,000–30,000 Mc/s	1–10 cm

The last three groups in the table are sometimes lumped together under the description " extra-high frequency ".

What has been said about currents applies to voltages, too; it requires an alternating voltage to drive an alternating current.

The last two chapters have shown that when currents and voltages are varying there are two circuit effects—capacitance and inductance —that have to be taken into account as well as resistance. We shall therefore be quite right in expecting a.c. circuits to be a good deal more complicated and interesting than d.c. Before going on to consider these circuit effects there are one or two things to clear up about a.c. itself.

THE SINE WAVE

It is easy to see that an alternating current might reverse abruptly or it might do so gradually and smoothly. In Fig. 34a we have an example of the former. There is, in fact, an endless variety of ways in which current or voltage can vary with time, and when graphs are drawn showing how they do so we get a corresponding variety of wave shapes. The steepness of the wave at any point along the time scale shows the rapidity with which the current is changing at that time.

Fortunately for the study of alternating currents, all wave shapes, however complicated, can be shown to be built up of waves of one fundamental shape, called the *sine wave* (adjective: sinusoidal). Fig. 8c is an example of this. Note the smooth, regular alternations of the component sine waves, like the swinging of a pedulum. Waves of even such a spiky appearance as those in Fig. 34 can be analysed into a number of sine waves of different frequencies.

Most circuits used in wireless and other communications consist basically of sources of alternating e.m.f. (hereinafter called *generators*) connected to combinations of resistance, inductance and/or capacitance (often called *loads*). With practice one can reduce even very complicated-looking circuits to standard generator-and-load combinations.

Fig. 43—Circuit consisting of an a.c. generator (G) feeding a purely resistive load (R)

We have just seen that although there is no end to the variety of waveforms that generators can produce, they are all combinations of simple sine waves. So it is enough to consider the sine-wave generator. Sources of more complicated waveforms can be imitated by combinations of sine-wave generators. Theoretically this dodge is always available, but in practice (as, for example, with square waves) there are sometimes easier alternatives. Unless the contrary is stated, it is to be assumed from now on that a generator means a sine-wave generator.

CIRCUIT WITH RESISTANCE ONLY

The simplest kind of a.c. circuit is the one that can be represented as a generator supplying current to a purely resistive load (Fig. 43).

We have already found (p. 41) how to calculate the current any given e.m.f. will drive through a resistance. Applying this method to an alternating, e.m.f. involves nothing new. Suppose, for example, that the voltage at the crest of each wave is 200, and that its frequency is 50 c/s. Fig. 44 shows a graph of this e.m.f. during rather more than one cycle. And suppose that R is 200 Ω. Then we can calculate the current at any point in the cycle by dividing the voltage at that point by 200, in accordance with Ohm's Law.

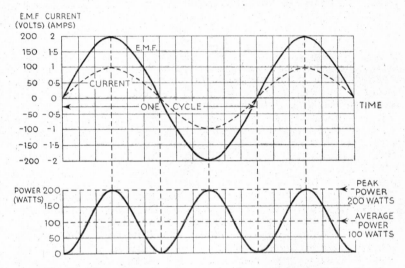

Fig. 44—Time graphs of e.m.f., current and power in the circuit Fig. 43

At the crest it is, of course, 200/200 = 1 A; half-way up the wave it is 0·5 A. Plotting a number of such points we get the current wave, shown dotted. It is identical in shape, though different in vertical scale.

How is an electricity supply that behaves in this fashion to be rated? Can one fairly describe it as a 200-volt supply, seeing that the actual voltage is changing all the time and is sometimes zero? Or should one take the average voltage?

The answer that has been agreed upon is based on comparison with d.c. supplies. It is obviously very convenient for a lamp or fire intended for a 200-V d.c. system to be equally suited to a.c. mains of the same nominal voltage. This condition will be fulfilled if the average *power* taken by the lamp or fire is the same with both types of supply, for then the filament will reach the same temperature and the light or heat will be the same in both cases.

We know (p. 53) that the power in watts is equal to the voltage multiplied by the amperage. Performing this calculation for a sufficient number of points in the alternating cycle in Fig. 44, we

77

get a curve showing how the power varies. To avoid confusion it
has been drawn below the E and I curves. A significant feature of
this power curve is that although during half of every cycle the
voltage and current are negative, their negative half-cycles always
exactly coincide, so that even during these half-cycles the power is
(by the ordinary rules of arithmetic) positive. This mathematical
convention agrees with and represents the physical fact that although
both current and voltage reverse their direction the flow of power is
always in the same direction, namely, out of the generator. We
used this convention in Figs. 34c and 41c, and will do so again
very soon.

R.M.S. VALUES

Another thing one can see by looking at the power curve is that its
average height is half the height of the crests—which, incidentally,
occur 100 times per second when the frequency of the voltage and
current are 50 c/s. The crest height is $200 \times 1 = 200$ W; so the
average power must be 100 W. The next step is to find what
direct voltage would be needed to dissipate 100 W in 200 Ω ; the
answer is on page 54—$P = E^2/R$, from which $E^2 = PR$, which in
this case is $100 \times 200 = 20,000$. So $E = \sqrt{20,000} = 141$
approximately.

Judged on the basis of equal power, then, an a.c. supply with a
maximum voltage of 200 is equivalent to a d.c. supply at 141 V.

Generalizing this calculation, we find that when an alternating
voltage is adjusted to deliver the same power to a given resistance
as a direct voltage, its crest voltage—called its *peak* value—is $\sqrt{2}$
times the direct voltage, or about 1·414 times as great. Put the
other way round, its nominal or equivalent or effective voltage—
called its *r.m.s.* (root-mean-square) value—is $1/\sqrt{2}$ or about
0·707 times its peak value. Since the resistance is the same in
both cases, the same ratio exists between r.m.s. and peak values of
the current. What is called a 230 V a.c. supply therefore alternates
between zero and $\pm \sqrt{2} \times 230 = 325$ V peak.

The r.m.s. value is *not* the same as the average voltage or current
(which is actually 0·637 times the peak value). If you have followed
the argument carefully you will see that this is because we have been
comparing the a.c. and d.c. on a power basis, and power is proportional to voltage or current *squared*.

It is important to remember that the figures given above apply
only to the sine waveform. With a square wave, for example, it is
obvious that peak, r.m.s., and average (or mean) values are all
the same.

There is one other recognized " value "—the instantaneous
value, changing all the time in an a.c. system. It is the quantity
graphed in Fig. 44.

As regards symbols, plain capital letters such as E, V and I are
generally understood to mean r.m.s. values unless the contrary is
obvious. Instantaneous values, when it is necessary to distinguish

78

them, are denoted by small letters, such as i; peak values by I_{max}; and average values by I_{ave}.

Using r.m.s. values for voltage and current we can forget the rapid variations in instantaneous voltage, and, *so long as our circuits are purely resistive*, all a.c. calculations can be carried out according to the rules discussed in Chapter 2.

A.C. Meters

If alternating current is passed through a moving-coil meter (p. 67) the coil is pushed first one way and then the other, because the current is reversing in a steady magnetic field. The most one is likely to see is a slight vibration about the zero mark. Certainly it will not indicate anything like the r.m.s. value of the current.

If, however, the direction of magnetic field is reversed at the same times as the current, the double reversal makes the force act in the same direction as before, and the series of pushes will cause the pointer to take up a position that will indicate the value of current. The obvious way to obtain this reversing magnetic field is to replace the permanent magnet by a coil and pass through it the current being measured. When the current is small, the field also is very weak, and the deflection too small to be read; so this principle is seldom used, except in *wattmeters*, in which the main current is passed through one coil, and the other—the *volt coil*—is connected across the supply.

A more usual type is that in which there is only one coil, which is fixed. Inside are two pieces of iron, one fixed and the other free to move against a hairspring. When either d.c. or a.c. is passed through the coil, both irons are magnetized in the same polarity, and so repel one another, to a distance depending on the strength of current. These *moving-iron* meters are useful when there is plenty of power to spare in the circuit for working them, but they tend to use up too much in low-power circuits.

Another method is to make use of the heating effect of the current. When a junction of two different metals is heated a small unidirectional e.m.f. is generated, which can be measured by a moving coil meter. Instruments of this kind, called *thermojunction* or *thermocouple* types, if calibrated on d.c. will obviously read r.m.s. values of a.c. regardless of waveform. They are particularly useful for much higher frequencies than can be measured with instruments in which the current to be measured has to pass through a coil.

The electrostatic instrument (p. 51) can be used for alternating voltages and responds to r.m.s. values.

But perhaps the most popular method of all is to convert the alternating current into direct by means of a *rectifier*—a device that allows current to pass through it in one direction only—so that it can be measured with an ordinary moving-coil meter. The great advantage of this is that by adding a rectifier a multirange d.c. instrument can be used on a.c. too. Most of the general-purpose test meters used in radio are of this kind. Because the moving-coil instrument measures the average current, which in general is not the same as the r.m.s. current, the scale is marked off in such a way as to take account of the factor necessary to convert one to the other. This, as we have seen, is approximately 0·707/0·638 (= 1·11) for sine waves. It is different for most other waveforms, so the rectifier type of meter reads them incorrectly.

PHASE

Looking again at the current graph in Fig. 44 we see that it not only has the same shape as the e.m.f. that causes it but it is also exactly in step with it. Consideration of Ohm's Law proves that this must be so in any purely resistive circuit. The technical word for being in step is being *in phase*. The idea of phase is very important, so we had better make sure we understand it.

Suppose we have two alternating generators, A and B. The exact voltages they give will not matter, but to make it easier to distinguish their graphs we shall suppose A gives about double the voltage of B. If we start drawing the voltage graph of A just as it begins a cycle the result will be something like waveform A in Fig. 45*a*. Next, consider generator B, which has the same frequency,

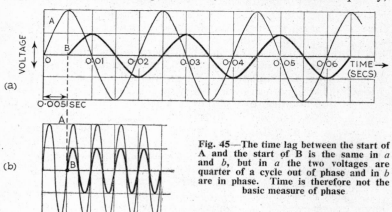

(a)

(b)

Fig. 45—The time lag between the start of A and the start of B is the same in *a* and *b*, but in *a* the two voltages are quarter of a cycle out of phase and in *b* are in phase. Time is therefore not the basic measure of phase

but is out of step with A. It starts each of its cycles, say, quarter of a cycle later than A, as shown by waveform B. This fact is expressed by saying that voltage B lags voltage A by a phase difference of quarter of a cycle. Seeing that it is a *time* graph, it might seem more natural to say that B lagged A by a phase difference of 0·005 sec. The disadvantage of doing so is shown in Fig. 45*b*, where the frequency of A and B is four times as great. The time lag is the same as before, but the two voltages are now *in phase*. So although phase is usually very closely related to time, it is not advisable to think of it as time. The proper basis of reckoning phase is in fractions of a cycle.

80

VECTOR DIAGRAMS

The main advantage of a time graph of alternating voltage, current, etc., is that it shows the waveform. But on those very many occasions when the form of the wave is not in question (because we have agreed to stick to sine waves) it is a great waste of effort to draw a number of beautifully exact waves merely in order to show the relative phases. Having examined Figs. 8, 44 and 45, we ought by now to be able to take the sine waveform as read, and be prepared to accept a simpler method of indicating phases.

In Fig. 46, imagine the line OP to be pivoted at O and to be capable of rotating steadily in the direction shown (anticlockwise). (The arrowhead at P is there to show which end of OP is moving, not the direction in which P is moving.) Then the height of the end P above a horizontal line through O varies in exactly the same way as a sine wave. Assuming OP starts, as shown in Fig. 46, at " 3 o'clock ", P is actually on the hori-

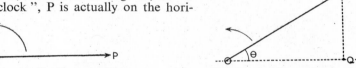

Fig. 46—Starting position of an alternative method of representing sinusoidal variation

Fig. 47—The Fig. 46 vector after having turned through an angle, θ. The height PQ represents an instantaneous voltage or other sinusoidally varying quantity. PQ/PO is the sine of the angle

zontal line, so its height above it is, of course, nil. That represents the starting point of a sine-wave cycle. As OP rotates, its height above the line increases at first rapidly and then more slowly, until, after a quarter of a revolution, it is at right angles to its original position. That represents the first quarter of a sine-wave cycle. During the third and fourth quarter of the revolution, the height of P is negative, corresponding to the same quarters of a cycle.

Readers with any knowledge of trigonometry will know that the ratio of the height of P to its distance from O is called the sine of the angle that OP has turned through (Fig. 47)—hence the name given to the waveform we have been considering and which is none other than a time graph of the sine of the angle θ (abbreviated " sin θ ") when θ (pronounced " theta ") is increasing at a steady rate.

We now have a much more easily drawn diagram for representing sine waves. The length of a line such as OP represents the peak value of the voltage, etc., and the angle it makes with the " 3 o'clock " position represents its phase. The line itself is called a *vector*. The angle it turns through in one whole revolution (which, of course, brings it to the same position as at the start) is 360°, and that corresponds to one whole cycle of the voltage. So a common way

81

of specifying a phase is in angular degrees. Quarter of a cycle is 90°, and so on. Sometimes even a time or waveform diagram such as Fig. 45 is marked in degrees.

Besides the common angular measure, in which a whole revolution is divided into 360 degrees, there is the mathematical angular measure in which it is divided into 2π *radians*. Seeing that π is a very odd number (p. 12) this may seem an extremely odd way of doing things. It arises because during one revolution P travels 2π times its distance from O. Even this may not seem a good enough reason, and as we shall be using the 360° scale there is no need to worry about it just now; but if you intend to study a.c. further you will certainly see more of 2π.

As an example of a vector diagram, Fig. 48 is the equivalent of Fig. 45a. In the position shown it is equivalent to it at the beginning or end of each cycle, but since both vectors rotate at the same rate the 90° phase difference shown by it between A and B is the same at any stage of any cycle.

ADDING ALTERNATING VOLTAGES

A great advantage of the vector diagram is the way it simplifies adding and subtracting alternating voltages or currents that are not

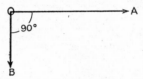

Fig. 48—Vector diagram corresponding to Fig. 45a

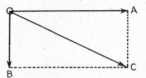

Fig. 49—OC is the vector representing the result of adding the sinusoidal quantities represented by OA and OB. It is obviously itself sinusoidal

in phase. To add voltages A and B in Fig. 45a, for example, one would have to add the heights of the A and B waves at close intervals of time and plot them as a third wave. This would be a very laborious way of finding how the peak value and phase of the combined voltage (or *resultant*, as it is called) compared with those of its component voltages. In the vector diagram it is quickly done by dotting in from A a line equal in length and direction to OB (Fig. 49), to arrive at point C. Then OC is the vector representing voltage A plus voltage B. Alternatively, a line can be drawn from B equal to OA. Note that the result of adding two voltages that are not in phase is less than the result of adding them by ordinary arithmetic, and its phase is somewhere between those of the components.

If you mean to study a.c. seriously you should read a good elementary book on vectors and also learn the corresponding algebraical method of calculation, using the symbol "j" to distinguish vertical from horizontal distances.*

The phase relationship between voltage and current in a purely resistive circuit is shown vectorially as in Fig. 50. The length of OE relative to OI represents the resistance of the circuit; but at the moment we are not concerned with that, so any arbitrary lengths will do.

Fig. 51a shows a simple resistive circuit at the instant when the alternating e.m.f. is at its maximum positive clockwise, as indicated by the + and — sign at the generator, and the E vector in Fig. 51b. It is driving a current in the same direction (indicated by the arrow in a and the I vector in b) against the resistance of the circuit. The

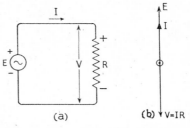

(a) (b) V=IR

Fig. 50—Vectorial representation of the conditions in the circuit Fig. 43, where the current is in phase with the e.m.f. A convenient convention is to distinguish current vectors by filled-in arrow heads

Fig. 51—(a) A.c. circuit at the instant when the e.m.f. is at its positive maximum, and (b) the corresponding vector diagram

p.d. across the resistance is, of course, equal to that across the generator terminals, but its direction is anticlockwise. We can therefore draw a p.d. vector (OV), equal and opposite to E. This is merely the vectorial way of expressing the Kirchhoff Law we studied in connection with d.c. circuits (p. 48), by which the sum of all the voltages round a circuit must be equal to zero.

If there were several resistances in the circuit, each would have across it an alternating p.d. which could be represented by its own vector; and these separate vectors, all in the same direction, would add up to one p.d. equal and opposite to the e.m.f.

* For example, " Basic Mathematics for Radio Students ", by F. M. Colebrook, B.Sc., D.I.C., A.C.G.I. Published for *Wireless World* by Iliffe & Sons, Ltd., 10s. 6d. net.

CHAPTER 6

Capacitance in A.C. Circuits

CURRENT FLOW IN A CAPACITIVE CIRCUIT

THE NEXT TYPE of basic circuit to consider is the one shown in Fig. 52. If the generator gave an unvarying e.m.f. no current could flow, because there is a complete break in the circuit. The most that could happen would be a momentary current when switching on, as shown in Fig. 34.

Some idea of what is likely to happen when an alternating e.m.f. is applied can be obtained by an experiment similar to Fig. 33 but with an inverted battery in the B path, as shown in Fig. 53a. Moving

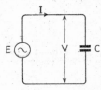

Fig. 52—Circuit consisting of an a.c. generator with a purely capacitive load

the switch alternately to A and B at equal time intervals will then provide an alternating voltage of square waveform (Fig. 53b).

Whenever the switch is moved to A there is a momentary charging current in one direction, and moving it to B causes a similar current in the reverse direction.

We know that for a given voltage the quantity of electricity transferred at each movement of the switch is proportional to the capacitance (p. 57).

And it is obvious that the more rapidly the switch is moved to and fro (that is to say, the higher the frequency of the alternating e.m.f.) the more often this quantity of electricity will surge to and fro in the circuit (that is to say, the greater the quantity of electricity that will move in the circuit per second, or, in other words, the greater the current).

Thus, although the circuit has no conductance, so that no continuous d.c. can flow, an alternating e.m.f. causes an alternating current, flowing not *through* but *in and out* of the capacitor. And the amount of current due to a given voltage will depend on two

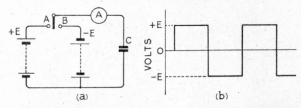

Fig. 53—If the generator in Fig. 52 consisted of the periodically switched batteries as shown at *a*, the waveform would be as at *b*, and the current (assuming a certain amount of resistance) could be calculated as discussed in connection with Fig. 34

things—the capacitance and the frequency. The greater they are, the greater the current.

The truth of the first statement—that an alternating e.m.f. causes a current to flow in a circuit blocked to d.c. by a capacitance in series—can easily be demonstrated by bridging the open contacts

Fig. 54—If a capacitor of about 2 μF is connected across the open contacts of an a.c. lighting switch so that it is in series as here, the lamp will light steadily, though at reduced brightness

of an electric light switch by a capacitor; say 2 μF for a 40 W lamp (Fig. 54). The lamp will light and stay alight as long as the capacitor is connected. But its brilliance will be below normal.

CAPACITIVE CURRENT WAVEFORM

Let us now consider the action of Fig. 52 in greater detail, by drawing the graph of instantaneous e.m.f. (Fig. 55) exactly as for the resistive circuit, in which we assumed a sine waveform. But unlike the resistive case there is no Ohm's Law to guide us in plotting the current waveform. We have, however, a rather similar relationship (p. 57)—V = Q/C, where V is the p.d. across C and Q is the charge in C. This is true at every instant, so we can rewrite

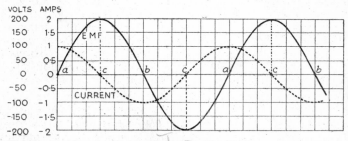

Fig. 55—E.m.f. and current diagram for Fig. 52, drawn to correspond with Fig. 44

it $v = q/C$, to show that we mean instantaneous values. In Fig. 52, v is always equal in magnitude to e, the instantaneous e.m.f. So we can say with confidence that at the moments when e is zero the capacitor is completely uncharged, and at all other moments the charge is exactly proportional to e. If we knew the right scale, the voltage wave in Fig. 54 would do also as a charge curve. But we are not so much interested in the charge as in the current—that is to say, the rate at which charging takes place. At points marked a, although the voltage and charge are zero they are growing faster than at any other stage in the cycle. So we may expect the current to be greater than at any other times. At points marked b, the

85

charge is decreasing as fast as it was growing at a, so the current is the same in magnitude but opposite in direction and sign. At points marked c, the charge reaches its maximum, but just for an instant it is neither growing nor waning; its rate of increase or decrease is zero, so at that instant the current must be zero. At intermediate points the relative strength of current can be estimated from the steepness of the voltage (and charge) curve. Joining up all the points gives a current curve shaped like the dotted line.

If this job is done carefully it is clear that the shape of the current curve is also sinusoidal, as in the resistive circuit, but out of phase, being quarter of a cycle (or 90°) ahead of the voltage.

On seeing this, students are sometimes puzzled and ask how the current *can* be ahead of the voltage. " How does the current know what the voltage is going to be, quarter of a cycle later?" This difficulty arises only when it supposed, quite wrongly, that the current maximum at a is caused by the voltage maximum quarter of a cycle later, at c; whereas it is actually caused by the fact that at a the voltage is increasing at its maximum rate.

THE " OHM'S LAW " FOR CAPACITANCE

What we want to know is how to foretell the actual magnitude of the current, given the necessary circuit data. Since, as we know (p. 57), 1 volt established between the terminals of a 1-farad capacitor causes a charge of 1 coulomb to enter it, we can see that if the voltage were increasing at the rate of 1 volt per second the charge would be increasing at 1 coulomb per second. But we also know that 1 coulomb per second is a current of 1 amp; so we can express our basic relationship, $Q = VC$, in the form:

Amps = Volts-per-second × Farads.

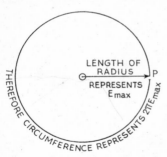

Fig. 56—From this diagram it can be inferred that the maximum rate at which E increases is $2 \pi f E_{max}$ volts per second

The problem is how to calculate the volts-per-second in an alternating e.m.f., especially as it is varying all the time. All we need do, however, is find it at the point in the cycle where it is greatest—at a in Fig. 55. That will give the peak value of current, from which all its other values follow (p. 78).

Going back to Fig. 47, you may remember that one revolution of P about O represents one cycle of alternating voltage, the fixed length OP represents the peak value of the voltage, and the length of PQ (which, of course, is varying all the time) represents the instantaneous voltage. When P is on the starting line, as in Fig. 46, the length of PQ is zero, but at that moment it is increasing at the rate at which P is revolving around O. Now the distance travelled by P during one cycle is 2π times the length of OP. And if the frequency is 50 c/s, it does this distance 50 times per second. Its rate is therefore $2\pi \times 50$ times OP. More generally, if f stands for the frequency in cycles per second, the rate at which P moves round O is $2\pi f$ times OP. And as OP represents E_{max}, we can say that P's motion represents $2\pi f\, E_{max}$ volts per second (Fig. 56). But we have just seen that it also represents the maximum rate at which PQ, the instantaneous voltage, is growing. So, fitting this information into our equation, we have

$$I_{max} = 2\pi f\, E_{max}\, C$$

where I is in amps, E in volts, and C in farads. Since I_{max} and E_{max} are both $\sqrt{2}$ times I and E (the r.m.s. values) respectively, it is equally true to say

$$I = 2\pi f\, EC.$$

And if we rearrange it like this

$$\frac{E}{I} = \frac{1}{2\pi f\, C}$$

and then take another look at one of the forms of expressing Ohm's Law:

$$\frac{E}{I} = R$$

we see they are the same except that $1/2\pi f\, C$ takes the place of R in the role of limiting the current in the circuit. So, although $1/2\pi f\, C$ is quite a different thing physically from resistance, for purposes of calculation it is of the same kind, and it is convenient to reckon it in ohms. To distinguish it from resistance it is named *reactance*. To avoid having to repeat the rather cumbersome expression $1/2\pi f\, C$, the special symbol X has been allotted. The "Ohm's Law" for the Fig. 52 circuit can therefore be written simply as

$$\frac{E}{I} = X \quad \text{or } I = \frac{E}{X} \quad \text{or } E = IX.$$

For example, the reactance of a 2 μF capacitor to a 50 c/s supply is $1/(2\pi \times 50 \times 2 \times 10^{-6}) = 1{,}590\ \Omega$, and if the voltage across it were 230 V the current would be $230/1590 = 0\cdot145$ A.

CAPACITANCES IN PARALLEL AND IN SERIES

The argument that led us to conclude that the capacitance between parallel plates is proportional to the area across which they face one another (p. 59) leads also to the conclusion that capacitances in parallel add up just like resistances in series.

Fig. 57—In this circuit, each capacitor takes its own charging current without being affected by the other. Since capacitances are rated by their charging current, the capacitance equal to these two in parallel is equal to $C_1 + C_2$

87

We can arrive at the same conclusion by simple algebraic reasoning based on the behaviour of capacitors to alternating voltage. Fig. 57 represents an a.c. generator connected to two capacitors in parallel. The separate currents in them are respectively $E \times 2\pi f C_1$ and $E \times 2\pi f C_2$. The total current is thus $E \times 2\pi f(C_1 + C_2)$, which is equal to the current that would be taken by a single capacitance equal to the sum of the separate capacitances of C_1 and C_2.

We also saw (p. 59) that if a single capacitor is divided by a plate placed midway between its two plates, the capacitance between the middle plate and either of the others is twice that of the original capacitor. In other words, the capacitance of two equal capacitors in series is half that of each of them. Let us now consider the more general case of any two capacitances in series.

If X_1 and X_2 are respectively the reactances of C_1 and C_2 in Fig. 58, their combined reactance X is $(X_1 + X_2)$, as in the case of resistances in series. By first writing down the equation $X = X_1 + X_2$, and then replacing each X by its known value, of form $1/2\pi f C$,

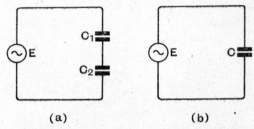

(a)   **(b)**

Fig. 58—If the one capacitor C in *b* is to take the same current as the two in series at *a*, its capacitance must be equal to $1/(1/C_1 + 1/C_2)$

we deduce that $1/C = 1/C_1 + 1/C_2$. That is, the sum of the reciprocals of the separate capacitances is equal to the reciprocal of the total capacitance.

So the rule for capacitances in series is identical with that for resistances or reactances in parallel. From the way it was derived it is evidently not limited to two capacitances only, but can be applied to any number. It implies that if capacitors are connected in series, the capacitance of the combination is always less than that of the smallest.

Applied to two capacitances only, the rule can, as with resistances, be put in the more easily manageable form $C = C_1 C_2/(C_1 + C_2)$.

POWER IN A CAPACITIVE CIRCUIT

Fig. 55 was drawn to match Fig. 44 as regards peak voltage and current. The only difference is the current's 90° phase lead. Let us now complete the picture by calculating the wattage at a sufficient number of points to draw the power curve (Fig. 59). Owing to the

88

phase difference between E and I, there are periods in the cycle when they are of opposite sign, giving a negative power. In fact, the power is alternately positive and negative, just like E and I except for having twice the frequency. The net power, taken over a whole cycle, is therefore zero. In accordance with the usual convention (p. 64), if " + " distinguishes power going out of the generator, the negative sign signifies power returned by the load to the generator. We have already seen something like this, in Fig. 34, except that there the action was complicated by resistance.

The power curve in Fig. 59 represents the fact that although a pure capacitance draws current from an alternating generator it

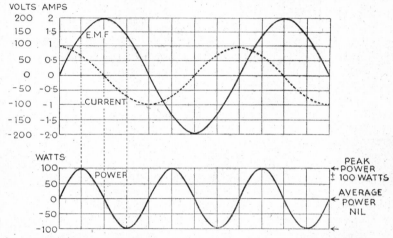

Fig. 59—The current and voltage graphs for a capacitance load (Fig. 55) are here repeated, with a power graph derived from it plotted below. Note that over any complete cycle the total power is zero, because the exact amount put into the capacitor during one half is returned during the other half

does not permanently draw any power—it only borrows some twice per cycle, repaying it with a promptitude that might be commended to human borrowers.

An experimental demonstration of this fact is given by the capacitor in series with the lamp (Fig. 34). The lamp soon warms up, showing that electrical power is being dissipated in it, but although the capacitor is carrying the same current it remains quite cold.

CAPACITANCE AND RESISTANCE IN SERIES

Fig. 34 is an example of the next type of circuit to be considered— C and R in series. We know how to calculate the relationship (magnitude and phase) between voltage and current for each of these separately. When they are in series the same current will flow through both, and this current cannot at one and the same time be in phase with the generator voltage and 90° ahead of it. But it

89

is quite possible—and in fact essential—for it to be in phase with the voltage across the resistance and 90° ahead of the voltage across the capacitance. These two voltages, which must obviously be 90° out of phase with one another, must add up to equal the generator voltage. We have already added out-of-phase voltages by two different methods (Fig. 45 and Fig. 49), so that part of it should not be difficult. Because the current, and not the voltage, is common to both circuit elements, it will be easier to reverse the procedure we have adopted until now, and, starting with a current, find the e.m.f.

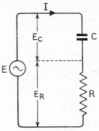

Fig. 60—For finding the current, I, caused by E to flow in a circuit comprising C and R in series, it is helpful to split E up into the two parts needed to drive I through C and R separately

required to drive it. When we have in that way discovered the key to this kind of circuit, we can easily use it to calculate the current resulting from a given e.m.f.

For brevity, let E_C and E_R denote the e.m.fs needed for C and R (Fig. 60). We could, of course, represent E_C and E_R by drawing waveform graphs, and, by adding them, plot the graph of E, the total generator e.m.f., and compare it for phase and magnitude with the current graph. But seeing we have taken the trouble to learn the much quicker vector method of arriving at the same

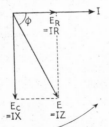

Fig. 61—Vector diagram relating to Fig. 60. E_R is in phase with I, but E_C lags I by 90°. E is the vector sum of E_R and E_C, and lags I by the angle ϕ

result, we might as well use it. (If you find the vector method unconvincing, there is nothing to stop you drawing the waveforms.)

The first thing, then, is to draw a vector of any convenient length to represent the current, I (Fig. 61). Since we are concerned only with *relative* phases, it can be drawn in any direction. The E_R vector must be drawn in the same direction, to represent the fact that the current driven through a resistance is in phase with the e.m.f. Its length represents the voltage of the e.m.f. ($=IR$) to any convenient scale. The length of the E_C vector represents E_C ($=IX$ or $I/2\pi fC$) to the same scale, and since we know the current

90

is 90° ahead of it we must draw it 90° behind the current vector. The vector representing E in magnitude and phase is then easily found as explained in connection with Fig. 49.

IMPEDANCE

A new name is needed to refer to the current-limiting properties of this circuit as a whole. *Resistance* is appropriate to R and *reactance* to C; a combination of them is called *impedance* (symbol: Z). Resistance and reactance themselves are special cases of impedance. So we have still another relationship in the same form as Ohm's Law; one that covers the other two, namely:

$$I = \frac{E}{Z}$$

Although Z combines R and X, it is not true to say $Z = R + X$. Suppose that in Fig. 60 C is the 2 μF capacitor which we have already calculated has a reactance of 1,590 Ω at 50 c/s, and that R is a round 1,000 Ω. I, shall we say, is 0·1 A. Then E_R must be 100 V and E_C 159 V. If the vector diagram is drawn accurately to scale it will show E to be 188 V, so that Z must be 1,880 Ω, which is much less than $1,590 + 1,000$. It should be obvious from Fig. 61 that the three voltage vectors could, by suitable choice of scale, be used to represent the respective impedances. Then, since these three vectors placed together make a right-angled triangle, the celebrated Theorem of Pythagoras tells us that $Z^2 = R^2 + X^2$, or $Z = \sqrt{(R^2 + X^2)}$. So we have an alternative of calculating Z by arithmetic instead of drawing a vector diagram or a waveform diagram accurately to scale. Since the voltages are proportional to the impedances, $E = \sqrt{(E_R^2 + E_C^2)}$.

The angle by which I leads E in Fig. 61 is marked φ, which is the usual symbol for a phase difference. It is the Greek small letter " phi ". (We have already used the capital, Φ, to mean flux.) The trigonometrists will see that $\tan \varphi = X/R$.

Given the values of R and C, and the frequency, we now have three alternative methods of finding their series impedances and the phase difference between current and voltage; also, given either current or voltage, of finding the other. Although the method of adding out-of-phase voltages by drawing their waveforms takes longest to do, it does perhaps bring out most clearly the reason why the total voltage is less than the sum of the two separate voltages—namely, that their peak values occur at different times.

From what has already been said about power in a.c. circuits it should be clear that in Fig. 60, for example, the wattage dissipated is given by multiplying I by E_R (*not* by E), so that only part of the volt-amps supplied by the generator (EI) represents power permanently delivered.

CAPACITANCE AND RESISTANCE IN PARALLEL

In solving this type of circuit, Fig. 62, we revert to the practice of starting with the voltage E, because that is common to both.

91

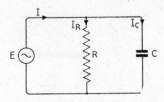

Fig. 62—The branch currents in this circuit, I_R and I_C, are 90° out of phase with one another

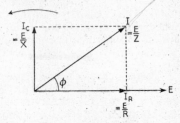

Fig. 63—Vector diagram relating to Fig. 62

What we do, in fact, is exactly the same as for the series circuit except that currents and voltages change places. We now have two currents, I_R and I_C, one in phase with E and the other 90° ahead of it; and by adopting the same methods we find that $I = \sqrt{(I_R^2 + I_C^2)}$. Fig. 63 is a typical vector diagram, which should need no further explanation.

Calculating the impedance is slightly more complicated, however, because the currents are *inversely* proportional to the impedances through which they flow. So $1/Z = \sqrt{(1/R^2 + 1/X^2)}$, or

$$Z = \frac{1}{\sqrt{\dfrac{1}{R^2} + \dfrac{1}{X^2}}}$$

which can be simplified to

$$Z = \frac{RX}{\sqrt{R^2 + X^2}}$$

Compare the formula for two resistances in parallel, p. 45.

It should be noted that this addition of squares applies only to circuits in which the two currents or voltages are exactly 90° out of phase, as when one element is a pure resistance and the other a pure reactance. Combining series impedances which are themselves combinations of resistance and reactance in parallel, or vice versa, is a rather more advanced problem than will be considered here. Such a circuit as Fig. 64, however, can be tackled by rules already given. R_2 and R_3 are reduced to a single equivalent resistance (p. 44) which is then added to R_1. C_1, C_2 and C_3 are just added together, and so are C_4 and C_5; the two resulting capacitances in series are reduced to one (p. 88). The circuit has now boiled down to Fig. 62.

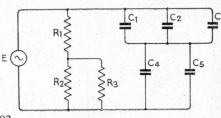

Fig. 64—Example of a complex circuit that can be reduced to Fig. 62 by applying the rules for resistances and capacitances in series and in parallel

CHAPTER 7

Inductance in A.C. Circuits

CURRENT FLOW IN AN INDUCTIVE CIRCUIT

ALTHOUGH THE PHENOMENON of magnetism, which gives rise to inductance, differs in many ways from electrostatics, which gives rise to capacitance, it is helpful to draw a very close parallel or analogy between them. Inductance and capacitance are, in fact, like opposite partners; and this chapter will in many ways be a repetition of the last one, but with a few basic situations reversed.

You probably noticed some striking similarities, as well as differences, between Figs. 34 and 41. One thing that can be seen by comparing them is an exchange of roles between voltage and current. In Fig. 34 (and Fig. 53) the effect of capacitance is to cause a transient current at each movement of the switch, and the full voltage across the capacitance (which gives rise to the electric field) is delayed until this current has ceased. In Fig. 41 the effect of inductance is to cause a transient voltage at each movement of the switch, and the full current through the inductance (which gives rise to the magnetic field) is delayed until this voltage has ceased.

The simple experiment of Fig. 53 showed that, in a circuit consisting of a square-wave alternating-voltage generator in series with a capacitor, the current increased with frequency, beginning with zero current at zero frequency. This was confirmed by examining in more detail a circuit (Fig. 52) with a sine-wave generator, in which the current was found to be exactly proportional to frequency.

Comparing Fig. 41 with Fig. 34, we can expect the opposite to apply to inductance. At zero frequency, it has no restrictive influence on the current, which is limited only by the resistance of the circuit. But when a high-frequency alternating e.m.f. is applied, the current has very little time to grow (at a rate depending on the inductance) before the second half-cycle is giving it the " about turn ". The gradualness with which the current rises, you will remember, is due to the magnetic field created by the current, which generates an e.m.f. opposing the e.m.f. that is driving the current. It is rather like the gradualness with which a heavy truck gains speed when you push it. If you shake it rapidly to and fro it will hardly move at all.

INDUCTIVE CURRENT WAVEFORM

For finding exactly how much current a given alternating voltage will drive through a given inductance (Fig. 65) we have the basic relationship (p. 68):

$$\text{Volts} = \text{Amps-per-second} \times \text{Henries}$$

It looks as if it is going to be difficult to find what we want directly from this; so let us tackle it in reverse, beginning with a sinusoidal current and seeing what voltage is required. The dotted curve in Fig. 66 represents such a current during rather more than one cycle. At the start of a cycle (*a*), the current is zero, but is increasing faster than at any other phase. So the amps-per-second is at its maximum, and so therefore must be the voltage. After half a cycle (*b*) the current is again zero and changing at the same rate, but this time it is *decreasing*, so the voltage is a maximum *negative*. Half-way between (*c*), the current is at its maximum, but for an instant it is neither increasing nor decreasing, so the voltage must be zero. And so on. Completing the voltage curve in the same way as we did the current curve in Fig. 55, we find that it also is sinusoidal. This is very fortunate, for it allows us to say that if the sinusoidal voltage represented by this curve were applied to an inductance, the current curve would represent the resulting current, which would be sinusoidal.

Fig. 65—Circuit consisting of an a.c. generator with a purely inductive load

THE "OHM'S LAW" FOR INDUCTANCE

We have already found (p. 86) that when an alternating e.m.f. E, of frequency *f*, is sinusoidal, its r.m.s. volts-per-second is $2\pi f$E.

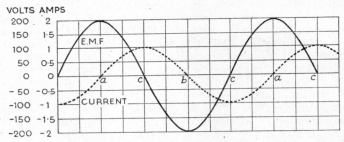

Fig. 66—E.m.f. and current graphs for Fig. 65, drawn to correspond with Figs. 44 and 55

The same method applies equally to current, so the r.m.s. amps-per-second is $2\pi f$I. Fitting this fact into our basic principle we get

$$E = 2\pi f IL,$$

where L is the inductance in henries.

What we set out to find was the current due to a given e.m.f., so the appropriate form of the above equation is

$$I = \frac{E}{2\pi f L}$$

Again, this is in the same form as Ohm's Law, $2\pi f$L taking the place of R. This $2\pi f$L can therefore also be reckoned in ohms,

94

and, like $1/2\pi f C$, it is called reactance and denoted by X. Whenever it is necessary to distinguish between inductive reactance and capacitive reactance they are denoted by X_L and X_C respectively. X is the general symbol for reactance.

A question that may come to mind at this point is: Can X_L and X_C in the same circuit be added in the same simple way as resistances? The answer is so important that it will have to be reserved for the next chapter.

Note in the meantime that X_L is proportional to f, whereas X_C is proportional to $1/f$; this expresses in exact terms what our early experiments had led us to expect about the opposite ways in which frequency affected the current due to a given voltage.

An example may help to clinch the matter. What is the reactance of a 2 H inductor at 50 c/s? $X = 2\pi f L = 2\pi \times 50 \times 2 = 628 \ \Omega$. So if the voltage is 230, the current will be $230/628 = 0 \cdot 366$ A.

The 'multiple of frequency, $2\pi f$, occurs so often in electrical calculations that it has been given a special symbol, the Greek letter ω (omega). (We have already met capital omega, Ω.)

INDUCTANCES IN SERIES AND IN PARALLEL

The previous section has shown that the reactive impedance of an inductance is directly proportional to the inductance—oppositely to that of capacitance (which is proportional to $1/C$), but exactly like resistance. So inductances can be combined in the same way as resistances. The total effect of two in series, L_1 and L_2, is equal to that of a single inductance equal to $L_1 + L_2$. And inductances in parallel follow the reciprocal law: $1/L = 1/L_1 + 1/L_2$, or $L = (L_1 L_2)/(L_1 + L_2)$. These principles can easily be verified by adding the reactances when they are in series, and the currents when the inductances are in parallel.

The above rules are subject to one important condition, however; that the inductors are so placed that their magnetic fluxes do not interlink appreciably—in other words, their mutual inductance (p. 73) or magnetic coupling must be negligible. If mutual inductance, M, does exist between two coils, the total of the two in series is $L_1 + L_2 + 2M$ or $L_1 + L_2 - 2M$, according to whether the coils are placed so that their separate magnetic fields add to or subtract from one another. The reason M is doubled is that each coil is affected by the other, so in the combination the same effect occurs twice.

The corresponding elaboration of the formula for two inductances in parallel gives the result $L = (L_1 \pm M)(L_2 \pm M)/(L_1 + L_2 \pm 2M)$.

Complications arise also when the fields of two capacitors interact, but with the usual forms of construction such interaction is seldom enough to trouble about.

POWER IN INDUCTIVE CIRCUIT

Comparing Figs. 55 and 66 we see one difference. Whereas the capacitive current leads its terminal voltage by quarter of a cycle

(90°), the inductive current lags by that amount. If you want something to do you might care to calculate the instantaneous power at intervals throughout the cycle in Fig. 66 and draw a power curve, as in Fig. 59. But the same result can be achieved with less trouble simply by reversing the time scale in Fig. 59, making it read from right to left. So except for relative phases the conclusions regarding power in a pure inductance are exactly the same as for a capacitance—the net power taken over a whole cycle is zero, because during half the time the generator is expending power in building up a magnetic field, and during the other half the energy thus built up is returning power to the generator. So in the example we took, with 230 V passing 0·366 A through 2 H, the result of multiplying 230 by 0·366 does not represent watts dissipated in the circuit (as it would with resistance) but volt-amps tossed to and fro between generator and inductor at the rate of 100 times a second.

If you try an experiment similar to Fig. 47, but using a coil of several henries in place of the capacitor, you may find that it does become perceptibly warm. This will be because the coil is not

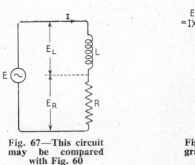

Fig. 67—This circuit
may be compared
with Fig. 60

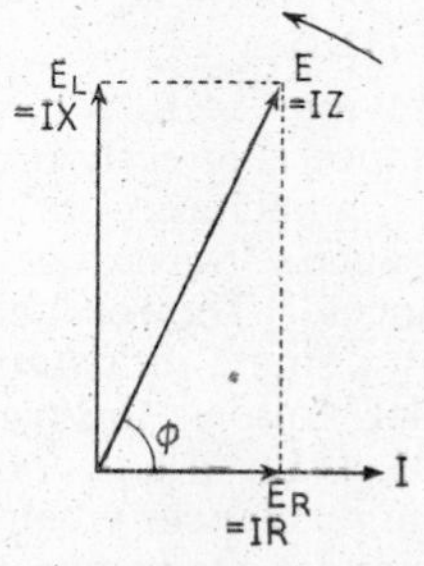

Fig. 68—Vector dia-
gram relating to
Fig. 67

purely inductive. Whereas the resistance of the plates and connections of a capacitor is usually negligible compared with its reactance, the resistance of the wire in a coil is generally very appreciable. Although the resistance and inductance of a coil can no more be separate than the body and soul of a live person, it is allowable to consider them theoretically as separate items in series with one another (Fig. 67).

INDUCTANCE AND RESISTANCE IN SERIES

R in Fig. 67 represents the resistance of the inductor whose inductance is represented by L, plus any other resistance there may be in series. This circuit can be tackled in exactly the same manner as Fig. 60. E_L is the e.m.f. required to drive a sinusoidal current I through L, and is exactly equal to the back e.m.f. generated by the alternating magnetic field linking the turns of the coil. E_R is, as before, the e.m.f. required to drive the same current through R. E_L and E_R must be 90° out of phase with one another, because

96

whereas I is in phase with E_R it lags 90° behind E_L. So E_L and E_R cannot be added straightforwardly to give E, but by the same method as we found for Fig. 60, namely $E = \sqrt{(E_R^2 + E_L^2)}$. The vector diagram is obviously the same except for the current lagging E_L instead of leading E_C; compare Fig. 68 with Fig. 61.

In the same way, too, the impedance of the circuit is $Z = \sqrt{(R^2 + X^2)}$.

INDUCTANCE AND RESISTANCE IN PARALLEL

This circuit, Fig. 69, corresponds with Fig. 62, and its impedance is found in the same way, by combining the branch currents, remembering that this time the reactive current *lags* by 90°. The

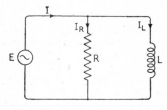

Fig. 69—As in Fig. 62, the branch currents are 90° out of phase with one another, the only difference being that the reactive current I_L is 90° later than I_R

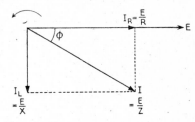

Fig. 70—Vector diagram relating to Fig. 69

vector diagram, Fig. 70, is therefore with this exception the same as Fig. 63. So we have for the total current $I = \sqrt{(I_R^2 + I_L^2)}$; and as the impedances are inversely proportional to the currents, $1/Z = \sqrt{(I/R^2 + 1/X^2)}$, giving as before

$$Z = \frac{RX}{\sqrt{R^2 + X^2}}.$$

These calculations give only the magnitudes of the impedances, without regard for the amount of the phase angle ϕ, or whether it is leading or lagging. So for a complete specification of an impedance it is necessary to add this information.

The more advanced books extend the methods and scope of circuit calculation enormously; but before going on to them one should have thoroughly grasped the contents of these last two chapters. Some of the most important results can be summarized like this:

			Current
Impedance, Z ohms	Resistance, R ohms		In phase with e.m.f.
	Reactance, X ohms	Capacitive, $X_C = 1/2\pi f C$	Leads e.m.f. by 90°
		Inductive, $X_L = 2\pi f L$	Lags

$$\text{R and X} \begin{cases} \text{in series} & : \quad Z = \sqrt{(R^2 + X^2)} \\ \text{in parallel} & : \quad Z = \dfrac{RX}{\sqrt{(R^2 + X^2)}} \end{cases}$$

But the most important thing is not to memorize results but to understand the methods used for obtaining them, so as to be able to tackle new problems.

TRANSFORMERS

On page 73 we had a brief introduction to the transformer, which is an appliance very widely used in radio and electrical work generally. The main features of its action can be grasped by considering the simple arrangement shown in Fig. 71a. Such complications as resistance of the windings are conveniently assumed

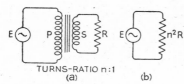

TURNS-RATIO n:1
(a)　　　　　(b)

Fig. 71—(a) Iron-cored transformer drawing current from the generator E and delivering it, at a voltage equal to E/n, to the load R. From the point of view of loading the generator, diagram b represents an equivalent circuit (assuming a perfect transformer)

to be absent. An iron core is used, not only to increase the amount of magnetic flux and hence the e.m.f. generated by a given current, but also to ensure that practically all of it links both primary and secondary windings. It will be seen later that transformers used for high-frequency a.c. often have no iron core, and only part of the field due to one winding links with the other; in other words, the coupling is loose. It is much simpler, to begin with, to assume that the coupling is 100 per cent.

Firstly, consider what happens when the resistance R is disconnected. There being no resistance in the primary circuit either, the generator e.m.f. E is opposed solely by the back voltage caused by the varying of the magnetic flux. The situation is exactly as described with reference to Fig. 66. To build up sufficient flux to generate an e.m.f. similar to that of the supply necessitates a certain number of ampere-turns; with an iron core that number is far smaller than it would be without. If the number of turns is large the current is small. It is called the *magnetizing current*.

How about the secondary coil? Because R is disconnected, the circuit is broken and no current can flow; but as we have assumed that the whole of the sinusoidally varying magnetic flux associated with the primary links with the secondary, too, an e.m.f. is generated in the secondary. The e.m.f. generated by a given change of flux linked with a coil is proportional to the number of turns. The e.m.f. generated in the primary must be equal to E. As the secondary has one nth as many, we get E/n volts across its terminals.

For example, suppose P is connected to a 200-V supply. The magnetizing current rises until sufficient alternating magnetic flux is developed to generate 200 V. Suppose 100 amp-turns are necessary to do this. Then if P has 2,000 turns, the magnetizing current is 100/2,000 = 0·05 A, and since we are assuming that the coil P is a pure inductance this current must be 90° out of phase with E. Suppose *n* is 32, so S has 2,000/32 = 63 turns; then the secondary voltage is 200/32 = 6·3 V, which might be used to heat the valves in a radio set. In practice it is not uncommon to have several secondary windings delivering different voltages for different purposes, all energized by a single primary.

The Primary Load Current

Now suppose R to be connected, and its value to be 1·4 Ω. The secondary voltage, 6·3, causes a current of 6·3/1·4 = 4·5 A, which thus introduces a magnetizing force of 4·5 × 63 = 283 amp-turns. As the secondary current is flowing in a resistive circuit, the current and the resulting flux must be in phase with the secondary and primary voltages, not 90° out of phase as is the magnetizing current. We now have 283 amp-turns due to the secondary, and (90° out of phase with it) 100 amp-turns due to the primary. We could work out the total in the now-familiar square-root manner of dealing with quantities 90° out of phase with one another, but there is no need to bother, because it is obviously not going to be equal to the original 100 amp-turns alone—the only magnetizing force that can provide the correct back-e.m.f. to balance E. The only thing that can happen to end this impossible situation is for sufficient additional current to flow in the primary to provide 283 amp-turns in exactly opposite phase to those due to the secondary, neutralizing them.

If you are guaranteed a net income of £100 a year, and your expenses in a certain year are £283, the matter can only be put right by paying £283 into your account to neutralize the outgoings.

The extra primary current—in this case 283/2,000 = 0·1415 A —is called the *load current*, because it is the current needed to make good the results of connecting the secondary load, R. Even if one did not know how a transformer worked, one would expect it to be in phase with E. This is because the secondary is delivering 6·3 × 4·5 = 28·3 watts of power, and this can only come from the primary. 28·3 W at the supply voltage, 200, is 28·3/200 = 0·1415 A, which agrees with what we have already found in another way.

Fig. 72—Simplified vector diagram of a transformer primary circuit, showing the two components, I_M and I_W, making up the total primary current, I_P. I_M is required in any case, to generate the back-e.m.f. by magnetizing the core; I_P is required to deliver power to the secondary circuit, and varies according to what is connected to the secondary winding

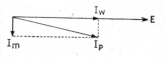

The phase relationships are shown in the vector diagram, Fig. 72. I_m denotes the magnetizing current, lagging the applied e.m.f. E by 90° and therefore causing no power loss. I_w is the load current, in phase with E. It neutralizes the secondary flux, so the secondary current must be 180° out of phase with it, and therefore also 90° out of phase with I_m as already mentioned. I_p is the total primary current; in our example it would be $\sqrt{(0.05^2 + 0.1415^2)} = 0.15$ A.

TRANSFORMER LOSSES

In practice the magnetizing current is not quite wattless, because it has to flow through the primary winding, which inevitably has some resistance. Moreover, the alternating flux in the core generates a certain amount of heat in it, which has to come from somewhere, and in accordance with our wider definition of resistance (p. 54) can be considered as equivalent to some extra resistance in the primary. The primary resistance, augmented in this way, causes I_m to lag E by less than 90°.

Nor is the power from the supply transferred to the load without the transformer taking its rake-off. The primary and secondary load currents have to contend with the resistance of the windings, so there is bound to be some loss of voltage when R is connected. The output wattage is therefore somewhat less than the input, the difference being dissipated in the transformer.

The foregoing example is typical of a small " mains " transformer. Although the same principles apply, the emphasis is rather different in a.f. and r.f. types, which will be considered later.

IMPEDANCE TRANSFORMATION

We already know that (neglecting the losses) the secondary voltage given by a transformer with a $n : 1$ turns ratio is E/n. You will probably have realized by now that the secondary current is n times the primary load current. For one thing, it must be so to make the input and output wattages equal. For another, it must be so to make the primary load current exactly neutralize the secondary current by providing an equal number of amp-turns.

Now if the primary voltage (E) is n times as great as the secondary voltage, and the primary load current is one-nth, connecting R to the secondary draws the same load current from the supply as connecting a resistance equal to $n^2 R$ directly to the supply. So, except for magnetizing current and losses, the transformer and its load R can be replaced by a resistance $n^2 R$ (Fig. 71b), without making any difference from the generator's point of view. This principle applies not only to resistances but to any type of impedance.

One of the uses of a transformer is for making a load of a certain impedance, say Z_s, equivalent to some other impedance, say Z_p. So it is often necessary to find the required turns ratio. Since $Z_p = n^2 Z_s$, it follows that n must be $\sqrt{(Z_p/Z_s)}$.

Another use is for insulating the load from the generator. That is why 1 : 1 transformers are occasionally seen. But if it is not necessary to insulate the secondary winding from the primary, there is no need for two separate coils. The winding having the smaller number of turns can be abolished, and the connections tapped across the same number of turns forming part of the other winding. This device is called an *auto-transformer*.

100

CHAPTER 8

The Tuned Circuit

INDUCTANCE AND CAPACITANCE IN SERIES

IN THE PREVIOUS chapter we have seen what happens in a circuit containing capacitance *or* inductance (with or without resistance), and the question naturally arises: What about circuits containing both? We know that two or more reactances of either the inductive or capacitive kind in series can be combined just like resistances, by adding; and either sort of reactance can be combined with resistance by the more complicated square-root process. The outcome of combining reactances of opposite kinds is so fundamental to wireless that it needs a chapter to itself.

We shall begin by considering the simplest possible series circuit, Fig. 73. The method is exactly the same as for reactance and resistance in series; that is to say, since the current is common to both it is easiest to start from it and work backwards to find the e.m.f. needed to drive it. We already know how to find the separate

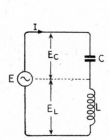

Fig. 73—Circuit consisting of an a.c. generator in series with capacitance and inductance

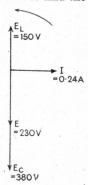

Fig. 74—Vector diagram relating to Fig. 73, when $E = 230$ V, $X_c = 1,590$ Ω and $X_L = 628$ Ω

e.m.fs for C and L; Figs. 55 and 61 are respectively the waveform and vector diagrams for C, and Figs. 66 and 68 for L. It is therefore an easy matter to combine them in a diagram to represent the Fig. 73 situation. With either type of diagram it is clear that the e.m.fs are exactly in opposition; 180° out of phase, as one would say. This can only mean that one e.m.f. must be *subtracted* from the other to give the necessary driving e.m.f. And since reactance is equal to e.m.f. divided by current (the same in both cases) it

101

follows that the total reactance of the circuit is also equal to one of the separate reactances *less* the other.

Which e.m.f. or reactance must be subtracted from which to give the total? There is no particular reason for favouring either, but the agreed convention is to call X_L positive and X_C negative.

For example, suppose L in Fig. 73 is 2 H, C is $2\mu F$, and E is 230 V at 50 c/s. We have already calculated the reactances of 2 H and 2 μF at 50 c/s (p. 95 and p. 87) and found them to be 628 Ω and 1,590 Ω. So the total reactance must be $628 - 1,590 = -962 \ \Omega$, which at 50 c/s is the reactance of a 3·3 μF capacitor. The generator, then, would not notice any difference if a 3·3 μF capacitor were substituted for the circuit consisting of 2 μF in series with 2 H. The magnitude and phase of the current would be the same in both cases; namely, $230/962 = 0.24$ A, leading by 90°.

To make sure, let us check it by calculating the voltage needed to cause this current. E_C is equal to $IX_C = 0.24 \times 1,590 = 380$ V, and its vector must be drawn so that I leads it by 90° (Fig. 74). E_L is $IX_L = 0.24 \times 628 = 150$ V, drawn so that I lags it by 90°. The resultant of E_C and E_L, represented in Fig. 74 by the net effect of a distance downwards representing 380 V and one upwards of 150 V, is clearly 230 V.

The fact that the voltage across the capacitor is greater than the total supplied may be difficult to believe at first, but it is nothing to what we shall see soon!

L, C AND R ALL IN SERIES

Bringing R into the circuit introduces no new problem, because we have just found that L and C can always be replaced (for purposes of the calculation) by either L *or* C of suitable value, and the method of combining this with R was covered in the previous chapter. Elaborating the equation given therein (p. 91) to cover the new information, we have:

$$Z = \sqrt{(X_L - X_C)^2 + R^2}$$

Faced with a circuit like Fig. 75, we might feel inclined to begin by combining R_1 with X_C and R_2 with X_L, afterwards combining the two results. But a little thought will show that neither of these pairs would be either a pure resistance or a pure reactance, so that we should have no immediate knowledge of the relative phases

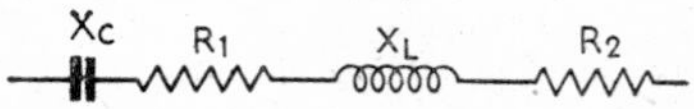

Fig. 75—Capacitance, inductance and resistance in series

of the voltages across them. The final stage of the process would therefore be outside the range of the methods we have discussed. We get round the difficulty by first subtracting X_C from X_L to find the total reactance of the circuit, then finding the total resistance by adding R_1 to R_2, and finally working out the impedance as for any other simple combination of reactance and resistance. The fact that neither the two reactances nor the two resistances are neighbours

102

in the circuit does not matter, for the same current flows through all in series.

THE SERIES TUNED CIRCUIT

We have already seen that the reactance of a capacitor falls and that of an inductor rises (p. 95) as the frequency of the current supplied to them is increased. It is therefore going to be interesting to study the behaviour of a circuit such as Fig. 76 over a range of frequencies. For the values given on the diagram, which are typical of practical broadcast receiver circuits, the reactances

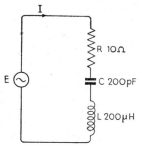

Fig. 76—The way the reactances in this circuit vary with the frequency of E, graphed in Fig. 77, leads to interesting conclusions regarding this type of circuit in general

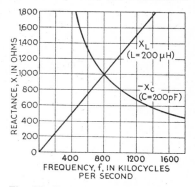

Fig. 77—Reactances of the coil and capacitor in Fig. 76 plotted against frequency. At 800 c/s, where the curves intersect, they are equal, but of opposite sign

of coil and capacitor for all frequencies up to 1,800 kc/s are plotted as curves in Fig. 77. The significant feature of this diagram is that at one particular frequency, about 800 kc/s, L and C have equal reactances, each amounting to about 1,000 Ω. So the total reactance, being the difference between the two separate reactances, is zero. Put another way, the voltage developed across the one is equal to the voltage across the other; and since they are, as always, in opposition, the two voltages cancel out exactly. The circuit would therefore be unaltered, so far as concerns its behaviour *as a whole* to a voltage of this particular frequency, by completely removing from it both L and C. This, leaving only R, would result in the flow of a current equal to E/R.

Let us assume a voltage not unlikely in broadcast reception, and see what happens when E = 5 mV. The current at 800 kc/s is then 5/10 = 0·5 mA, and this current flows, not through R only, but through L and C as well. Each of these has a reactance of 1,000 Ω at this frequency; the potential across each of them is therefore 0·5 × 1,000 = 500 mV, which is just one hundred times the voltage E of the generator to which the flow of current is due.

That so small a voltage should give rise to two such large voltages elsewhere in the circuit is one of the queer paradoxes of alternating currents that make wireless possible. If the foregoing paragraphs have not made clear the possibility of the apparent absurdity, the reader should construct for himself a waveform or vector diagram for the circuit of Fig. 76 at 800 kc/s, noting that the presence of two large voltages in opposition is inevitable.

MAGNIFICATION

In the particular case we have discussed, the voltage across the coil (or across the capacitor) is one hundred times that of the generator. This ratio is called the *magnification* of the circuit.

We have just worked out the magnification for a particular circuit; now let us try to obtain a formula for any circuit. The magnification is equal to the voltage across the coil divided by that from the generator, which is the same as the voltage across R. If I is the current flowing through both, then the voltage across L is $2\pi f$ LI, or X_L I; and that across R is IR. So the magnification $= 2\pi f$ L/R, or X_L/R or (because in the circumstances considered $X_0 = X_L$) X_0/R. At any given frequency, it depends solely on L/R, the ratio of the inductance of the coil to the resistance of the circuit.

To obtain high magnification of a received signal (for which the generator of Fig. 76 stands), it is thus desirable to keep the resistance of the circuit as low as possible.

The symbol generally used to denote this voltage magnification is Q* (not to be confused with Q denoting quantity of electricity).

RESONANCE CURVES

At other frequencies the impedance of the circuit is greater, because in addition to R there is some net reactance. At 1,250 kc/s, for example, Fig. 77 shows that the individual reactances are 1,570 and 636 Ω, leaving a total reactance of 934 Ω. Compared with this, the resistance is negligible, so that the current, for the same driving voltage of 5 mV, will be 5/934 mA, or, roughly, 5 μA. This is approximately one hundredth of the current at 800 kc/s. Passing through the reactance of L (1,570 Ω) it gives rise to a voltage across it of $1,570 \times 5 = 7,850$ μV $= 7.85$ mV, which is only about one sixty-fourth as much as at 800 kc/s.

By extending this calculation to a number of different frequencies we could plot the current in the circuit, or the voltage developed across the coil, against frequency. This has been done for two circuits in Fig. 78. The only difference between the circuits is that in one the resistance is 15 Ω, giving Q = 75, and in the other it is 5.66 Ω, giving Q = 200. In both, the values of L and C are such that their reactances are equal at 1,000 kc/s. These curves illustrate one thing we already know—that the *response* (voltage developed

* In any real tuned circuit the coil is not pure inductance as shown in Fig. 76, but contains the whole or part of R and also has some stray capacitance in parallel with it. Consequently the magnification obtained in practice is generally not exactly equal to Q (as calculated by X_L/R); but the difference is usually unimportant.

across the coil) when the reactances are equal is proportional to Q. They also show how it falls off at frequencies on each side, due to unbalanced reactance. At frequencies well off 1,000 kc/s the reactance is so much larger than the resistance that the difference between the two circuits is insignificant. The shapes of these curves show that the response of a circuit of the Fig. 76 type is enormously greater to voltages of one particular frequency—in this case 1,000 kc/s—than to voltages of substantially different frequencies. The circuit is said to be *tuned* to, or to *resonate* to, 1,000 kc/s; and the curves are called *resonance* curves. This electrical resonance is very closely parallel with acoustical resonance — the way in which hollow spaces or pipes magnify sound of a particular pitch.

The principle on which a receiver is tuned is now beginning to be evident; by adjusting the values of L or C in a circuit such as that under discussion it can be made to resonate to any desired frequency. Any signal voltages received from the aerial at that frequency will receive

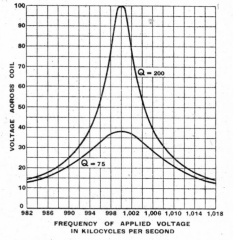

Fig. 78—Showing how the voltage developed across the coil in a tuned circuit varies with frequency. Curves are plotted for L = 180 μH, C = 141 pF, E (injected voltage) = 0·5 V, and R = 15 Ω for the Q = 75 circuit and 5·66 Ω for the Q = 200 circuit

preferential amplification; and the desired sender, distinguished from the rest by the frequency of the wave that it emits, will be heard to the comparative exclusion of the others.

SELECTIVITY

This ability to pick out signals of one frequency from all others is called *selectivity*. It is an even more valuable feature of tuned circuits than magnification. There are alternative methods (which we shall consider later) of magnifying incoming signal voltages, but by themselves they would be useless, because they fail to distinguish between the desired programme and others.

The manner in which the curves in Fig. 78 have been plotted focuses attention on how the value of Q affects the response at resonance. The conditions of actual reception are better represented, however, if the curves are plotted to give the same voltage at resonance, as has been done in Fig. 79. It must be borne in

105

mind, of course, that this implies raising the input to the low-Q circuit from 0·5 V to 1·32 V. Although Fig. 79 presents the same information as Fig. 78, it brings out more clearly the superior selectivity of the high-Q circuit. For a given response to a desired station working on 1,000 kc/s, the 200-Q response to 990 kc/s

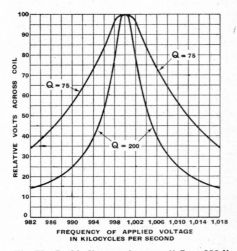

FREQUENCY OF APPLIED VOLTAGE
IN KILOCYCLES PER SECOND

Fig. 79—In this diagram the curve " Q = 200 " is the same as in Fig. 78, but, to enable the selectivity of the Q=75 circuit to be more easily compared, the voltage injected into it has been raised from 0·5 V to 1·32 V, so as to make the output voltage at resonance equal to that across the Q = 200 circuit

voltages is less than half that of the 75-Q circuit. In general, the rejection of frequencies well off resonance is nearly proportional to Q.

Broadcasting stations work at intervals of 9 or 10 kc/s, and although a Q of 200 is rather better than the average, Fig. 79 shows that the response at 10 kc/s off resonance is as much as one quarter that at resonance. This amount of selectivity is quite insufficient to keep out a possible interfering station, especially if it is stronger than the wanted one. So nearly all receivers include several tuned circuits. A second one of the same Q would reduce the quarter to one sixteenth; a third would reduce it to a quarter of one sixteenth—one sixty-fourth—and so on.

FREQUENCY OF RESONANCE

It is obviously important to be able to calculate the frequency at which a circuit containing known L and C resonates, or (performing the same process in reverse) to calculate the L and C required to tune to a given frequency. The required equation follows easily from the fact that resonance takes place at the frequency which makes the reactance of the coil equal that of the capacitor:

$$2\pi f_r L = \frac{1}{2\pi f_r C}$$

where the symbol f_r is used to denote the frequency of resonance. Rearranging this, we get:

$$f_r = \frac{1}{2\pi\sqrt{LC}}$$

106

If L and C are respectively in henries and farads, f_r will be in cycles per second; if L and C are in henries and microfarads, f_r will be in kc/s. But perhaps the most convenient units for radio purposes are μH and pF, and when the value of π has been filled in the result is then:

$$f_r = \frac{159,200}{\sqrt{LC}} \ (f_r \text{ in kc/s}) \text{ or } f_r = \frac{159\cdot2}{\sqrt{LC}} \ (f_r \text{ in Mc/s})$$

If the answer is preferred in terms of wavelength, we make use of the relationship $f = 3 \times 10^8/\lambda$ (p. 31) to give:

$$\lambda_r = 1\cdot885 \sqrt{LC} \quad (\lambda_r \text{ in metres; L in } \mu\text{H; C in pF})$$

One thing to note is that f_r and λ_r depend on L multiplied by C; so in theory a coil of any inductance can be tuned to any frequency by using the appropriate capacitance. In practice the capacitance cannot be reduced indefinitely, and there are disadvantages in making it very large. Most variable tuning capacitors give a range of about 30–530 pF. The capacitance of the wiring and circuit components necessarily connected in parallel may add another 30 pF. This gives a ratio of maximum to minimum of $560/60 = 9\cdot35$. But the square root sign in the above equations means that if the inductance is kept fixed the ratio of maximum to minimum f_r (or λ_r) is $\sqrt{9\cdot35}$, or $3\cdot06$. Any band of frequencies with this range of maximum to minimum can be covered with such a capacitor, the actual frequencies in the band being dependent on the inductance chosen for the coil.

Suppose we wished to tune from 1,605 kc/s to $1,605/3\cdot06$ or 525 kc/s, corresponding to the range of wavelengths 187 to 572 metres. For the highest frequency or lowest wavelength the capacitance will have its minimum value of 60 pF; by filling in this value for C and $1\cdot605$ Mc/s for f_r, we have $1\cdot605 = 159\cdot2/\sqrt{60L}$, from which $L = 164 \ \mu\text{H}^*$.

If we calculate the value of L necessary to give $0\cdot525$ Mc/s with a capacitance of 560 pF, the same value will again be found.

In the same way the inductance needed to cover the short-wave band $9\cdot8$ to 30 Mc/s ($30\cdot6$ to 10 metres) can be calculated, the result being $0\cdot471 \ \mu\text{H}$.

Observe how large and clumsy numbers are avoided by a suitable choice of units; but, of course, it is essential to use the equation with its appropriate numerical " constant ". If one is in any doubt it is best to go back to first principles ($2\pi f_r L = 1/2\pi f_r C$) and use henries, farads, and c/s.

---

* For this reverse process it saves time to adapt the formula, thus:

$f_r = 159\cdot2/\sqrt{LC}$ (μH, pF, Mc/s).

$\therefore f_r^2 = 159\cdot2^2/LC$

$\therefore L = 25,350/f_r^2 C$

The corresponding adaptation for calculating C is

$C = 25,350/f_r^2 L$

L and C in Parallel

If the input voltage, instead of being applied in series with L and C as in Fig. 73, is in parallel (Fig. 80), the result is a system which is in many ways similar, but in which voltage and current have changed places. In elucidating the series circuit we started with the current— because that was common to both L and C—and found the voltages across each and hence across the whole. In Fig. 80 the currents through L and C are not necessarily equal, but the voltages across them obviously must be, both being equal to E. So we start the vector diagram (Fig. 81) by drawing an E vector.

With no resistance, the current in the L-branch will be determined by the reactance $2\pi f L$ of the coil; it will be $E/2\pi f L$. In the C-branch, it will similarly be $E/(1/2\pi f C) = E.2\pi f C$. We know,

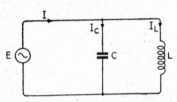

Fig. 80—Parallel resonant circuit, which may be compared with the series resonant circuit, Fig. 73

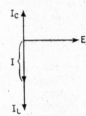

Fig. 81 — Vector diagram relating to Fig. 80

too, that I_L will lag E by 90°, and I_C will lead E by 90°; so the currents must be in exactly opposite phase, as were the voltages in Fig. 74. The net current taken from the generator will, therefore, be the simple difference between the two individual currents.

Suppose now that the frequency is such as to make the reactances equal. The currents will therefore be equal, so that the difference between them will be zero. We then have a circuit with two parallel branches, both with currents flowing in them, and yet the current supplied by the generator is nil!

It must be admitted that such a situation is impossible, because no practical circuits are entirely devoid of resistance. But if the resistance is small, the system does behave approximately as just described, when the two currents are equal. It is a significant fact that the frequency which makes them equal is obviously the same as the frequency at which L and C in a series circuit would resonate.

The Effect of Resistance

When the resistance of a circuit such as Fig. 80 has been reduced to a minimum, the resistance in the C-branch is likely to be negligible compared with that in the L-branch. Assuming this to be so, let us consider the effect of resistance in the L-branch (Fig. 82), representing it by the symbol r as a reminder that it is small compared with the reactance. We have already studied this branch on its

own (Fig. 67) and noted that one effect of the resistance is to cause the phase angle by which the current lags the total applied voltage to be less than 90°; the greater the resistance the less the angle (Fig. 68). Applying the same principle, we modify Fig. 81 as shown
in Fig. 83a. (If you have any
difficulty in seeing that the principle is the same, look at Fig 68
with the right-hand edge of the page
at the bottom, so that the two
diagrams are in phase with one
another.) The angle between E
and I_L is now less than 90°, but
since we are assuming that the
resistance in the C-branch is
negligible we must draw the I_C
vector at right angles to E. We

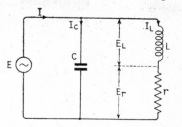

Fig. 82—Parallel resonant circuit with resistance in the inductive branch, which may be compared with Fig. 76

are also assuming that $I_C = I_L$, but as they are now not exactly opposite in phase the result of combining them is a small current I, being the current supplied by the generator. To avoid confusing Fig. 83a this combining process has been transferred to Fig. 83b.

One detail that should be noticed about Fig. 83b is that although I is nearly in phase with E it is not exactly so. If $I_C = I_L$, I must be exactly midway between them in phase, whereas E is 90° from I_C

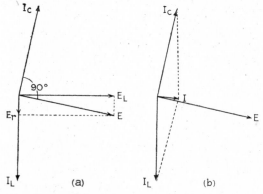

Fig. 83—(a) Modification of Fig. 81 to allow for the presence of resistance as in Fig. 82. As the two branch currents I_C and I_L are not exactly opposite in phase, the result of combining them is a small current I (b) nearly in phase with E

and less than 90° from I_L. It is easy to see that I could be brought exactly into phase with E by a slight reduction in frequency, which would increase I_L and reduce I_C. But if (as we are supposing) r is much smaller than X_L there is no need to worry about this, because the difference in phase between E and I will then be negligible. In

109

Fig. 83 we have had to make r nearly a quarter of X_L to show any difference at all, whereas in practice r is more likely to be 10–50 times smaller still. And, of course, that will make I very small indeed compared with I_L or I_C.

What all this amounts to is that under the conditions named (inductive reactance of the coil much greater than its resistance, and frequency such as to make the currents in the two branches equal) the current that has to be supplied by the generator is very small and in phase with its e.m.f. In other words, it is identical with the current that would flow if the two reactive branches were replaced by one consisting of a high resistance.

DYNAMIC RESISTANCE

It is a matter of considerable practical interest to know how high this resistance is (let us call it R), and how it is related to the values of the real circuit—L, C and r. We have already seen that if $r = 0$ the current I is zero, so in that case R is infinitely large. Fig. 83 shows that as r is increased the voltage E_r increases, bringing I_L more nearly into phase with E and therefore with I_C, so that I increases, representing a decrease in R. Whereas when r is much less than X_L the value of R is much greater than X_L, you can find by drawing the vector diagram that when r is about equal to X_L then R will be not very much more than X_L. So at least we can say that the smaller we make r in Fig. 82, the greater is the resistance which the circuit as a whole presents to the generator.

It can be shown mathematically that, so long as r is much less than X_L, the resistance R, to which the parallel circuit *as a whole*

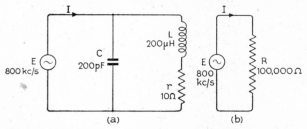

Fig. 84—The circuit composed of C, L and r having the values marked (*a*) can *at 800 kc/s* be replaced by a high resistance (*b*), so far as the phase and magnitude of the current taken by the generator is concerned

is equivalent at a certain frequency, is practically equal to X_L^2/r. The proof by algebra is given in standard textbooks, but geometry-minded readers should not find it difficult to prove from the vector diagram, Fig. 83.

To take an example, suppose C and L are the same as in Fig. 76, and r is equal to 10 Ω (Fig. 84*a*). At 800 kc/s the reactances are each 1,000 Ω (Fig. 77). So R is $1,000^2/10 = 100,000$ Ω (Fig. 84*b*). If L, C and r were hidden in one box and R in another, each with a

110

pair of terminals for connecting the generator, it would be impossible to tell, by measuring the amount and phase of the current taken, which box was which. Both would appear to be resistances of 100,000 Ω, *at that particular frequency.* We shall very soon consider what happens at other frequencies, but in the meantime it should be noted that the apparent or equivalent resistance, which we have been denoting by R, has the special name *dynamic resistance.*

PARALLEL RESONANCE

Suppose E in Fig. 84 is 1 V. Then under the conditions shown the current I must be 1/100,000 A, or 10 μA. Since the reactances are each 1,000 Ω, and the impedance of the L-branch is not appreciably increased by the presence of r, the branch currents are each 1,000 μA. But let us now change the frequency to 1,000 kc/s. Fig. 77 shows that this makes X_C and X_L respectively 800 Ω and 1,250 Ω. The current I_C taken by C is then 1/800 A = 1,250 μA and I_L is 1/1,250 A = 800 μA. Since r is small, these two currents are so nearly in opposite phase that the total current is practically equal to the difference between them, 1,250 − 800 = 450 μA. This balance is on the capacitive side, so at 1,000 kc/s the two branches can be replaced by a capacitance having a reactance = E/I = 1/0·00045 = 2,222 Ω, or 112·5 pF. The higher the frequency the greater is the current, and the larger this apparent capacitance; at very high frequencies it is practically 200 pF—as one would expect, because the reactance of L becomes so high that hardly any current can flow in the L-branch.

Using the corresponding line of argument to explore the frequencies below 1,000 kc/s, we find that the current becomes larger and larger, and that its phase is very nearly the same as if C were removed, leaving an inductance rather greater than L but not much greater at very low frequencies.

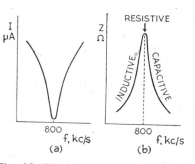

Plotting the current over a range of frequency, we get the result shown in Fig. 85a, which looks like a series-circuit resonance curve turned upside down.

Fig. 85—Plotting the current and impedance of the Fig. 84a circuit as a whole at various frequencies gives the shapes shown here; (a) current, (b) impedance

The graph of impedance against frequency (Fig. 85b) is still more clearly a resonance curve.

THE FREQUENCY OF PARALLEL RESONANCE

Before we complicated matters by bringing in r we noticed that the frequency which would make L and C resonate in a series

111

circuit had the effect of reducing I to zero and making the impedance of the parallel circuit infinitely great. In these circumstances the frequency of parallel resonance is obviously the same as that of series resonance. But actual circuits always contain resistance, which raises some awkward questions about the frequency of resonance. In a series circuit it is the frequency that makes the two reactances equal. But in a parallel circuit this does not make the branch impedances exactly equal unless both contain the same amount of resistance, which is rarely the case. The two branch currents are not likely to be exactly equal, therefore. And even if they were, Fig. 83 shows that it would not bring the total current I exactly into phase with E. So are we to go on defining f_r as the frequency that makes $X_L = X_C$, or as the frequency which brings I into phase with E so that the circuit behaves as a resistance R, or as the frequency at which the current I is least?

Fortunately it happens that in normal radio practice this question is mere hair-splitting; the distinctions only become appreciable when r is a large-sized fraction of X_L; in other words, when Q ($=X_L/r$) is abnormally small—say less than 5. *On the understanding that such unusual conditions are excluded, therefore,* the following relationships are so nearly true that the inaccuracy is of no practical importance. The frequency of parallel resonance (f_r) is the same as that for series resonance, and it makes the two reactances X_L and X_C equal. The impedance at resonance (R) is resistive, and equal to X_L^2/r and also to X_C^2/r. And, because $X_L = X_C$ at resonance, $R = X_L X_C/r = 2\pi f_r L/2\pi f_r Cr = L/Cr$, and $r = L/CR$. r can be regarded as the whole resistance in series with L and C, regardless of how it is distributed between them. Since $Q = X/r$, $R = QX$, $r = X/Q$, and $R/Q = Q/r$. All these relationships apply, of course, only at resonance.

SERIES AND PARALLEL RESONANCE COMPARED

The resonance curve in Fig. 85b showing R = 100,000 Ω applies to the circuit in Fig. 84a, in which $Q = X_L/r = 2\pi f L/r = 2\pi \times 800,000 \times 0.0002/10 = 100$. If r were reduced to 5 Ω, Q would be 200, and R would be 200,000 Ω. But reducing r would have hardly any effect on the circuit at frequencies well off resonance; so the main result would be to sharpen the resonance peak. Increasing r would flatten the peak. This behaviour is the same as with series resonance, except that a peak of impedance takes the place of a peak of voltage across the coil or of current from the generator. Current from the generator to the parallel circuit reaches a minimum at resonance (Fig. 85a), as does impedance of the series circuit.

At resonance a series circuit is (except for r) a perfect short-circuit to the generator, so is called an *acceptor circuit*. A parallel circuit at resonance is (except for R, which is an inversion of r) a perfect open-circuit to the generator, so is called a *rejector circuit*. One should not be misled by these names into supposing that there is some inherent difference between the circuits; the only difference is in the way they are used. To a generator connected in one of the branches, Fig. 84a is an acceptor circuit at the same time as it is a rejector circuit to the generator shown.

If the generator in a circuit such as Fig. 84a were to deliver a constant current instead of a constant e.m.f., the voltage developed across it would be proportional to its impedance, and so would vary with frequency in the manner shown in Fig. 85b. So the result is the same, whether a tuned circuit is used in series with a source of voltage or in parallel with a source of current. We shall come across examples of both in later chapters.

THE RESISTANCE OF THE COIL

In the sense that it cannot be measured by ordinary direct-current methods—by finding what current passes through on connecting it across a 2 V cell, for example—it is fair to describe R as a fictitious resistance. Yet it can quite readily be measured by any method suitable for measuring resistances at the frequency to which the circuit is tuned; in fact, those methods by themselves would not disclose whether the thing being measured was the dynamic resistance of a tuned circuit or the resistance of a resistor.

If it comes to that, even r is not the resistance that would be indicated by any d.c. method. That is to say, it is not merely the resistance of the wire used to make the coil. Although no other cause of resistance may be apparent, the value of r measured at high frequency is always greater, and may be many times greater, than the d.c. value.

One possible reason for this has been mentioned in connection with transformers (p. 100). If a solid iron core were used, it would have currents generated in it just like any secondary winding: the laws of electromagnetism make no distinction. These currents passing through the resistance of the iron represent so much loss of energy, and, as we have seen, that necessitates an e.m.f. in phase with the primary current, just as if there were some extra resistance in the coil to be overcome. To stop these *eddy currents*, as they are called, iron cores are usually made up of thin sheets arranged so as to break up circuits along the lines of the induced e.m.f. At radio frequencies even this is not good enough, and iron is either avoided altogether or used in the form of a fine dust.

There is a further source of loss in iron cores, called *hysteresis*, due to a slight lag in magnetic response, which shifts the phase of the primary current.

The warming-up of cores in which a substantial number of watts are being lost in these ways is very noticeable.

Although an iron core introduces the equivalent of resistance into the circuit, its use is worthwhile if it enables a larger amount of resistance to be removed as a result of fewer turns of wire being needed to give the required inductance. Another reason for using iron cores, especially in r.f. coils, is to enable the inductance to be varied (by moving the core in and out).

113

Even the metal composing the wire itself has e.m.fs induced in it in such a way as to be equivalent to an increase in resistance. As the frequency is raised, the current is confined more and more to the surface of the wire. This *skin effect* occurs even in a straight wire; but when wound into a coil each turn lies in the magnetic field of other turns, and the resistance is further increased—so much so that using a thicker gauge of wire sometimes actually increases the r.f. resistance of a coil.

DIELECTRIC LOSSES

In the circuits we have considered until now, r has been shown exclusively in the inductive branch. While it is true that the resistance of the capacitor plates and connections is usually negligible (except perhaps at very high frequencies), insulating material coming within the alternating electric field introduces resistance rather as an iron core does in the coil. It is as if the elasticity of the " leashes " (p. 59) were accompanied by a certain amount of friction, for the extra circuit current resulting from the electron movements is not purely capacitive in phase. The result is the same as if resistance were added to the capacitance.

Such materials are described as poor dielectrics, and obviously would not be chosen for interleaving the capacitor plates. Air is an almost perfect dielectric, but even in an air capacitor a part of the field traverses solid material, especially when it is set to minimum capacitance. Apart from that, valve holders, valve bases, terminal blocks, wiring, and other parts of the circuit—including the tuning coil—have " stray " capacitances; and if inefficient dielectrics are used for insulation they will be equivalent to extra resistance.

R.F. RESISTANCE

All these causes of loss in high-frequency circuits come within the general definition of resistance (p. 54), as (electrical power dissipated) ÷ (current-squared). In circuit diagrams and calculations it is convenient to bring it all together, with the ordinary wire resistance, in a single symbol such as in Fig. 84a, in conjunction with a theoretically perfect inductor and capacitor, L and C. But we have seen that at resonance the whole tuned circuit can also be represented as a resistance R (Fig. 84).

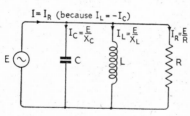

$I = I_R$ (because $I_L = -I_C$)

$I_C = \dfrac{E}{X_C}$ $I_L = \dfrac{E}{X_L}$ $I_R = \dfrac{E}{R}$

E   C   L   R

Fig. 86—An alternative way of representing a circuit such as Fig. 84 (a). If r is small compared with X, $R = X^2/r$

We also know that a perfect L and C at resonance have an infinite impedance, so could be shown connected in parallel with R as in Fig. 86; and as this tuned circuit would carry the large circulating currents I_L and I_C it would represent the actual circuit more closely. Furthermore, it represents the circuit not only at resonance but (except in so far as R varies somewhat with frequency) at frequencies on each side of resonance.

More generally, for every resistance and reactance in series one can calculate the values of another resistance and reactance which, connected in parallel, at the same frequency, are equivalent. And if (as we are assuming) the reactance is much greater than the resistance, it has very nearly the same value in both cases. The values of series and parallel resistance, r and R respectively, are connected by the same approximate formula $R = X^2/r$, which we have hitherto regarded as applying only at the frequency of resonance (p. 110). This ability to reckon resistance as either in parallel or in series is very useful. It may be, for example, that in an actual circuit there is resistance connected both ways. Then for simplifying calculations it can be represented by a single resistance, either series or parallel.

An example, worked out with the help of relationships explained in this chapter, may make it clearer. A certain coil has, say,

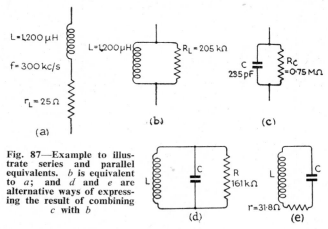

Fig. 87—Example to illustrate series and parallel equivalents. b is equivalent to a; and d and e are alternative ways of expressing the result of combining c with b

an inductance of 1,200 μH, and at 300 kc/s its r.f. resistance, reckoned as if it were in series with a perfect inductance, is 25 Ω (Fig. 87a). At that frequency the reactance, X_L, is $2\pi f L = 2\pi \times 300 \times 1\cdot2 = 2,262 \ \Omega$. So $Q_L = 2,262/25 = 90\cdot6$. ($Q_L$ is the Q of the coil, defined as X_L/r_L; it is also the magnification of a resonant circuit consisting of this coil and a perfect capacitor.) The same coil can be represented as a perfect inductance of very nearly 1,200 μH in parallel with a resistance $R_L = X_L^2/r_L = 2,262^2/25 = 205,000 \ \Omega$ or 205 kΩ (Fig. 87b). If r_L remained the same at 200 kc/s, the value of R_L would be $(2\pi \times 200 \times 1\cdot2)^2/25 = 462$ kΩ; so when the equivalent parallel value has been found for one frequency it must not be taken as holding good at other frequencies. As a matter of fact, neither r_L nor R_L is likely to remain constant, but in most

115

practical coils Q is fairly constant over the useful range of frequency. So it is likely that at 200 kc/s R_L would be somewhere around 300 kΩ, and r_L would be about 17 Ω.

The capacitance required to tune the coil to 300 kc/s, or 0·3 Mc/s, is $C = 25{,}350/f_r^2 L = 25{,}350/(0·3^2 \times 1{,}200) = 235$ pF. This, of course, includes not only the tuning capacitor itself but also the stray capacitance of the wiring and of the coil. The whole of this is equivalent to a perfect 235 pF in parallel with a resistance of, shall we say, 0·75 MΩ (Fig. 87c). The reactance, X_C, is bound to be the same as X_L at resonance; but to check it we can work it out from $1/2\pi f C = 1/(2\pi \times 0·3 \times 0·000235) = 10^6/(2\pi \times 0·3 \times 235) = 2{,}262$ Ω. Q_C is therefore $R_O/X_C = 750{,}000/2{,}262 = 332$. (This figure is the magnification of a resonant circuit consisting of this capacitor and a perfect coil, but as real coils are far from perfect it is more useful as a measure of the " goodness " of the capacitor.)

If the two components are united as a tuned circuit, the total loss can be expressed as a parallel resistance, R, by reckoning R_L and R_C in parallel—$R_L R_C/(R_L + R_C) = 0·205 \times 0·75/0·955 = 0·161$ MΩ (Fig. 87d). Although this is less than R_L, it indicates a greater loss. The Q of the tuned circuit as a whole is $161{,}000/2{,}262 = 71$. [Incidentally, it may be seen that this is $Q_L Q_C/(Q_L + Q_C)$.] The total loss of the circuit can also be expressed as a series resistance, $r = 2{,}262^2/161{,}000 = 31·8$ Ω (Fig. 87e). Calculating Q from this, 2,262/31·8, gives 71 as before.

Before going on, the reader would do well to continue calculations of this kind with various assumed values, taking note of any general conclusions that arise. For instance, a circuit to tune to the same frequency could be made with less inductance; assuming the same Q, would the dynamic resistance be lower or higher? Would an added resistance in series with the lower-L coil have less or more effect on its Q? And what about a resistance in parallel?

CHAPTER 9

Valves: The Simpler Types

LIBERATED ELECTRONS

IN DISCUSSING THE NATURE of an electric current (p. 38) we saw that it consists of a stream of electrons along a conductor. The conductor is necessary in order to provide a supply of loose electrons, ready to be set in motion by an e.m.f. An e.m.f. applied to an insulator causes no appreciable current because the number of loose electrons in it is negligible.

To control the current, it is necessary to move the conductor, as is done in a switch or rheostat (a variable resistor). This is all right occasionally, but quite out of the question when (as in radio) we want to vary currents millions of times a second. The difficulty is the weight of the conductor; it is mechanically impracticable to move it at such a rate.

This difficulty can be overcome by releasing electrons, which are inconceivably light, from the relatively heavy metal or whatever conductor is used. Although in constant agitation in the metal, they have not enough energy at ordinary temperature to escape beyond its surface. But if the metal is heated they " boil off " from it. A source of free electrons, such as this, is called a *cathode*. To prevent the electronic current from being hindered by the surrounding air, the space in which it is to flow is enclosed in a glass bulb and as much as possible of the air pumped out, giving a vacuum. We are now well on the way to manufacturing a *thermionic valve*, or, as it is called in America, a vacuum tube.

Cathodes are of two main types—*directly heated* and *indirectly heated*. The first, more usually known as a *filament*, consists of a fine wire heated by passing a current through it. To minimize the current needed, the wire is usually coated with a special material that emits electrons freely at the lowest possible temperature. Valves with this type of cathode are used chiefly in battery-driven sets. The indirectly heated cathode is a very narrow tube, usually of nickel, coated with the emitting material and heated by a separate filament, called the *heater*, threaded through it. Since the cathode is insulated from the heater, three connections are necessary compared with the two that suffice when the filament serves also as the source of electrons, unless two are joined together as in certain rectifier valves.

In all essentials the two types of cathode work in the same way; in dealing with valves we shall therefore omit the heater or filament circuit altogether after the first few diagrams, indicating the cathode by a single connection. The operation of a valve depends upon the emission from the cathode; the means by which the cathode is

117

heated to obtain this emission has little significance except in connection with the design of a complete receiver.

The free electrons do not tend to move in any particular direction unless urged by an electric field. In the absence of such a field they gather round the cathode, enclosing it in an electronic cloud known as the *space charge*. Because the charge consists of electrons, it is negative, and repels new arrivals back again to the cathode, so preventing any further accumulation of electrons in the vacuous space.

THE DIODE VALVE

To overcome the stoppage caused by the negative space charge it is necessary to apply a positive potential. This is introduced into the valve by means of a metal plate called the *anode*. The simplest type of valve—the diode—contains only two *electrodes*—cathode and anode.

When the anode is made positive relative to the cathode, it attracts electrons from the space charge, causing its repulsion to diminish

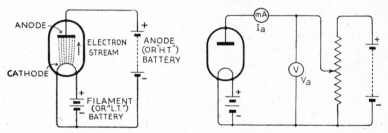

Fig. 88—Electron flow from cathode to anode in a directly-heated diode valve

Fig. 89—Circuit for finding the relationship between the anode voltage (V_a) and the anode current (I_a) in a diode

so that more electrons are emitted from the cathode, so that a current can flow, through the valve, round a circuit such as that of Fig. 88. But if the battery is reversed, so that the anode is more negative than the cathode, the electrons are repelled towards their source, and no current flows. The valve will therefore permit current to flow through it in one direction only, and it is from this property that its name is derived.

If the anode of a diode is slowly made more and more positive with respect to the cathode, as, for example, by moving the slider of the potentiometer in Fig. 89 upwards, the attraction of the anode for the electrons is slowly augmented and the current increases. To each value of anode voltage V_a, there corresponds some value of anode current I_a, and if each pair of readings is recorded on a graph a curve like that of Fig. 90 (called a valve *characteristic curve*) is obtained.

The shape of the curve shows that the anode collects few electrons at low voltages, being unable to overcome the repelling effect of the space-charge. The greater the positive anode voltage the greater the negative space charge it is able to neutralize; that is to say, the greater the number of electrons that can be on their way between cathode and anode; in other words, the greater the anode current.

By the time the point C is reached the voltage is so high that electrons are reaching the anode practically as fast as the cathode can emit them; a further rise in voltage collects only a few more strays, the current remaining almost constant from C to D and beyond. This is called *saturation*.

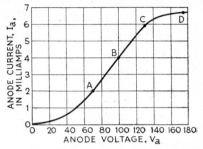

Fig. 90—Typical characteristic curve of a diode

At B an anode voltage of 100 V drives through the valve a current of 4 mA; the valve could therefore be replaced by a resistance of $100/4 = 25$ kΩ without altering the current flowing at this voltage. This value of resistance is therefore the equivalent d.c. resistance of the valve at this point. Examination of the curve will show that although the valve is in this sense equivalent to a resistor, it does not conform to Ohm's Law; its resistance depends on the voltage applied. To drive 1 mA, for example, needs 50 V; $V/I = 50/1 = 50$ kΩ.

This is because the valve, considered as a conductor, is quite different from the material conductors with which Ohm experimented. Its so-called resistance—really the action of the space charge—is like true resistance in that it restricts the current that flows when a given voltage is applied, but it does not cause the current to be exactly proportional to the voltage as it was in Fig. 18. In other words, it is non-linear.

Anode A.C. Resistance

One can, however, reckon the resistance of a valve in another way. The portion of the curve round about B is nearly linear (i.e., straight). Within it, an increase or decrease of 30 anode volts causes an increase or decrease in anode current of 2 mA. The resistance over this region of the curve would therefore appear to be $30/2 = 15$ kΩ. This resistance is effective towards current *variations* within the range A to C; if, for example, a steady anode voltage of 100 V were applied (point B) and then an alternating voltage of peak value 20 V were superposed on this, the resulting alternating current through the valve would be 1·33 mA peak. Based on this, the resistance, as before, comes out to $20/1·33 = 15$ kΩ. Thus the figure derived in this way is the resistance offered to an alternating voltage superposed on a steady anode voltage; it is therefore called the *anode a.c. resistance* of the valve. Its importance in wireless technique is so great that it has had the special symbol r_a allotted to

119

it. It is also, but not so precisely, called the " impedance " of the valve. The number of steps up in current for one step up in voltage is the *slope* of the curve. But r_a is the number of voltage steps for one current step, so it is 1 divided by the slope, or, as it is called, the reciprocal of the slope, at the particular point selected on it. As can be seen from Fig. 90, a steep slope means a low anode a.c. resistance.

The equivalent d.c. resistance of a valve is a quantity seldom used or mentioned; it was discussed here only for the sake of bringing into prominence the non-linearity of the valve's resistance.

THE TRIODE VALVE

As we shall see in Chapter 13, the one-way traffic of the diode makes it very useful for converting a.c. to d.c.—*rectifying*. But if a mesh of fine wire is inserted between cathode and anode, in such a way that before they can get to the anode all the electrons emitted from the cathode have to pass through the meshes of this extra electrode, a much fuller control of the electron current becomes possible.

We are, in effect, altering the space-charge, which, as we have seen, is the only thing (short of saturation) affecting the amount of current that a given anode voltage causes to flow.

It is fairly evident that if this new electrode, the *grid*, is made

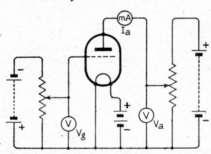

Fig. 91—Circuit for taking characteristic curves of a triode

positive it will assist the anode to neutralize the space charge, so increasing the anode current; and, being nearer to the cathode, one grid volt will be more effective than one anode volt. If, on the other hand, it is made negative it will assist the space charge in repelling electrons back towards the cathode. Fig. 91 shows the rather more complicated apparatus needed to take

characteristic curves of a three-electrode valve, or *triode*. And in Fig. 92 are some such curves, showing the effects of both anode and grid voltages. Each of these curves was taken with a fixed grid voltage, indicated against each curve. It is to be noticed that this voltage, like all others relating to a valve, is reckoned from the cathode as zero. If, therefore, the cathode of a valve is made two volts positive with respect to earth, while the grid is connected to earth, it is correct to describe the grid as " two volts negative," the words " with respect to the cathode " being understood. In a directly heated valve, voltages are reckoned from the negative end of the filament.

120

AMPLIFICATION FACTOR

Except for a successive shift to the right as the grid is made more negative, the curves in Fig. 92 are practically identical. This means that while a negative grid voltage reduces the anode current in the way described, this reduction can be counterbalanced by a suitable increase in anode voltage. In the valve of which curves are shown, an anode current of 10 mA can be produced by an anode voltage of 120 if the grid is held at zero potential ($V_g = 0$). This is indicated by the point A. If the grid is now made 6 V negative the current drops to 4 mA (point B), but can be brought up again to its original value by increasing the anode voltage to 180 V (point C).

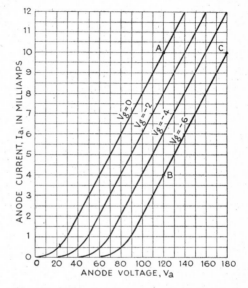

Fig. 92—Characteristic curves of triode valve, each showing change of anode current with change of anode voltage. (These curves are somewhat idealized, being straighter and more parallel than in actual practice)

Looked at another way, the distance A to C represents 60 V on the V_a scale and -6 V on the V_g scale, with no change in I_a. So we can say that a change of 6 V at the grid can be compensated for by a change of 60 V, or ten times as much, at the anode. For reasons that will presently appear, this ratio of 10 to 1 is called the *amplification factor* of the valve. It is one more thing to be denoted by μ.

As in the case of the diode, the anode resistance of the valve can be read off from the curves. All four curves of Fig. 92 will give the same value over their upper portions, since they all have the same slope; over the lower parts, where the steepness varies from point to point, a whole range of values for the anode resistance exists. Over the linear portions of the curves this resistance is 10 kΩ, as can be seen from the fact that the anode voltage must change by 10 to alter the anode current by 1 mA.

When reckoning the r_a of a triode, it is most important that the change in anode voltage should not be accompanied by any change in grid voltage.

MUTUAL CONDUCTANCE

We have seen that 1 V on the grid is equivalent to 10 V on the anode; a change of 1 V at the grid will, therefore, also cause a change in the anode current of 1 mA. This can also be read directly from the curves by observing that at $V_a = 100$, the anode current for $V_g = 0$ and $V_g = -2$ are 8 and 6 mA respectively, again a change of 1 mA for each 1-V change on the grid.

The response of the anode current of a valve to changes in grid voltage is a useful measure of the control that the grid exercises over the electron stream through the valve. It is called the *mutual conductance* (symbol: g_m), and in basic units would be expressed in amps per volt, of mhos (p. 48); but because valve currents usually amount only to milliamps it is nearly always in mA/V, which could also be called millimhos.

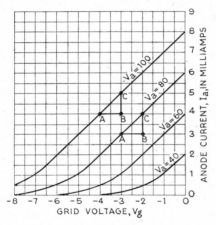

Fig. 93—Four samples of anode-current/grid-voltage characteristic curve, each taken at a different anode voltage

Most Americans use a smaller unit still, the μA/V or micromho.

The value of g_m can, as we have seen, be derived from an $I_a - V_a$ diagram such as Fig. 92, provided that there are curves for at least two different grid voltages, by noting the change in I_a corresponding to a change in V_g. And, of course, the pair of readings marking out this change must both be at the same anode voltage. An alternative form of characteristic curve is obtained by plotting I_a at a fixed V_a for various values of V_g, as in Fig. 93; a single curve of this kind is obviously sufficient to indicate g_m. For instance, BC represents the increase in I_a caused by an increase in V_g represented by AB; so g_m is given by the ratio BC/AB—in this case 1 mA/V. Since this ratio also defines the slope of the curve, it is quite common to refer to the mutual conductance as the *slope* of the valve. But it must be clearly understood that it is only the slope of this particular kind of valve characteristic curve. The slope of the $I_a - V_a$ curve (Fig. 92) is obviously different, and, in fact, is the anode conductance, $1/r_a$. It, too, can be measured in mA/V, the volts being anode volts instead of grid volts. But we know that one grid volt is equivalent to μ anode volts, in its effects on I_a. So the mutual conductance must be μ times the anode conductance. In symbols:

$$g_m = \mu \times \frac{1}{r_a}, \text{ or } g_m = \frac{\mu}{r_a}, \text{ or } \mu = g_m r_a, \text{ or } r_a = \frac{\mu}{g_m}.$$

122

If r_a is in ohms, g_m will be in A/V; and if g_m is in mA/V, r_a will be in kΩ.

We see, then, that if any two of these valve *parameters* are known, the third follows. It must not be forgotten that the values of them all depend on the part of the valve curve selected; that is to say, on the steady voltages applied to the electrodes. The more nearly linear the curves, the more nearly constant the parameters. At the bends, they vary enormously, especially r_a and g_m; μ is the most nearly constant.

ALTERNATING VOLTAGE AT THE GRID

In Fig. 94 we have an I_a — V_g curve for a typical triode. As the slope of the curve shows, its mutual conductance g_m is about $3\frac{1}{2}$ to 4 mA/V for anode currents greater than about 4 mA, but less for lower currents. Suppose that, as suggested in the inset to that figure, we apply a small alternating e.m.f., e_g, to the grid of the valve, what will the anode current do? If the batteries supplying anode and grid give 200 and $-2\frac{1}{2}$ V respectively, the anode current will set itself at about $5\frac{3}{4}$ mA— point A on the curve.

If the alternating voltage applied to the grid has a peak value of 0·5 V, the total voltage on the grid will swing between -3 and -2 V, alternate half-cycles adding to or subtracting from the steady voltage E_g. The anode current will swing correspondingly with

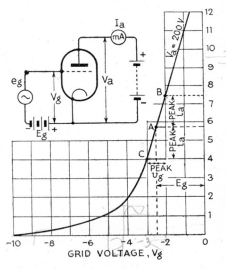

Fig. 94—The result of applying an alternating e.m.f. (e_g) to the grid of a triode can be worked out from the I_a — V_g curve, as here. The fixed starting voltage, E_g, is —2·5 V in this case

the changes in grid voltage, the points B and C marking the limits of the swing of both. The current, swinging between $7\frac{1}{2}$ and 4 mA, is reduced by $1\frac{3}{4}$ mA on the negative half-cycle and increased by the same amount on the positive one. The whole is therefore equivalent to the original steady current with an alternating current of $1\frac{3}{4}$ mA peak superposed on it.

THE LOAD LINE

There are two ways in which this a.c. in the anode circuit can be usefully employed. It can be used for producing an alternating voltage, by passing it through an impedance, of which the simplest

123

sort to consider is a resistance (Fig. 95). If the voltage so obtained is larger than the alternating grid voltage that caused it, we have a voltage amplifier. Alternatively, if the alternating current is strong enough it can be used to operate a loudspeaker or other device.

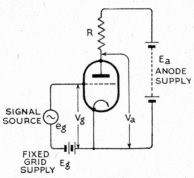

Fig. 95—When an impedance, such as the resistance R, is connected in the anode circuit, the anode voltage V_a varies as V_g is varied

But as the loudspeaker, etc., inevitably offers some impedance to the current, in principle the circuit is the same.

This complicates matters, because V_a will no longer be equal to the fixed voltage E_a supplied by the battery, but will be E_a less the voltage drop in R. And, if the current through R is varying due to the alternating voltage e_g, the voltage drop—and hence V_a— will vary too. The awkward thing is that in order to find how much I_a varies we have to know how much V_a (as well as V_g) varies; and to find how much V_a varies we have to know how much I_a varies.

One way of overcoming this difficulty is by means of a set of $I_a — V_a$ curves for different values of V_g, such as Fig. 96. Let us suppose that E_a, the fixed anode battery e.m.f., is 240 V, and R is

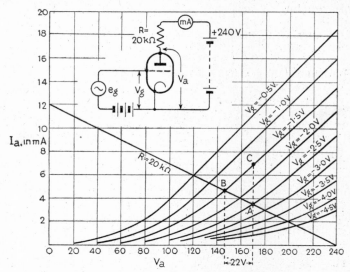

Fig. 96—An example of the problem set by Fig. 95 is here worked out on an $I_a — V_a$ curve sheet

20 kΩ. Knowing this, we can at once say what V_a will be when any given anode current is flowing. Thus, when $I_a = 0$, the voltage drop (which, of course, is equal to I_aR) is also zero, and therefore the full battery voltage reaches the anode; $V_a = 240$ V. When $I_a = 1$ mA, I_aR is 20 V, so $V_a = 240 - 20 = 220$ V. When $I_a = 2$ mA, $V_a = 200$ V. And so on. Plotting all these points on Fig. 96, we get the straight line marked " $R = 20$ kΩ ". The significance of this line is that it marks out the only combinations of I_a and V_a that are possible when the resistance R is 20 kΩ. Since R is a load resistance, the line is called a load line. It would be equally easy to draw a load line for $R = 10$ kΩ or any other value.

At the same time, the valve curves mark the only possible combinations of I_a, V_a and V_g, when that particular valve is used. So when that valve and that resistance are used together, as in the inset to Fig. 96, the only possible combinations of I_a and V_a are those marked by points located both on the load line and on the appropriate valve curves; for example, point A, which indicates $I_a = 3\frac{1}{2}$ mA at $V_a = 170$ V. A current of $3\frac{1}{2}$ mA flowing through 20 kΩ drops $3\frac{1}{2} \times 20 = 70$ V, so the total voltage to be supplied is $170 + 70 = 240$ V, which is correct. Since the valve curve on which A falls is marked " $V_g = -2\cdot5$ V ", that is the only grid voltage that will satisfy all the conditions.

VOLTAGE AMPLIFICATION

Suppose now we alter the grid voltage to $-1\cdot5$ V. The working point (as it is called) must move to B, because that is the only point on both the " $V_g = -1\cdot5$ V " curve and the load line. The anode current rises from $3\cdot5$ mA to $4\cdot6$ mA—an increase of $1\cdot1$ mA. The voltage drop due to R therefore increases by $1\cdot1 \times 20 = 22$ V. So the voltage at the anode (V_a) falls by that amount.

Note that a grid voltage change equal to 1 V has caused an anode voltage change of 22 V, so we have achieved a voltage multiplication —called amplification or *gain*—of 22. If the anode had been connected direct to E_a, there would have been no change in V_a at all, of course; and the working point would have moved to C, representing an I_a increase of $3\cdot3$ mA. The reason why the increase with R in circuit was only $1\cdot1$ mA was the drop of 22 V in V_a, which partly offset the rise in V_g.

Another thing to note is that making the grid less negative caused the anode to become less positive. So an amplifier of this kind reverses the sign of the signal being amplified.

THE " VALVE EQUIVALENT GENERATOR "

It would be very convenient to be able to calculate the voltage amplification when a set of curves was not available and only the valve parameters, μ and r_a, were known. To understand how this can be done, let us go back to Fig. 91 with its controls for varying anode and grid voltages. First, leaving the V_g control untouched, let us work the V_a control. The result, indicated on the milliammeter, is a variation in anode current. The same current variation for a given variation in V_a would be obtained if an ordinary resistance equal to r_a were substituted for the valve (p. 119). Considering only the variations, and ignoring the initial V_a and I_a needed to make the valve work over an approximately linear part of its characteristics, we can say that from the viewpoint of the anode voltage supply the valve looks like a resistance r_a.

Now keep V_a steady and vary V_g. To the surprise of the V_a supply (which does not understand valves!), I_a again starts varying. If the V_a supply could think, it would deduce that one (or both) of two things was happening: either the resistance r_a was varying, or the valve contained a source of varying e.m.f. To help it to decide between these, we could vary V_a slightly—enough to check the value of r_a by noting the resulting change in I_a—at various settings of the V_g control. Provided that we took care to keep within the most linear working condition, the value of r_a measured in this way would be at least approximately the same at all settings of V_g. So that leaves only the internal e.m.f. theory in the running.

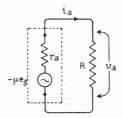

Fig. 97—The " equivalent generator " circuit of a valve, which can be substituted for Fig. 95 for purposes of calculating the performance of the valve

We (who do understand valves) know that varying V_g has μ times as much effect on I_a as varying a voltage directly in the anode circuit (namely, V_a).

So we can now draw a diagram, Fig. 97 (which should be compared with Fig. 95) to show what the valve looks like from the point of view of the anode circuit. Its behaviour can be accounted for by supposing that it contains a source of e.m.f., μe_g, in series with a resistance, r_a. We have already come across examples of substituting (on paper or in the imagination) something that, within limits, behaves in the same way as the real circuit, but is easier for calculation. One of them was a dynamic resistance in place of a parallel resonant circuit (Fig. 84). And now this trick of the *valve equivalent generator*, which is one of the most important and useful of all.

But " within limits " must be remembered. In this case there are two limits: (1) for a valve to behave like an ohmic resistance it must be working at anode and grid voltages corresponding to linear parts of its characteristic curves, and they are never *perfectly* linear, so at best r_a is no more than a good approximation to an ohmic resistance; and (2) the initial values of V_a, V_g, and I_a are

126

left out of account—they are merely incidental conditions necessary to achieve (1)—and variations or alternating signal voltages and currents within the linear region are considered on their own. For example, if I_a is alternating between 3 mA and 5 mA, then the valve equivalent generator regards only i_a, the anode signal current, peak value 1 mA, and ignores the initial 4 mA on which it is based.

It is failure to separate these two things (the " feed " current and the " signal " current) in one's mind that leads to confusion about the next idea—the minus sign in front of μe_g in Fig. 97. Some people argue that, because a positive movement in e_g (say from $-2 \cdot 5$ V to $-1 \cdot 5$ V) *increases* I_a, the imaginary signal voltage μe_g must also be positive. And then they are stuck to account for v_a, the amplified signal voltage, being negative as we found on page 125. But if they realized that the feed voltage and current E_a and I_a have nothing to do with Fig. 97 they would avoid this dilemma. For it just happens that the feed current flows anticlockwise round the circuit; but as we are ignoring this there is nothing to stop us from taking the logical view that the signal current flows clockwise. If e_g is positive, $-\mu e_g$ is negative and its negative clockwise i_a is equivalent to a positive anticlockwise current (increasing I_a in Fig. 95) but making v_a negative—both in agreement with known facts.

CALCULATING AMPLIFICATION

Now let us apply this valve equivalent generator technique to the problem we set out to solve—finding the amplification of a valve. The signal current i_a in Fig. 97 is (by Ohm's Law) the signal e.m.f. divided by the total circuit resistance, $-\mu e_g/(R + r_a)$. The signal output voltage, v_a, is caused by this current flowing through R, so is $-\mu e_g R/(R + r_a)$. The voltage amplification (which is often denoted by A) is v_a/e_g, so

$$A = \frac{-\mu R}{R + r_a}$$

This minus sign agrees with our finding on page 125. Let us apply this to the case we considered with the help of Fig. 96. Using the methods already described (p. 119 and p. 121) we find that in the region of A the valve in question has a r_a of about 14·5 kΩ and μ about 39. Substituting these, and R = 20 kΩ, in the formula: $A = -39 \times 20/(20 + 14 \cdot 5) = -22 \cdot 6$, which agrees pretty well with the figure obtained graphically. Since it is understood that v_a is in opposite phase to e_g, the minus is often omitted.

THE EFFECT OF LOAD ON AMPLIFICATION

The amplification formula that we have just used shows at once that making R = 0 would make A = 0. It also shows that making R so large that r_a was negligible in comparison with it would make A almost equal to μ, which is the reason for calling this parameter the amplification factor. What happens at intermediate

127

values of R can best be seen by using the formula to plot a graph of A against R—the full-line curve in Fig. 98.* In case this suggests that the best policy is to use the largest possible R, it should be mentioned that in order to keep r_a from increasing too much it is necessary to apply sufficient battery voltage to maintain the anode feed current. If R were raised from 20 kΩ to 100 kΩ in order to raise A from 22 to 34, an extra $80 \times 3 \cdot 5 = 280$ V would be needed to keep at the same 3·5 mA working point. Any gain above about two-thirds μ is obtained at an uneconomical cost in supply voltage.

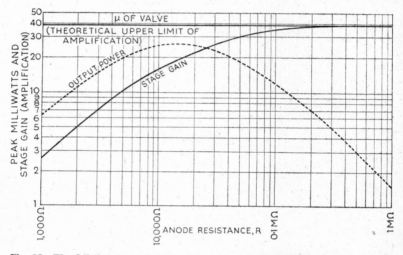

Fig. 98—The full line shows how the voltage amplification depends on the value of load resistance R. It is calculated for a valve with $\mu = 39$ and $r_a = 14 \cdot 5$ kΩ. The dotted line shows the peak milliwatts delivered to R for a grid input of 1 V peak. The maximum power is obtained when $R = r_a$

All these facts can be deduced also from Fig. 96. For a higher R than 20 kΩ the load line would be more nearly horizontal, and to keep it passing through the same working point A it would have to pivot around A so that its left-hand end would touch the voltage scale at a higher point than 240 V. At the same time the anode current would be kept more nearly constant as V_g varied, so the resulting variation in V_a would necessarily be more nearly equal to μe_g. And vice versa for lower values of R.

THE MAXIMUM-POWER LAW

For some purposes (such as working loudspeakers) we are not interested in the *voltage* output so much as the *power* output. This, of course, is equal to $i_a v_a$ or $i_a^2 R$, and can therefore be calculated by filling in the value of i_a we found overleaf— $- \mu e_g/(R + r_a)$.

* Logarithmic scales are used (p. 20) in order to cover wide ranges of values without squeezing most of them into a corner.

Denoting the power by P, we therefore have

$$P = \left(\frac{\mu e_g}{R + r_a} \right)^2 R.$$

A graph of this rather complicated expression, for $e_g = 1$ V, and $\mu \doteq 39$ and $r_a = 14 \cdot 5$ as before, is shown dotted in Fig. 98. The interesting thing about it is that it has a maximum value when R is somewhere between 10 kΩ and 20 kΩ. The only thing in the circuit that seems to give any clue to this is r_a, 14·5 kΩ. Could the maximum power result when R is made equal to r_a?

It could, and does; as can be proved mathematically. This fact is not confined to this particular valve, or even to valves in general, but (since, you remember, it was based on Fig. 97) it applies to all circuits which consist basically of a generator having internal resistance and working into a load resistance. Making the load resistance equal to the generator resistance is called *load matching*.

It does not follow that it is always desirable to make the load resistance equal to the generator resistance. Attempting to do so with a power-station generator would cause so much current to flow that it would be disastrous! But it is true, and can be confirmed by experiment, that the greatest power output *for a given signal voltage applied to the grid* is obtained when the load resistance is made equal to the valve resistance r_a. Again, the usual assumptions about linear characteristics apply.

POWER IN THE GRID CIRCUIT

You may have been wondering why the grid of the valve has always been shown as negative with respect to the cathode. The reason is the desire to expend as little power as possible in the grid circuit. If the grid were allowed to run positive it would act as an anode and collect electrons instead of making them all pass through its meshes, and a current would then flow round the grid circuit, absorbing power from the signal source. Since this may be, in practice, a tuned circuit of high dynamic resistance, this absorption of power would have markedly ill effects in reducing the voltage across it and in decreasing the effective selectivity.

Provided no current flows in the grid circuit the valve absorbs no power in that circuit. This condition will normally be fulfilled if the initial negative voltage, known as *grid bias*, makes the grid negative enough to prevent the flow of grid current even at the peak of the positive half-cycle of signal voltage. The bias required is equal to, or a volt or so greater than, the peak of the signal that the valve has to accept.

At very high frequencies, such as 30 Mc/s and above, other more subtle effects come into play, which are equivalent to placing a comparatively low resistance across the grid input points, causing it to absorb power.

In spite of the fact that at low and medium frequencies the power consumed in the grid circuit is negligibly small, alternating voltages applied to the grid can, as we have seen, release an appreciable amount of a.c. power in the anode circuit. We have just discussed a case in which 1·1 mA peak of a.c. developed 22 V across a resistance, making $(22 \times 1·1) = 24$ peak or 12 r.m.s. milliwatts of power. This power is, of course, derived from the anode battery, which is continuously supplying 3·5 mA at a total of 240 V, which is 840 mW.

Behind all the curves and calculations there lies the simple basic fact that the valve is able to convert the d.c. power from the battery into a.c. power in response to a practically wattless a.c. driving-voltage on its grid.

Seven Important Points

As a summary of this chapter, we will enumerate the most important points about the triode valve.

(1) One volt at the grid controls the anode current to the same extent as μ volts at the anode; μ is the amplification factor of the valve.

(2) Towards a.c. the valve has an anode resistance r_a, depending for its exact value upon the steady voltages applied.

(3) The control of anode current by grid voltage is given by the ratio μ/r_a, known as the mutual conductance, g_m.

(4) It follows that a valve can be represented as a resistance r_a in series with a generator the voltage of which is μ times the alternating voltage applied to the grid. This representation (Fig. 97) takes no account whatever of steady voltages and currents, except through their influence in determining μ and r_a.

(5) The voltage amplification, A, given by a valve in conjunction with a load resistance R is $\dfrac{\mu R}{R + r_a}$, as the application of Ohm's Law to Fig. 97 clearly shows.

(6) A condition for maximum power from a valve (or any other generator) is that the load resistance is equal to the internal resistance (of the generator).

(7) Since r_a, μ, and g_m all depend, more or less, on actual operating voltages, all *detailed* study of a valve's behaviour must be made by drawing load-lines across its actual curves, as in Fig. 96.

CHAPTER 10

Oscillation

GENERATING AN ALTERNATING CURRENT

IN THE LAST FEW chapters we have considered alternating currents in a variety of circuits, but have taken the generator of such currents for granted, representing it in diagrams by a conventional symbol. The only sort of a.c. generator actually shown (Fig. 53) is incapable of working at the very high frequencies necessary in radio, and produces a square waveform which is generally less desirable than the " ideal " sine shape (Fig. 44).

The alternating currents of power frequency—usually 50 c/s in Great Britain and many other countries—are generated by rotating machinery which moves conductors through magnetic fields produced by electromagnets (p. 67). Such a method is quite impracticable for frequencies of millions per second. This is where the curious properties of inductance and capacitance come to the rescue.

THE OSCILLATORY CIRCUIT

Fig. 99 shows a simple circuit consisting of inductance and capacitance in parallel, connected between the anode of a valve and its positive source. The valve is not essential in the first stage of the experiment, which could be performed with a battery and switch, but it will be needed later on. With the grid switch as shown, there is no negative bias, and we can assume that the anode current flowing through the coil L is fairly large. It is a steady current, and therefore any voltage drop across L is due to the resistance of the coil only. As none is shown, we assume that it is too small to take into account, and therefore there is no appreciable voltage across L and the capacitor is completely uncharged. The current through L has set up a magnetic flux which by now has reached a steady state, and represents a certain amount of energy stored up, depending on the strength of current and on the inductance L. This condition is represented in Fig. 100 by *a* so far as the circuit LC is concerned. The conventional direction of current (opposite to electron flow) is indicated.

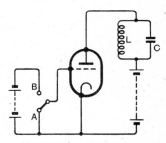

Fig. 99—Valve-operated device for setting up oscillations in the circuit LC

Now suppose the switch is moved from A to B, putting such a large negative bias on the grid that anode current is completely cut off. If the current in L were cut off instantaneously, an infinitely high voltage would be self-induced across it (p. 68), but this is impossible owing to C. What actually happens is that directly the current through L starts to decrease, the collapse of magnetic flux induces an e.m.f. in such a direction as to oppose the decrease, that

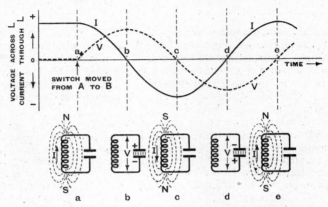

Fig. 100—Sequence of events in Fig. 99 after the switch has been moved to B. Stages *a* to *e* cover one complete cycle of oscillation

is to say, it tends to make the current continue to flow. It can no longer flow through the valve, but there is nothing to stop it from flowing into the capacitor C, charging it up. As it becomes charged, the voltage across it rises (p. 57), demanding an increased charging voltage from L. The only way in which the voltage can rise is for the current through it to fall at an increasing rate, as shown in Fig. 100 between *a* and *b*.

After a while the current is bound to drop to zero, by which time C has become charged to a certain voltage. This state is shown by the curves of I and V and by the circuit sketch at the point *b*. The magnetic field has completely disappeared, its energy having been transferred to C as an electric field.

The voltage across C must be balanced by an equal voltage across L, which can result only from the current through L continuing to fall at the same rate; that means it must become negative, reversing its direction. The capacitor must therefore be discharging through L. Directly it begins to do so it inevitably loses volts, just as a punctured tyre loses pressure. So the rate of change of current (which causes the voltage across L) gradually slackens, until, when C is completely discharged and there is zero voltage, the current is momentarily steady at a large negative value (point *c*). The whole of the energy stored in the electric field between the plates of C has been returned to L, but in the opposite polarity.

132

Assuming no loss in the to-and-fro movement of current (such as would be caused by resistance in the circuit), it has now reached a negative value equal to the positive value with which it started.

This current now starts to charge C, and the whole process just described is repeated (but in the opposite polarity) through d to e. This second reversal of polarity has brought us to exactly the same condition as at the starting point a. And so the whole thing starts all over again and continues to do so indefinitely, the original store of energy drawn from the battery being forever exchanged between coil and capacitor; and the current will never cease oscillating.

It can be shown mathematically that voltage and current vary sinusoidally.

FREQUENCY OF OSCILLATION

From the moment the valve current was switched off in Fig. 99 the current in L was bound to be always equal to the current in C (shown by the curve I in Fig. 100) because, of course, it was the same current flowing through both. Obviously, too, the voltage across them must always be equal. It follows that the reactances of L and C must be equal, that is to say $2\pi f L = 1/2\pi f C$. Rearranging this we get $f_0 = 1/2\pi\sqrt{LC}$, where f_0 denotes frequency of oscillation. This is the same as the formula we have already had (p. 106) for the frequency of resonance. It means that if energy is once imparted to an oscillatory circuit (i.e., L and C joined together as shown) it goes on oscillating at a frequency called the natural frequency of oscillation, which depends entirely on the values of inductance and capacitance. By making these very small—using only a few small turns of wire and small widely-spaced plates—very high frequencies can be generated, running if necessary into hundreds of millions per second.

DAMPING

The non-stop oscillator just described is as imaginary as perpetual motion. It is impossible to construct an oscillatory circuit entirely

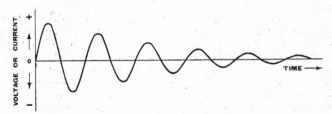

Fig. 101.—The first few cycles of a train of damped oscillations

without resistance of any kind. Even if it were possible it would be merely a curiosity, without much practical value as a generator, because it would be unable to yield more than the limited amount of

133

energy with which it was originally furnished. After that was exhausted it would stop.

The inevitable resistance of all circuits—using the term resistance in its widest sense (p. 54)—dissipates a proportion of the original energy during each cycle, so each is less than its predecessor, as in Fig. 101. This effect of resistance is called *damping*; a highly damped oscillatory circuit is one in which the oscillations die out quickly. If the total effective series resistance r is equal to $2\sqrt{L/C}$ the circuit is said to be critically damped; with less resistance the circuit is oscillatory, with more it is non-oscillatory and the voltage or current does not reverse after the initial kick due to an impulse but tends towards the shape shown in Figs. 34 and 41.

The Valve-Maintained Oscillator

What we want is a method of keeping an oscillator going, by supplying it periodically with energy to make good what has been usefully drawn from it as well as what has unavoidably been lost in its own resistance. We have plenty of energy available from batteries, etc., in a continuous d.c. form. The problem is to apply it at the right moments.

The corresponding mechanical problem is solved in a clock. The pendulum is an oscillatory system which on its own soon comes to a standstill owing to frictional resistance. The driving energy of the mainspring is " d.c." and would be of no use if applied direct to the pendulum. The problem is solved by the escapement, which is a device for switching on the pressure from the spring once in each oscillation, the " switch " being controlled by the pendulum itself.

Turning back to Fig. 99 we have the oscillatory circuit LC which is set into oscillation by moving the switch from A to B at the stage marked *a* in Fig. 100. By the time marked *e* a certain amount of the energy would have been lost in resistance, but by operating the switch from B to A at point *c* the current will be built up to its full amplitude, at the expense of the anode battery, by the time *e* is reached.

What is needed, then, is something (an actual switch is not practicable for high frequencies) to make the grid more negative from *a* to *c* and more positive from *c* to *e*, and so on for each cycle.

At the frequency of oscillation the circuit LC is effectively a high resistance (p. 110). So we have all the essentials of a resistance-coupled amplifier (p. 124). Because the valve amplifies, quite a small part of the oscillating anode voltage, if applied to the grid, would release sufficient energy from the anode battery to cancel losses. From *a* to *c* the anode is more positive than its average, and from *c* to *e* more negative, which is just the opposite to what we have just seen to be necessary at the grid. We have already noticed (p. 125) that in a stage of valve amplification the anode voltage is opposite in polarity to the grid voltage causing it.

134

Suppose, as in Fig. 102*a*, a small generator of the required frequency is available to apply an alternating voltage v_g to the grid. LC at that frequency being equivalent to a resistance, an amplified voltage v_a, A times as large, appears across it (Fig. 102*b*). If now

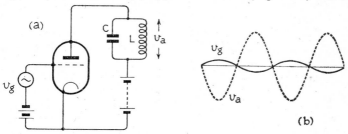

Fig. 102—Diagram *b* shows the relative amplitude and phase of grid and anode voltages when their frequency is the same as the natural frequency of the circuit LC

a fraction 1/A of this output voltage is turned upside down and applied to the grid there is no need for the generator; the amplifier provides its own input and has become a generator of sustained oscillations, or, briefly, a valve oscillator.

VALVE OSCILLATOR CIRCUITS

The most obvious practical method of doing what has just been described is to connect a coil in the grid circuit and couple it magnetically to L until it has induced in it sufficient voltage to " oscillate " (Fig. 103). The arrow indicates a variable coupling, obtained by varying the distance between the coils. The grid coil—called a *reaction* (or, more correctly, *retroaction*) coil—can be connected either way round in the circuit; one of these ways gives the reversal of sign necessary to maintain oscillation. The reaction process is sometimes called positive feedback. When the coupling is sufficiently close and in the right direction for oscillation it is not necessary to take any trouble to start it going; the ceaseless random movements of electrons in conductors (p. 38) are enough to start a tiny oscillation that very quickly builds up.

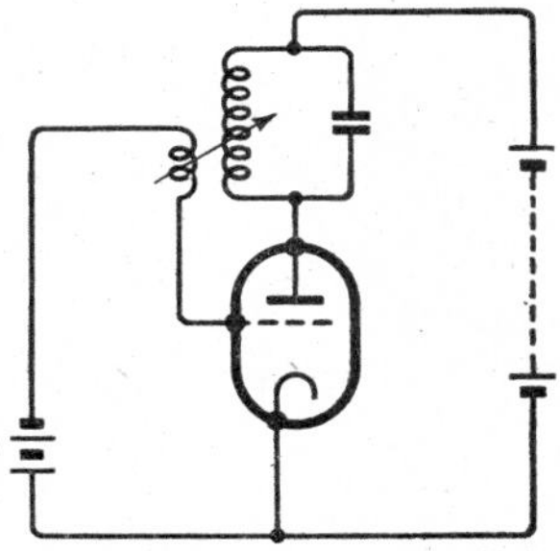

If the grid and anode are connected to opposite ends of the oscillatory coil, and some point in between is connected through the anode battery to the cathode and is thereby kept at a fixed potential, the alternating grid voltage is always opposite to the alternating

Fig. 103—The reaction-coil valve oscillator circuit

anode voltage, and can be adjusted in relative magnitude by choosing the tapping point on L (Fig. 104). Two extra components are

135

required, because if the grid were connected straight to the coil it would receive the full positive voltage of the anode battery which would upset things badly (p. 129). C_g is used as a *blocking capacitor* to stop this (p. 63), and R is used to connect a suitable grid bias. The capacitance of C_g is sufficient for its reactance to offer little obstruction at the oscillatory frequency compared with the resistance of R, which is made large. This circuit, known as the Hartley, is a very effective oscillator, useful when the losses are so great that it

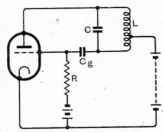

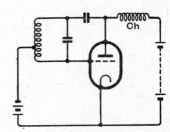

Fig. 104—The series-fed Hartley circuit, showing parallel-fed grid bias using a grid leak R and capacitor C_g

Fig. 105 — Parallel-fed Hartley circuit with the anode current supplied through a choke Ch. The grid bias is series-fed

might be difficult to obtain sufficiently close coupling to get Fig. 103 to oscillate.   Fig. 104 shows the *series-fed* variety, so called because the anode feed current flows through the oscillatory circuit. The grid bias is parallel-fed through R.

In the *parallel-fed* Hartley (Fig. 105) the anode is connected in this way, but to avoid loss of anode supply volts a choke coil Ch is generally used instead of a high resistance. The grid is shown series-fed, but it is more often parallel-fed in order to allow the coil to be connected to the cathode, which is usually earthed. Moreover, for reasons to be explained in Chapter 12, the combination of C_g, R and the valve generates its own grid bias and the battery can be left out.

An alternative intermediate-potential point can be obtained on the oscillatory circuit by " tapping " the capacitor instead of the coil, in the Colpitts circuit, of which one variety is shown in Fig. 106. In this the capacitance of C_1C_2 together is made equal to that of the one capacitor shown in the preceding circuits. The Colpitts is particularly favoured for very high frequency oscillators. C_2 then sometimes consists merely of the small capacitor formed by the grid and cathode of the valve itself.

Another method of obtaining the necessary reversal between anode and grid is to take advantage of the fact, shown in Fig. 74, that when a current flows through a coil and capacitor in series the voltages across them (neglecting resistance) are 180° out of phase (i.e., in opposite directions). This coil and capacitor, L_1 and C_2 in Fig. 107, are proportioned so that the reactance of L_1, and hence

136

the voltage across it, is much less than that of C_2, so that the voltage across it is less and in opposite phase to that across C_2 and L_1 combined, which voltage is the same as that across the oscillatory circuit (battery voltages disregarded). In practice C_2 is usually the capacitance between the anode and grid themselves, while the inductive reactance between grid and cathode is adjusted by C_1. The name of this circuit, " tuned-anode tuned-grid ", then seems reasonable; but it should not be taken to mean that grid and anode

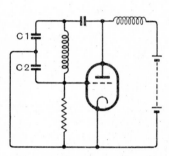

Fig. 106—Parallel-fed Colpitts circuit

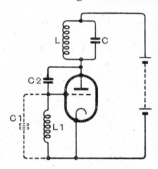

Fig. 107—Tuned-anode tuned-grid (T.A.T.G.) oscillator circuit. The phase-reversing part of the circuit is C_2 (normally the valve itself) and L

circuits are both tuned to the frequency of oscillation. If the combination $L_1 C_1$ were so tuned, it would be equivalent to a resistance, and not an inductive reactance as required; while LC must also be slightly off tune so that it has sufficient reactance to shift the phase slightly to make up for the fact that the phase shift in $C_2 L_1 C_1$ is less than 180°, due to their resistance.

The oscillator circuits shown in Figs. 103 to 107 look considerably different from one another at first glance, and can be modified to look even more different without affecting their basic similarity, which is that they are all valve amplifiers in which the grid *drive* or *excitation* is obtained by taking a part of the resulting anode alternating voltage and applying it in the opposite polarity, instead of going to some independent source for it.

AMPLITUDE OF OSCILLATION

It may be asked: What happens if the valve feeds back to its grid a greater voltage than is needed to maintain oscillation? The oscillation will grow in amplitude; the voltage at the grid will increase; that will be amplified by the valve, increasing the output at the anode; and so on. What stops it growing like a snowball?

Part of the answer is on page 129, where it was pointed out that if the grid is allowed to become positive with respect to the cathode, it causes current to flow in that circuit and absorb power. When

137

the amplitude of oscillation has grown to the point at which this loss of power due to grid current balances the surplus fed-back power, it will remain steady at that level.

If the grid bias is increased in an effort to obtain a greater amplitude of oscillation before grid current steps in to restrict it, another limiting influence is felt.

Look at Fig. 108 showing some typical valve characteristic curves of the same type as those in Fig. 96. Suppose the anode voltage is 300 V and the grid bias — 5 V. Then any greater amplitude (i.e., peak value) than about 5 V causes grid current. Suppose also, for example, that the anode oscillatory circuit is equivalent at its resonant frequency to a resistance of 8 kΩ (dynamic

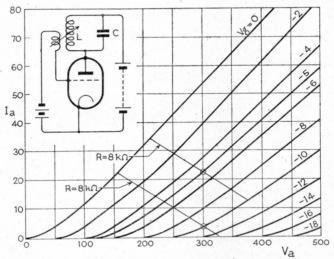

Fig. 108—The oscillatory circuit LC is equivalent at resonance to a high resistance R and the voltage across it can be derived from a load line on the valve characteristic curves. From this follows the proportion to be fed back to the grid to sustain oscillation

resistance) represented by the load line shown.* Then if the grid voltage has an amplitude of 5 V, the anode voltage swings from 210 to 380 V; i.e., it has an amplitude of 85 V. If one-seventeenth of this (5 V) is fed back to the grid in the correct phase, the conditions for oscillation are fulfilled. Any tendency for a slight overcoupling to the grid causes it to go positive, grid current flows, and by trans-former action (p. 100) this is equivalent to a resistance load in parallel with R, so reducing the anode voltage amplitude and hence the voltage fed back to the grid. And so a brake is put on any tendency for the amplitude of oscillation to increase indefinitely.

* Note that as the 8 kΩ applies only to a.c. of the resonant frequency, and not to d.c., the voltage actually reaching the anode is practically the same as that of the supply.

Now suppose the grid bias is increased, say to -10 V. The voltage amplitude at the grid can increase to about 10 V before grid current flows. Drawing the appropriate load line in Fig. 108, centred on $V_g = -10$, we see that the negative half-cycle of grid voltage cuts off the anode current altogether, so that it is distorted. The whole conception of dynamic resistance was based on a sinusoidal current (p. 76), and the simple method of calculation employèd above breaks down. It should be fairly clear, however, that if during a substantial part of each cycle of oscillation the resistance of the valve, r_a, is abnormally high, or even infinity, due to the oscillatory voltage reaching to and beyond the " bottom bend " of the characteristic curves, the average amplification of the valve is reduced, and the tendency to oscillate also reduced. So here is another factor limiting the amplitude of oscillation.

DISTORTION OF OSCILLATION

The previous section shows that if a valve oscillates fiercely the positive half-cycles of grid voltage cause grid current to flow, which imposes a heavy load on those parts of the cycle, and they are consequently clipped at the peaks. The corresponding anode-current peaks are therefore similarly distorted. The negative half-cycles may cause anode current to be cut off, so they are clipped too. The result in either or both cases is a distorted wave, which for some purposes is undesirable. Obviously, to obtain as nearly as possible a pure sine wave from a valve oscillator it is desirable so to adjust the back-coupling that a very slight clipping is sufficient to stop the amplitude of oscillation from growing any more.

It should be clear from Fig. 108 that the greater the dynamic resistance, R, of the anode circuit (load line more horizontal), the greater the amplitude that is possible before either grid current or bottom-bend limiting set in, and the less, in proportion, is a given amount of clipping at the peaks.

We have seen (p. 112) that the dynamic resistance is equal to QX, where X is the reactance of either L or C at resonance. So to obtain a pure waveform the tuned circuit should have a high Q. This, incidentally, tends to increase the amplification, so that the amount of feedback needed to maintain oscillation is comparatively small.

There is a more important effect of high Q in minimizing distortion. Fig. 83 showed how the smaller the series resistance, r, is in relation to the reactance X, the smaller is the external current fed to a parallel resonant circuit in relation to the current circulating round it. And we have seen that the ratio X/r is Q. The same thing can be seen in another way by considering the circuit, Fig. 99, with which we started to explain oscillation. Here we started a sinusoidal oscillation by means of a square waveform produced by switching grid bias on and off. If the circuit has a high Q, the oscillatory current will build up to a value many times greater—to be precise, Q times greater—than the valve anode current of that frequency. The valve anode current therefore is such a small proportion of the whole that it does not matter very much whether it is distorted or not.

For example, suppose Q is 100, and R is 20 kΩ. Then, as R = QX, X is 200 Ω. The impedance to alternating current of the resonant frequency from the valve is thus 100 times greater than the impedance of the coil or of the capacitor. As the voltage across them is the same, the valve current is only 1% of the oscillatory current circulating internally between coil and capacitor, and any distortion it may have hardly counts. The oscillatory current itself is always sinusoidal in normal circumstances.

To obtain as nearly as possible a pure sine waveform from an oscillator, then, use a high-Q circuit and the least back-coupling that will do.

STABILITY OF FREQUENCY

The frequency of an oscillator, as we have seen, is adjusted by varying the inductance and/or capacitance forming the oscillatory circuit. For most purposes it is desirable that when the adjustment has been made the frequency shall remain perfectly constant. This means that the inductance and capacitance (and, to a less extent, the resistance) shall remain constant. For this purpose inductance includes not only that which is intentionally provided by the tuning coil, but also the inductance of its leads and the effect of any coils or pieces of metal (equivalent to single short-circuited turns) inductively coupled to it. Similarly capacitance includes that of the coil, the wiring, valve electrodes, and valve and coil holders. Resistance is varied in many ways, such as a change in the supply voltages of the oscillator valve, causing r_a to alter.

Inductance and capacitance depend mainly on dimensions, which expand with rising temperature. If the tuning components are shut up in a box along with the oscillator valve, the temperature may rise considerably, and the frequency will drift for some time after switching on. Frequency stability therefore is aided by keeping the valve, and any resistors which develop heat, well away from the tuning components; by arranging effective ventilation; and by designing components so that expansion in one dimension offsets the effect of that in another. Fixed capacitors are obtainable employing a special ceramic dielectric material whose variations with temperature oppose those of other capacitors in the circuit; this reminds one of temperature compensation in watches and clocks.

CHAPTER 11

The Sender

ESSENTIALS OF A SENDER

THE LAST FEW CHAPTERS provide the material for tackling in greater detail what was indicated in barest outline in Fig. 15. Considering the sending or transmitting system first, we have as the essentials for, say, broadcasting:

(a) A radio-frequency generator.

(b) A microphone, which may be regarded as a low-frequency generator.

(c) A modulator, combining the products of (a) and (b).

(d) An aerial, radiating this combination.

THE R.F. GENERATOR

In the valve oscillator we have an r.f. generator capable of working at any frequency up to many millions of cycles per second. It is easily controlled, both in frequency and output. For short-range communication, or even long ranges in special circumstances, ordinary receiving valves can be used. But to broadcast over a large area, or consistently over a long range, it is necessary to generate a large amount of power.

The difference between a receiving valve generating a few milliwatts (or at the most a few watts) of r.f. power, and a sending valve generating 100 kilowatts, is in the construction rather than the basic principles; and as this book deals with the latter there is no need to go into the subject of high-power valves as such.

The higher the power the sender is required to produce, the more important it is that the percentage wasted shall be small. If, in generating 10 kW of r.f. power, 30 kW is wasted, the total power to be supplied is 40 kW, and the efficiency (ratio of useful power to the total power employed) is 25%. By increasing the efficiency to 75% it is possible to obtain 30 kW of r.f. for the same expenditure, or, alternatively, to reduce the power employed to 13·3 kW for the same output. In the latter case it would be possible to reduce the size and cost of the valves and other equipment as well.

Referring back to Fig. 108, suppose the upper load line, based on a grid bias of -5 V and an anode voltage of 300, represents the voltage swing of an oscillator, working under practically distortionless or so-called " Class A " conditions. The average anode voltage applied is 300, and the average current 23 mA, so the input power is 6·9 W.

The useful output is obtained by multiplying r.m.s. alternating voltage by r.m.s. current. The swing is 170 V; therefore peak

141

value 170/2 = 85 V; r.m.s. value 85/$\sqrt{2}$ = 60 V. Current swing 22 mA; r.m.s. value 7·7 mA; power 0·462 W. This example points the way to a short cut for working out the a.c. power:

Watts = (Voltage swing × Current swing)/8.

The efficiency is therefore 0·462/6·9 = 0·067, or 6·7%. This is very poor indeed, because under the conditions illustrated there is a considerable anode current flowing all the time and a considerable voltage between anode and cathode of the valve. The power represented by this is dissipated as heat at the anode, and in the larger valves it is difficult to carry away all this heat. Many normally run bright red hot.

HIGH-EFFICIENCY OSCILLATORS: "CLASS B"

Obviously the aim should be to pass as little current through the valve as possible, consistent with keeping the oscillation going; and to pass that current only at times when the voltage across the valve is low.

As it happens, we started off our study of oscillators on the right lines, because in Fig. 100 the valve was totally cut off by grid bias

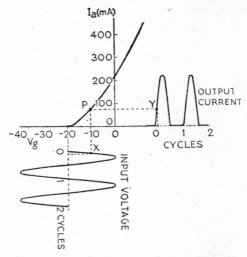

Fig. 109—Illustrating " Class B " operation with the aid of a valve anode-current/grid-voltage characteristic curve. The working grid bias nearly cuts off anode current, and only the positive half-cycles of grid signal are effective in reproducing themselves in the form of anode current

during half the cycle, from *a* to *c*; and was allowed to pass current only during the half-cycle from *c* to *e* when the voltage across the tuned circuit was in opposition to that of the supply, and therefore the anode voltage low. That is just what we want, and is obtained

142

by biasing the valve until it just fails to pass current (i.e., the working point is at the " bottom bend ").

These conditions are shown in Fig. 109, representing a valve with a negative bias of 20 V and the feedback adjusted to give a peak grid voltage of the same amount, shown by the sine waves below the grid voltage scale.* The resulting anode current has half of each cycle suppressed, shown by the waveform on the right; but, as we have seen (p. 139), this current is normally very small in comparison with the sinusoidal oscillatory current.

" Class C "

The process can be carried farther, and the efficiency further improved, by increasing the negative bias to well beyond cut-off. The grid swing has to be increased too, and the conditions, referred

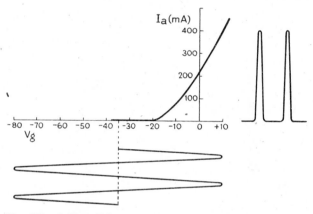

Fig. 110—" Class C " operation. Comparing this with Fig. 109, we see that the working grid bias (—35 V in this example) is considerably more than enough to cut off anode current, which flows during only part of the positive half-cycles of signal

to as " Class C ", are illustrated in Fig. 110. Note that the period during which anode current flows is less than half of each cycle, and is confined near the point d in Fig. 100, at which the anode voltage is a minimum, and therefore the power wasted in the valve is also very small.

Note too that it is advantageous to drive the grid positive, because, although there is a certain loss due to grid current, it occurs during only a small portion of each cycle, whereas the power developed in

* If the method of deducing the output waveform from the characteristic curve is unfamiliar it should be noted, as it will be used a good deal from now on. The output waveform is traced out point by point over the cycle; for example, at one-twelfth of a cycle (30°) from the start the input signal voltage is indicated by the point X. The corresponding point on the valve curve, P, is vertically above it, and indicates the anode current, which is then transferred horizontally to the left to give a point (Y) on the output waveform above 1/12th cycle on the output cycles scale. Points at other stages in the cycle are obtained similarly.

143

the anode circuit is much increased. Normally the valve is operated so that the positive grid voltage is nearly equal to the minimum anode voltage. Working efficiencies of the order of 75% are practicable, but beyond a certain point the power begins to drop off steeply. Moreover there may be difficulty in providing the very large grid swing.

Under Class C conditions the oscillator has either to be given a start or else begun with reduced bias, because full working bias cuts off anode current and prevents feedback. If worked as a self-oscillator (instead of merely a driven amplifier) the latter method is used. Chapter 13 will show a method of generating grid bias proportional to the amplitude of oscillation; an ideal arrangement for Class C, because it ensures the most powerful starting conditions.

CONSTANT FREQUENCY

The need for constancy of frequency (p. 140) applies with particular force to radio senders. To avoid confusion it is internationally agreed that their frequencies must keep within very narrow limits; and for special purposes—such as working more than one sender on the same frequency—it is now common practice to keep within less than one cycle in a million.

In early days, the tuned oscillatory circuit (sometimes called a *tank circuit*, because of its capability for storing oscillatory energy) was coupled straight to the aerial, either inductively or by a direct tapping, as in Fig. 111. Aerials will be discussed in detail in the next chapter; in the meantime they can be considered as opened-out capacitors (or, sometimes, inductors) necessary for effectively radiating waves over distances. They have both capacitance and inductance, which depend on their height above ground and

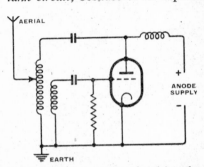

Fig. 111—Direct coupling of aerial to the tuned circuit of a self-oscillating sender. The other end is usually connected to earth. In this arrangement, any changes in the aerial alter the frequency of oscillation

other objects; so on a windy day are likely to vary erratically. Now, the frequency of an oscillator arranged as in Fig. 111 depends on the inductance and capacitance of the tuned circuit, of which the aerial forms part. The frequency stability of such a system is not nearly good enough for present-day needs.

Any circuits or components that can affect the frequency should be rigid and compact structures—compact, so that their electric or magnetic fields do not spread out where persons or things might move and upset the field distribution and hence the capacitance or inductance. We shall see (p. 204) that it is possible to prevent such

144

variations by shutting up the components in a metal box or *screen*. But, of course, this is no good for radiating.

The Master-Oscillator Power-Amplifier System

The way out of this dilemma is to separate the function of oscillating at the required frequency from that of feeding r.f. power to the aerial, instead of trying to make one valve do both. The oscillation frequency is generated by a valve oscillator in which all practicable precautions are taken to avoid frequency drift, and in which no attempt is made to obtain an extremely high power efficiency. This *master oscillator* is coupled, by some means that does not seriously affect the frequency stability, to one or more stages of amplification, the last of which is coupled to the aerial. Being designed to feed as much power to it as possible, this stage is called the *power amplifier*. The whole is therefore called a master-oscillator power-amplifier system; for short, M.O.P.A.

Crystal Control

To obtain extreme frequency stability even in a M.O.P.A. requires very good design and considerable expense. Where it is not necessary to cover a range of frequency, but is enough to be able to work on a few " spot " frequencies, a way of guaranteeing correct frequency to within very narrow limits quite simply and cheaply is

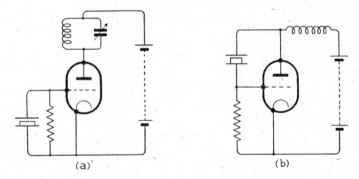

(a)   (b)

Fig. 112—Two types of crystal-controlled oscillator circuit

to exploit the remarkable properties of certain crystals, notably quartz. Such crystals are capable of vibrating mechanically at very high frequencies and in doing so develop an alternating e.m.f. between two opposite faces. Conversely, an alternating e.m.f. causes them to vibrate.

The subject is a large and specialized one, but for most purposes the crystal can be regarded as equivalent to a tank circuit of remarkably high inductance and Q. But unlike the coil-and-capacitor tank circuit, there is practically nothing that can be altered about it

145

by fair wear and tear. There is a small change of frequency with temperature; and where requirements are stringent the crystal is kept in a temperature-controlled box.

The crystal is mounted between two flat metal plates, generally with a small air gap intervening. Fig. 112 shows two varieties of crystal oscillator circuit.

Imagining the crystal to be a tuned circuit, we see *a* to be a T.A.T.G. circuit (compare Fig. 107), and *b* is a Colpitts circuit (compare Fig. 106). In *a* the tuning of the anode circuit is adjusted to a point at which oscillation takes place.

TELEGRAPH SENDERS: KEYING

We have now reached the point—in theory at any rate—at which we can send out into space a continuous stream of waves of constant frequency and (if desired) high power. This alone, however, is not enough to convey messages, still less speech or music. The simplest way of sending messages is to break up the stream of waves into short and long bursts that represent the dots and dashes of the Morse code.

To do this it is necessary to connect a Morse key—which is simply a form of switch that makes a contact when pressed and breaks it when let go—in such a way that it starts and stops the radiation from the transmitter.

It might appear that almost any part of the circuit would do. In practice there are quite a number of things that have to be considered. The key should not be asked to break large amounts of power, because the resulting sparking would soon burn the contacts away. It cannot break a very high voltage, which would just spark across; and there is safety to consider, too. Therefore the anode circuit is practically ruled out, and so is the aerial circuit. The filament circuit is no good, because of the time taken to heat and cool. And wherever the keying is done it must not affect the frequency of oscillation, so it is better not to keep stopping and starting the master oscillator.

A common method of suppressing radiation is to apply a large negative bias to a low-power r.f. amplifier valve by disconnecting the cathode.

RADIOTELEPHONY AND BROADCASTING: MODULATION

To convey speech and music, something more elaborate than simple interruption of the transmission is required. It must be, as it were, moulded into the shape of the sounds. This process is called *modulation*, and the raw material that is modulated is called the *carrier wave*.* Keying is an extreme and special case of modulation, in which the strength of the carrier wave is made to vary suddenly between zero and full power.

---

* Strictly, one should say " succession of waves " instead of " wave "; but that is taken as understood.

146

Suppose, however, that it is desired to transmit a pure note of 1 kc/s, available as an electric current derived, in the first place, from the microphone before which the note is being sounded (how, we shall see shortly). This current will have the form of a sine wave, as shown in Fig. 113*a*.

For the reasons given in Chapter 1, waves of such a low frequency cannot be radiated effectively through space. We therefore choose a r.f. carrier wave, say 1,000 kc/s. As 1,000 of its cycles occur in the time of every one of the a.f. cycles, they cannot all be drawn to the same scale, so the cycles in Fig. 113*b* are representative of the much greater number that have to be imagined. What we want is something which, like *b*, is entirely radio-frequency (so that it can be

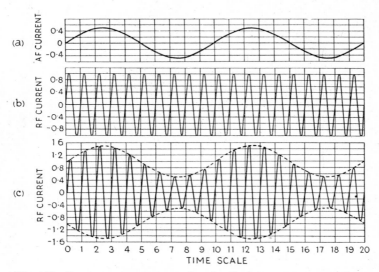

Fig. 113—Curve *a* represents two cycles of audio-frequency current, such as might be flowing in a microphone circuit; *b* represents the much larger number of radio-frequency cycles generated by the sender. When these have been modulated by *a*, the result is as shown at *c*

radiated), and yet carries the exact imprint of *a* (so that the a.f. waveform can be extracted at the receiving end). One way of obtaining it is to vary the amplitude of *b* in exact proportion to *a*, increasing the amplitude when *a* is positive and decreasing it when *a* is negative, the result being such as *c*. As we can see, this modulated wave is still exclusively r.f. and so can be radiated in its entirety. But although it contains no a.f. current, the tips of the waves trace out the shape of the a.f. waveform, as indicated by the dotted line, called the *envelope* of the r.f. wave train.

For simplicity we have considered a " programme " no more exciting than a tuning note; but the same principle applies to the far more complicated waveforms of music and speech—their

147

complexity can be faithfully represented in the envelope of a modulated carrier-wave.

DEPTH OF MODULATION

Since receivers are designed so that an unmodulated carrier wave (between items in the programme) gives rise to no sound in the loudspeaker, it is evident that a graph such as Fig. 113c represents a note of some definite loudness, the loudness depending on the amount by which the r.f. peaks rise and fall above and below their mean value. The amount of this rise and fall, relative to the normal amplitude of the carrier wave, is spoken of as the *depth of modulation*.

For distortionless transmission the increase and decrease in carrier amplitude, corresponding to positive and negative half-cycles of the modulating voltage, must be equal. The limit to this occurs when the negative half-cycles reduce the carrier-wave amplitude exactly to zero, as shown in Fig. 114. At its maximum it will then rise to double its steady value. Any attempt to make the maximum higher than this will result in the carrier actually ceasing for an

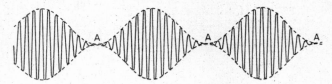

Fig. 114—Carrier-wave modulated to a depth of 100 per cent. At its minima (points A) the r.f. current just drops to zero

appreciable period at each minimum; over this interval the envelope of the carrier-amplitude can no longer represent the modulating voltage, and there will be distortion.

When the carrier has its maximum swing, from zero to double its mean value, it is said to be modulated to a depth of 100%. In general, half the variation in amplitude, maximum to minimum, expressed as a percentage of the mean amplitude, is taken as the measure of modulation depth. Thus, when a 100-V carrier wave is made to vary between 50 V and 150 V, the depth of modulation is 50%.

In transmitting a musical programme, variations in loudness of the received music are produced by variations in modulation depth, these producing corresponding changes in the amount of a.f. output from the receiver.

METHODS OF MODULATION

Without going into details, we may note that one basic method of amplitude modulation is to vary the anode voltage of a r.f. oscillator or amplifier valve. Fig. 115 shows an outline of this method applied to an oscillator.

148

The a.f. voltage is amplified by a modulator valve V_M which develops the amplified voltage at its anode, across the impedance of an inductor AFC (called an a.f. choke) in series with the anode supply to the oscillator valve V_O. A choke is preferred to a resistor, because of the large power to be carried. Suppose, for example, that the oscillator valve is normally fed at 5,000 V. To reduce the amplitude of oscillation to the verge of zero it would probably be necessary to reduce this to a few hundred volts; and to double the amplitude it might be necessary to raise it to nearly 10,000. So for 100% modulation the peak amplitude of the audio voltage would have to be nearly 5,000. This source of audio voltage would also have to handle the full anode current of the oscillator, so the amount of a.f. power to be supplied is comparable with the power

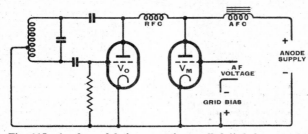

Fig. 115—Anode modulation, sometimes called " choke control " modulation because the audio voltage is developed across an a.f. choke, AFC, which forms the anode load of the modulator valve V_M and causes the anode voltage delivered to the oscillator valve V_O to vary in accordance with the audio voltage. V_M acts simply as a high-power a.f. amplifier. RFC is a r.f. choke for keeping r.f. current out of the modulator circuit

supplied to the oscillator. This is quite serious in a high-power sender, and involves large and expensive modulator valves as well as a considerable addition to the power consumption.

Another drawback of this simple arrangement is that the frequency of oscillation depends slightly on the anode voltage, and consequently varies during the cycle of modulation. This rules the method out from most modern practice, in which the frequency of the carrier wave must be kept constant within extremely narrow limits. It is therefore better to apply the method to an r.f. amplifier stage in a M.O.P.A. system.

Applying the modulating voltage to the grid of an oscillator or r.f. amplifier valve might seem to be a simpler and much more economical proceeding; but although grid modulation has been applied successfully it is by no means so straightforward as might appear, and generally results in more distortion than anode modulation.

There are a number of other methods of modulation, some of which are of practical value, especially in low-power senders. But the anode method, of which there are many variations, is the one generally favoured where freedom from distortion is important.

FREQUENCY MODULATION

Instead of keeping the frequency constant and varying the amplitude, one can do *vice versa*. Fig. 116 shows the difference; *a* represents a small sample—two cycles—of the a.f. programme, and *b* is the corresponding sample of r.f. carrier wave after it has been amplitude-modulated by *a*. If, instead, it were frequency-modulated it would be as at *c*, in which the amplitude remains constant but the frequency of the waves increases and decreases as the a.f. voltage rises and falls. In fact, with a suitable vertical scale of cycles per second, *a* would represent the frequency of the carrier wave.

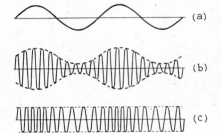

Fig. 116—Curve](*a*) represents 2 cycles of audio [frequency used to modulate a r.f. carrier wave. If amplitude] modulation is used, the result is represented by (*b*); if frequency modulation, by (*c*)

An advantage of frequency modulation, or "f.m.", is that under certain conditions reception is less likely to be disturbed by interference or noise. These conditions involve the use of very high frequency carrier waves; about fifty times as high as the "medium" broadcast frequencies (525–1,605 kc/s). Since with f.m. the sender can radiate at its full power all the time, it is more likely to outdo interference than with amplitude modulation ("a.m."), which has to use a carrier wave of half maximum voltage and current and therefore only one quarter maximum power. And the receiver can easily be arranged to cut off all peaks of interference without any risk of distorting the modulation.

The ordinary type of receiver designed for a.m. does not respond to f.m. when properly tuned in, but it can receive f.m. after a fashion if it is tuned to one slope of the resonance curve, so that the rise and fall of signal frequency varies the amplitude of response, as it would if an a.m. wave were applied.

F.m. has come into considerable use for broadcasting in America, and for very-high-frequency communication, but necessitates a rather more elaborate type of receiver and more precise tuning than a.m.

MICROPHONES

So far we have learnt something about two of the boxes at the sending end of Fig. 15—the r.f. generator and the modulator.

The device by which sound, consisting of air waves, is made to set up electric currents or voltages of identical waveform, which in turn are used to control the modulator, is one that most people handle more or less frequently, in telephones. It is the *microphone*; and the type used for most radio purposes other than broadcasting,

and in telephones everywhere, is essentially the same as the original
invention by Hughes in 1878.

Fig. 117 shows the principle. The sounds are directed on to a
thin carbon diaphragm D, behind which is fixed a carbon button B,
generally with a grooved or honeycombed inner surface. The
space between the two contains carbon granules, which are prevented
from falling out by some such device as a swansdown ring around
the edge of the button. Connections are taken from the diaphragm
and the button. Details vary (for example the diaphragm may be of
metal, carrying a carbon button) but the general idea is the same:
as the diaphragm vibrates under the alternating pressure of the air
waves of sound, it varies the pressure applied to the numerous carbon
contacts, and so varies the resistance between the terminals.

A carbon microphone is, in fact, a resistance that varies to
correspond with the sound waves, and so the current delivered by
the battery in Fig. 118 varies in the
same way. Since this current
passes through the primary of a
transformer, a varying voltage is
produced at the secondary terminals. Sound waves of normal

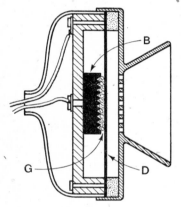

Fig. 117—Section of a typical
carbon microphone

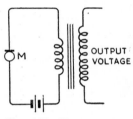

Fig. 118—How a micro-
phone (M) is connected to
give an a.f. voltage

intensity are very feeble, and even with a step-up transformer the
result is generally only a few volts at most: so for modulating a
powerful sender several stages of amplification may be necessary.

While such a microphone can be designed to give a reasonably
large output over the band of frequencies corresponding to the
essentials of intelligible speech, it does so by virtue of a certain
amount of mechanical resonance, and many of the frequencies
needed to give full naturalness to speech and music are not fairly
represented. If the resonance is reduced in order to give more
uniform response to all the audio frequencies, then the output
becomes less, and more amplification is needed. Compare electrical
resonance, as in Fig. 78. So various other systems have been tried;
but generally speaking it is true that the higher the quality—i.e., the
more faithfully the electrical output represents the sound—the lower
the output.

151

The electrostatic microphone consists of a diaphragm, generally metal, with a metal plate very close behind. When vibrated by sound, the capacitance varies, and the resulting charging and discharging currents from a battery, passed through a high resistance, set up a.f. voltages. Its disadvantages are very low output and high impedance.

The crystal or piezo-electric microphone depends on the same properties as are applied in crystal control (p. 145); the varying pressures directly give rise to a.f. voltages. Crystals of Rochelle salt are particularly effective.

The type most commonly used for broadcasting and the better class of " public address " is the electromagnetic. There are many varieties: in some an iron diaphragm varies the magnetic flux through a coil, so generating voltages; in others the diaphragm bears a moving coil in which the voltages are generated by flux from a stationary magnet; while in the most favoured types a metal ribbon is used instead of the coil.

COUPLING TO AERIAL

The last main component is the aerial. This is the subject of the next chapter; but one aspect that we can consider at this point is the way in which the sender is connected to the aerial, because the power efficiency is greatly affected thereby.

We saw (on p. 126) that a valve can be regarded as a generator having internal resistance (r_a), and that the maximum output power for a given alternating voltage at the grid is obtained by making the load resistance equal to the internal resistance. In a sender, the valve in question is the output or " last-stage " valve, and the load is the dynamic resistance of the tuning circuit combined with the aerial. Generally it is practicable to keep the losses in the tuning circuit relatively small, so we shall regard the aerial as the load. Assuming for the moment that it can be regarded as a resistance, should our aim be to make it equal to r_a? If so, the efficiency—which means the fraction of the power generated in the valve which is delivered to the aerial—is only 50%, because half the power is wasted in the valve resistance. But the real limiting factor is not the grid e.m.f.—which can readily be increased—but the amount of heat the valve can dissipate (p. 142). If, for example, the rated anode dissipation of a valve is 100 W, and the efficiency of power transfer to the aerial is 50%, then it can put up to 100 W into the aerial. But if, by increasing the load resistance *and* the input voltage, the efficiency is raised to $66\frac{2}{3}$%, the maximum output will be double the dissipation, namely, 200 W. For various reasons, the efficiency cannot be raised indefinitely in this way, so the valve manufacturer specifies the *optimum load resistance* for each type of valve.

Leaving detailed discussion of aerials as loads to the next chapter, we can assume in the meantime that their impedance varies greatly with frequency. If by some stroke of luck the aerial impedance at

152

the working frequency were to equal the optimum load resistance for the transmitting valve we could connect the aerial and earth terminals to opposite ends of the anode tuning coil. In general, however, the effective impedance between these terminals will not be equal to the optimum for the valve. A matching device is necessary.

On page 100 we saw that a transformer is just such a device, because by a suitable choice of turns ratio any resistance can be made equivalent to any other resistance. The rule was that to match R_s to R_p the transformer should have $\sqrt{(R_p/R_s)}$ primary turns for every secondary turn. That is the same thing as $\sqrt{(R_s/R_p)}$ secondary turns for every primary turn. For example, if our tuning

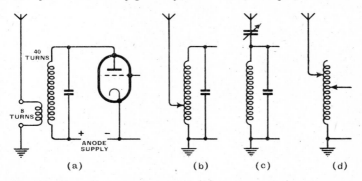

Fig. 119—Some of many varieties of method in coupling aerial to sender. *a* is the inductive coupling or r.f. transformer method, worked out in the text for a particular example; *b* is the aerial tapping or auto-transformer; *c* is the series capacitor method; and at *d* the valve is tapped down to reduce the effective load resistance

coil had 40 turns, and the optimum load for the valve was 3,000 Ω, and at the working frequency the aerial was equivalent to a resistance between aerial and earth terminals of 120 Ω, then it should be coupled to the tuning coil by a secondary winding of 40 $\times$ $\sqrt{120/3,000} = 8$ turns, as in Fig. 119*a*.

Alternatively, an auto-transformer (p. 100) may be used *b*. There are other ways of matching, such as *c*. Like method *a*, it insulates the aerial from the anode coil, which may be at anode potential. Method *d* is used when the optimum load is *less* than the aerial impedance.

Although it is easy to work out the right number of turns according to this simple theory (and rather less easy to calculate the right value of capacitance in Fig. 119*c*) there are complications that make it a more formidable task to calculate the best practical design. For example, we assumed that *all* the magnetic flux linked both primary and secondary coils, whereas this is far from being so in r.f. transformers. In practice, the right tapping or coupling is calculated as nearly as possible, and provision made for it to be varied until the best results are obtained. Fig. 98 shows that it is necessary to depart quite a lot from the optimum before there is a serious loss in output.

Another complication is that an aerial nearly always has reactance as well as resistance, which affects the tuning and makes it necessary to use less or more tuning capacitance; less, if the reactance effectively in parallel with the coil is capacitive, and greater if it is inductive.

CHAPTER 12

Radiation and Aerials

BRIDGING SPACE: RADIATION

IN THE FIRST CHAPTER of this book the processes of radio communication were very briefly traced from start to finish; since then we have considered the sender in some detail. Before going on to the receiver we should know something about how the space in between is bridged.

We know (p. 67) that a moving magnetic field generates an e.m.f., thereby setting up an electric field. We also know that an electric current consists of electric charges in motion, and charges are surrounded by an electric field. So an electric current is really a moving electric field, and we know that it generates a magnetic field. Put concisely:

Moving magnetic field causes electric field.

Moving electric field causes magnetic field.

Without going into the rather advanced mathematics of the thing, one might guess the possibility of the two fields in motion sustaining one another. Such a guess would be a good one, for they can and do. The speed of the motion is very great—in open space, about 186,000 miles per second—and the combination of fast-moving fields is known as an *electromagnetic wave*. The union of the two fields is so complete that each depends entirely upon the other and would disappear if it were destroyed.

We have come across electric and magnetic fields in the immediate neighbourhood of circuits. If they are stationary, there is no chance that they will suddenly dart off as electromagnetic waves. But if the current in the circuit is alternating at a very high frequency— so high that by the time the fields have had time to reach some distance from the circuit the current has already begun to reverse— a portion of the field combination breaks loose and keeps on travelling outwards on its own.

Steady electric and magnetic fields around a circuit are analogous to a perfectly steady current of air, which may cause a slight local increase in air pressure, but generates no waves, so is noiseless. Even if the air is waved to and fro with a fan, causing an alternating current, the production of sound waves is negligible. In the same way, alternating electric currents do not stir up appreciable electromagnetic waves if their frequency is low. So although we have referred to the waveforms of low-frequency a.c., this should not be taken to suggest that they *are* waves in the sense in which that word is to be used in this chapter—electromagnetic waves.

But if the sound pressure is varied rapidly, say by attaching the fan to something that is vibrating 1,000 or so times per second, even a small amplitude generates waves strong enough to be heard at a considerable distance. To radiate electromagnetic waves from a circuit effectively it is necessary for the frequency of the a.c. to be higher than the audible limit; hence the elaborate processes of generating and modulating a carrier wave having a much higher frequency than the sounds to be transmitted.

ELECTROMAGNETIC WAVES

If one end of a rope is waggled rapidly up and down, a vertical wave travels along the rope; that is to say, at right angles to the direction of waggling. This analogy represents the electric half of an electromagnetic wave. To complete the picture the magnetic part has to be imagined at right angles to both, and therefore in a side-to-side direction. Fig. 120 shows part of a wire in which an electric current must be supposed to be alternating, up and down. Then the electric part of the wave is parallel to the wire and alternates

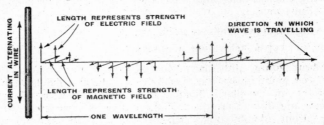

Fig. 120—Representing one and a half cycles of radiated electro-magnetic wave moving outwards from a wire carrying oscillatory current

as indicated by the varying lengths of the vertical arrows: the magnetic part is at right angles and is indicated by horizontal arrows (actually drawn as if viewed in perspective); and the combined wave moves outward from the wire and therefore its direction of motion is at right angles to both the fields. It is difficult to depict this three-dimensional phenomenon on paper; the complete wave-fronts could be better represented by a series of bubbles, one inside the other, expanding from the wire at their centre.

The electric field is measured in volts per metre, if close to the radiating wire, or microvolts per metre if far off. This voltage actually exists in space, but naturally cannot cause a current to flow unless it impinges on a conductor, such as a wire. The voltage may also be considered to be due to the cutting of the wire by the magnetic field.

A horizontal wire will have no voltage in the direction of its length when struck by waves due to a vertical wire radiator; and vice versa. This distinction is known as *polarization*; the waves due to a vertical wire radiator are conventionally called vertically polarized, that being the direction of their electric field. If a vertical wire half a metre long is located in vertically polarized radiation of strength 50 μV per metre, then an e.m.f. of 25 μV will be induced in it. But if either the wire or the radiation is horizontal, no e.m.f. is induced. At intermediate angles to the horizontal, the induced e.m.f. is proportional to the sine of the angle. To induce the maximum e.m.f. in a horizontal wire it is necessary for the radiation to be horizontally polarized, which can be arranged by placing the radiating wire horizontally. Because radiation starts off with a certain polarization, it does not follow that it will arrive with the same. If it has travelled far, and especially if on its way it has been reflected from earth or sky, it is almost certain to have become slightly disarranged, and at least part of it may be picked up by a wire at almost any angle.

The Inductor Radiator

It is time now to examine the radiating circuit a little more closely. Up to the present we have considered only a short section of wire in which a r.f. current is flow-ing, and have conveniently disregarded the rest of the circuit which is necessary for its existence. In Chapter 11 it was shown how oscillating currents of almost any fre-quency can be set up in a very simple circuit consisting of a coil and capacitor; and, later on, how by suitably connecting a valve to it the oscillations can be kept going continuously. We can fulfil

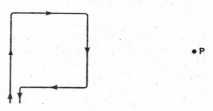

Fig. 121—From the point of view of the reader, the radiation due to different parts of a turn of wire carrying oscillatory current cancels out. Towards the point P, however, the difference in distance between the vertical sides of the square results in net radiation

the necessary condition for radiating waves, namely, causing a current to vary extremely rapidly—millions of times a second if need be. Yet such a circuit does not turn out to be a very efficient radiator. What is the trouble?

The difficulty is that for every short section of circuit tending to radiate electromagnetic waves there is another carrying the current in the opposite direction and therefore tending to cancel it out. Each turn of wire in the coil has to go up one side and down the other in order to complete itself; and, as the same current flows through the whole turn, the wave-producing efforts of the two sides of the turn are in opposition and largely counteract one another. Largely, but not altogether. Look at Fig. 121 and imagine it to be one turn of wire. Then you, looking at it, are an equal distance from two equal vertical lengths of wire carrying equal currents and therefore radiating with equal strength; but as the current in the two wires is always in opposite directions you receive no net radiation at all. The same argument applies to the top

157

and bottom sections. But now consider it from the point of view P. The down section is nearer than the up, and may therefore rather more than counteract the latter. Actually this disparity is quite negligible if P is miles away. But there is another thing to take into account. The radiation from the up section takes time—very little, it is true—to reach the down section on its way to P, and if the oscillations are very rapid indeed the current in the down section may have started to go up; in which case its radiation assists that coming from the previous up wire, and P will get the combined result. Even if the oscillation frequency is not high enough for a complete reversal, it may at least cause sufficient difference between the radiation from the two sections of wire to give a net result at P.

The best result is obtained when the diameter of the coil is half a wavelength (or any odd number of half wavelengths), because then the radiative efforts of both sections pull together in the direction P— and also in the opposite direction. If the coil is 2 inches in diameter —about 5 centimetres—the best wavelength is 10 (or $\frac{10}{3}$, $\frac{10}{5}$, etc.) centimetres, the frequency being 3,000 Mc/s. Instead of trying to fit the wavelength to the coil, we may fit the coil to a longer wavelength by making it larger. As one sometimes wants to radiate waves thousands of metres long, this suggestion has its difficulties, even bearing in mind that it is not essential for the diameter of the coil to be as much as half a wavelength in order to radiate a useful amount. For these and other reasons radiators in the form of a coil (known as frame or loop aerials) are comparatively seldom used.

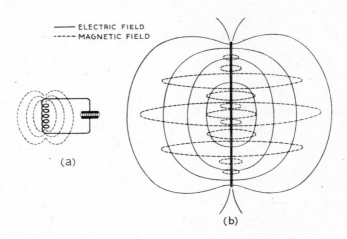

Fig. 122—In a concentrated tuned circuit (a) the electric and magnetic fiedsl are confined and radiation is slight. Opening out the circuit (b) extends the fields and also the radiation

THE CAPACITOR RADIATOR

How about the other element in an oscillatory circuit—the capacitor? As long as it is concentrated in a small space its radiating powers are almost negligible (Fig. 122*a*). But when opened out so that the lines of force form large loops, comparable with the wavelength, the vertical wires are carrying current in the same direction in all parts of them; and there is no return path to neutralize the resulting radiation. This arrangement (Fig. 122*b*) is a particularly efficient radiator; and it is actually used in large numbers in the form shown, although for convenience the coil is often separated from it as we shall see.

It is not essential for a circuit to be in resonance in order to radiate, but as the radiation is proportional to the current flowing, which is a maximum at resonance, the radiator is practically always tuned. So far we have considered tuned circuits made up of a coil and a capacitor as in Fig. 122*a*. These are devices embodying selected quantities of inductance and capacitance in concentrated form. But when the capacitor is replaced by long vertical wires as

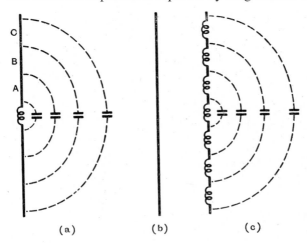

(a)   (b)   (c)

Fig. 123—The distributed capacitance of the radiator in Fig. 122 (*b*) is approximately represented by (*a*). A straight wire (*b*) actually has distributed capacitance and inductance, represented approximately by (*c*)

at *b* they possess capacitance which is distributed along their length. It could be approximately represented by a large number of small capacitors as in Fig. 123*a*. From this one can see that the current at the point A is greater than that at B, because some of it goes to charge the section of wire between A and B as well as all that beyond B. Similarly the current at B is greater than that at C, where there is such a small bit of wire to charge that it requires very little current indeed.

159

THE DIPOLE

As the wires carry this charging current to and fro, pushing electrons alternately towards the upper and lower halves of the system, they set up a magnetic field; and the wires, as well as the coil, therefore possess inductance, which is distributed along them. In fact, a tuned circuit can be constructed entirely of a straight wire (Fig. 123*b*), which can be approximately represented for electrical purposes as a number of tiny inductances and capacitances (*c*). There are, of course, moments in every part of the wire when the current is zero, when it is just about to turn and come back again; but, whereas at the extreme ends of the wire it is always zero (because there is nothing beyond to charge), at the middle it alternates with the maximum intensity. This distribution of current can be represented by the line marked I in Fig. 124, in which the distance it stands out from the wire at any point represents the r.m.s. or the peak value of the current at that point.

Each half of the wire becomes charged alternately positively and negatively; but the centre is always midway between these two charges and is therefore at zero alternating potential. The maximum potentials are reached at the ends, for there the charges all along the wire are pushing up behind one another, and the two ends are always at opposite polarity (except instantaneously twice every cycle when they are zero), so the alternating voltage distribution can be indicated by the line V.

Since the simple straight wire has both inductance and capacitance, and normally the resistance is comparatively small, it possesses all the qualifications of a resonant circuit, and can oscillate at its own natural frequency. A resonant radiator of this kind is known as a *dipole*. It turns out that the lengths of the resulting waves are almost exactly double the length of wire (actually a few per cent longer than double), and therefore the arrangement is called a half-wave dipole. For short waves, especially those classified as ultra-short (less than 10 metres), the dimensions of a dipole are so compact that it is a very convenient and popular form of radiator, and can be used for either vertically or horizontally polarized waves, according to the way it is erected.

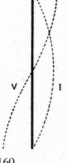

AERIAL AND EARTH

Until now we have assumed that the radiating wire is suspended in space, far away from any material substances such as the earth. The conclusions are not appreciably upset by placing it in air, but substances having relative permeability or permittivity greater than 1 increase the inductance and capacitance respectively and cause an increase in wavelength. The effect due to the necessary supporting insulators

Fig. 124—Diagrammatic method of showing the distribution of current (I) and voltage (V) in a half-wave resonant radiator

is very slight if they are kept small. But the effect of the earth is generally considerable. If the desired wavelength is very short, there is no difficulty in suspending the dipole many wavelengths above the ground; but as soon as radio began to be considered as a means of conveying messages it was found that the very short wavelengths, measured in centimetres rather than metres, have a very restricted range; and a dipole for much longer waves cannot in practice be more than a wavelength or so above ground and the wire itself may be of unwieldy length. Marconi used the ground to form the lower half of a vertical dipole; the remaining half sticking up out of it is therefore often known as the quarter-

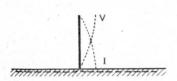

Fig. 125—The earth can be used as one half of a radiator, leaving a quarter - wavelength wire above earth. The horizontal broken line represents buried wires sometimes used to improve the conductivity of the ground

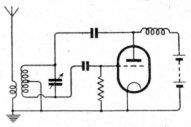

Fig. 126—Valve oscillator inductively coupled to a vertical aerial

wave Marconi aerial. The current and voltage distribution are shown in Fig. 125, which may be compared with the top half of Fig. 124.

For the earth to be a perfect substitute for the lower half of the dipole it must be a perfect conductor; which, of course, it never is, though sea-water is a good approximation to it. To overcome the loss due to semi-conducting earth forming a substantial part of the sphere of activity of the oscillating current and its resulting fields, it is a common practice to connect the lower end of the aerial to a radial system of copper wires. An insulated set of wires stretched just over the ground is known as a *counterpoise*. Alternatively, to prevent people or animals from tripping up, the wires are often buried just below the surface, as shown in Fig. 125, giving a low-resistance connection to earth.

AERIAL COUPLING AND TUNING

The next necessity is some means of maintaining oscillations in the aerial. Distributed inductance and capacitance, although satisfactory for composing the aerial itself, are not usually convenient for coupling to a source of oscillations such as a valve oscillator. Oscillatory power can be supplied to the aerial by either capacitive or inductive coupling. The latter is generally the more convenient, and it is therefore necessary to put back some of the concentrated inductance that we removed when arriving at the simple dipole. The result is shown in Fig. 126. The most effective point at which to insert the coil is that at which the current

F

is greatest. The Marconi aerial has a practical advantage here over the complete dipole, for the coil comes near the ground close to the other apparatus instead of awkwardly in mid-air.

The coil replaces some of the distributed inductance by concentrated inductance, leading to a shorter aerial for a given wavelength and therefore less radiation. To avoid this result, it is possible to neutralize the inductive reactance of the coil by an equal and opposite reactance furnished by a capacitor in series with the coil. But in many cases it may actually be desirable to reduce the height of the aerial below its natural quarter of a wavelength; for example, it would be unwise to erect a quarter-wave aerial to work on 10,000 metres—it would have to be about 8,000 feet high! Often, too, one wants to adjust the tuning by some more handy means than adjusting the length of the aerial wire. It is quite normal practice, then, for a considerable proportion of the tuning reactance of an aerial system, especially for medium and long waves, to be in concentrated form; but it must be remembered that this is at the expense of radiation efficiency.

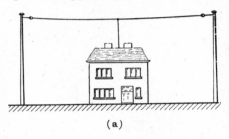

(a)

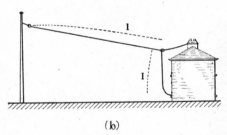

(b)

Fig. 127—To increase the radiation from a vertical aerial without increasing its height, a horizontal top is commonly added, forming *a* the T or *b* the inverted L type. Note the more uniform current distribution in the vertical part *b*

Where there are limitations in height, due to restrictions imposed by flying, or by the resources of the owner, it is possible to increase radiation by adding a horizontal portion, giving the familiar T or inverted L aerials (Fig. 127). The effect of the horizontal extension is to localize the bulk of the capacitance in itself so that the current in the vertical part, instead of tailing off to zero, remains at nearly the maximum value and therefore radiates more, as shown by the " I " line in Fig. 127*b*. The top portion radiates, too, but with a different polarization, so the addition due to it may not be very noticeable in a vertical receiving aerial.

CHOICE OF FREQUENCY

Talking about receiving aerials, the foregoing principles apply to them, because the factors that make for efficient radiation are identical with those for the inverse process of deriving the maximum signal power from an electromagnetic wave.

Before considering receiving aerials in detail, however, it will be as well to know what factors lead to the choice of frequency or wavelength. The shorter the wavelength, the higher the frequency, the smaller and cheaper the aerial, and the more efficiently it radiates. For example, as long ago as 1931 a radio link was established across the English Channel on a wavelength of 17 centimetres, a half-wave aerial for which is only about $3\frac{1}{2}$ inches long! Why, then, erect at vast expense aerials hundreds of feet high?

The main reason is that such waves behave very much like the still shorter waves of light, in not being able to reach anywhere beyond the direct line of " view " from the sending aerial. So either the aerials have to be put at the tops of high towers (in which case their cheapness disappears) or the range is restricted to a few miles. Wavelengths shorter than 10 metres are used for television, not because the shortness of wavelength in itself has any particular merit for that purpose, but because it corresponds to a very high frequency, which, as we shall see in Chapter 14, is necessary for a carrier wave that has to carry modulation frequencies of up to several Mc/s. They are also used for short-distance communication such as police cars, radiotelephone links between islands and mainland, and other specialized short-range purposes.

INFLUENCE OF THE ATMOSPHERE

At various heights between 60 and 300 miles above the earth, where the atmosphere is very rarified, there exist conditions which cause wireless waves to bend, rather as light waves bend when they pass from air into water. The very short (high-frequency) waves we have just been considering normally pass right through these layers and off into space, as shown in Fig. 128a. Where they are close to the ground, they are rapidly absorbed, as indicated by the shortness of the ground-level arrow. So their effective range is limited.

As the frequency is reduced below about 30 Mc/s—the exact dividing line depends on time of day, year, and solar activity cycle, and other conditions—the range of the wave-front travelling along the surface of the earth (and therefore termed the ground wave) increases slowly, while the sky wave is bent so much that it returns to earth at a very great distance, generally several thousands of miles (Fig. 128b). Between the maximum range of the ground wave and the minimum range of the reflected wave there is an extensive gap, called the skip distance, which no appreciable radiation reaches.

As the frequency is further reduced this gap narrows, and earth reflections may cause the journey to be done in several hops (c). Since the distances at which the sky waves return to earth vary according to time and other conditions as mentioned, it is rather a complicated business deciding which frequency to adopt at any given moment to reach a certain distance. But a vast amount of

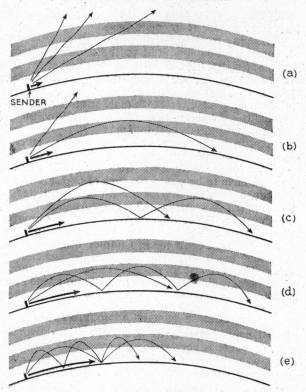

Fig. 128—Showing (not to scale) the relative ranges of ground
wave and reflected wave from very high frequencies (*a*) to very
low (*e*)

data has been accumulated on this and enables fairly reliable communication to be maintained at all times by a judicious choice. As waves usually arrive at the receiver by more than one path simultaneously, and tend to interfere with one another, fading and distortion are general unless elaborate methods are adopted for sorting them out. At a certain frequency, of the order of 2 Mc/s, the ground wave and reflected wave begin to overlap at night, while during daylight the reflected wave is more or less absent. Over the ranges at which there is overlap the two waves tend to interfere and cause fading and distortion, as they do with more than one reflected wave.

Finally, the range of the ground wave increases and becomes less affected by daylight or darkness, so that frequencies of 50–20 kc/s have a range of thousands of miles and are not at the mercy of various effects that make long-distance short-wave communication unreliable. For this reason they were originally selected as the only wavelengths suitable for long ranges, but now only a small fraction of long distance communication is borne by very long waves. The disadvantages of the latter are (1) the enormous size of aerial needed to radiate them; (2) the low efficiency of radiation even with a large and costly aerial system; (3) the higher power needed to cover long ranges, due largely to (4) the great intensity of atmospherics—interference caused by thunderstorms and other atmospheric electrical phenomena; and (5) the very limited number of stations that can work without interfering with one another, because the waveband is so narrow in terms of frequency—which is what matters; see Chapter 14.

The following table, which summarizes the foregoing, is due to Prof. F. E. Terman:

Frequency band: kc/s	Waveband: metres	Outstanding characteristics	Principal uses
Below 100	Over 3,000	Low attenuation at all times of day and year.	Long-distance trans-oceanic service requiring continuous operation.
100–1,500	3,000–200	Attenuation low at night and high in daytime; greater in summer than winter.	Range 100 to 500 kc/s used for marine communication, aircraft radio, direction finding, etc. Range 150 to 300 and 525 to 1,605 kc/s employed for broadcasting.
1,500–6,000	200–50	Attenuation low at night and moderate in daytime.	Moderate-distance communication of all types.
6,000–30,000	50–10	Transmission depends upon the ionization in the upper atmosphere, and so varies greatly with the time of day and season. Attenuation extremely small under favourable conditions.	Long-distance communication of all kinds; aircraft radio.
Above 30,000	Below 10	Waves travel in straight lines and are not reflected by ionized layers, so can only travel between points in sight of one another, or nearly so.	Short-distance communication; television; two-way police radio; portable equipment, aircraft landing beacons; radar.

BEAMS AND REFLECTORS

Because of the disadvantages, just mentioned, of very long waves, short waves are used wherever possible. A further point in their favour is that it is practicable to concentrate the radiation in any desired direction instead of wasting a large part of the power by indiscriminate distribution. When the wavelength is much greater than the dimensions of the aerial, radiation takes place fairly equally in all directions, and it is difficult to modify this. But when the aerial is half the wavelength, as in the simple dipole, the radiation varies from nil along its axis to a maximum all round its " equator " as indicated by the line drawn around the dipole in Fig. 129a. The distance of any point on this line from the centre is an indication of

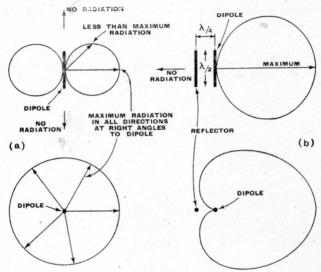

Fig. 129—Polar diagrams of radiation from a simple dipole aerial (a), and dipole with reflector (b). The upper diagrams are side views and the lower diagrams end views

the relative strength of radiation in that direction. If a second half-wave dipole, not fed with power, is placed quarter of a wavelength away, as shown at b, it is like a resonant coupled circuit and has oscillatory currents induced in it. These currents re-radiate, and the quarter-wave spacing causes the re-radiation to be in such a phase as to cancel out the original radiation on the side where the second dipole is placed, and to reinforce it on the opposite side. The second dipole therefore acts as a *reflector*. The same argument applies to a receiving aerial; and by using reflectors at both sending and receiving ends there is a considerable gain in signal strength.

But this is only the beginning of what can be done. By placing a number of dipoles in a row, or end-on, or both, the radiation from them adds up in phase in certain directions, and cancels out in others, and in general the greater the number of dipoles in such an array the narrower and more intense the beam of radiation. Obviously the size of such an array would be impracticable for long waves, whereas for very short waves it is reasonably compact. This compensates to a large extent for the difficulties in generating large amounts of power at very high frequencies.

The principle on which most of the directional aerial arrays, however elaborate, depend can be illustrated by a pair of dipoles shown end-on at DD in Fig. 130. They are fed with r.f. power of the resonant frequency (i.e., wavelength equal to twice the length of the dipoles) in phase, so that at any point O equidistant from the two dipoles the radiation from both arrives in phase and gives stronger reception than from one dipole only. But points such as P or Q are at unequal distances from the dipoles, and if the difference in distance happens to equal half a wave-length—or any odd multiple of half a wavelength—the radiation from the two arrives in opposite phase and cancels out. By using a sufficiently large number of dipoles, suitably arranged, the radiation can be concentrated into a narrow angle.

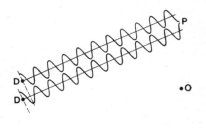

Fig. 130—Showing how the waves from two dipoles radiating in phase arrive at certain angles in completely opposite phase

It is necessary to consider, not only the distribution of radiation horizontally around the transmitter, but also the angle of elevation above the horizon. In this the ground has a large influence, and the height of the aerial above ground is an important factor. Obviously if the direct ground wave is being relied upon it is wasteful to direct most of the radiation upwards; while if reflected waves are necessary to reach the desired destination the upward angle should be adjusted accordingly. The design of an aerial array is therefore far from simple, especially as some of the data—conductivity of earth, and reflecting power of atmosphere, for example—are imperfectly known and subject to change.

RADIATION RESISTANCE

We have considered an aerial as just an opened-out resonant circuit, with its inductance and capacitance distributed along its length instead of being concentrated separately in an inductor and a capacitor—though in practice it is usually necessary to augment them by concentrated L and C for coupling and tuning purposes. The main difference—which will be no more than mentioned—between distributed and concentrated tuning is that a distributed

167

resonator such as an aerial resonates at certain additional frequencies, especially odd multiples of the main resonant frequency.

What about resistance? An aerial includes the various sources of loss resistance described on page 114, with one addition. The electromagnetic waves radiated from a sending aerial contain energy, otherwise they would not be able to cause currents to flow in receiving aerials. Departure of energy from a circuit can be expressed in terms of resistance (p. 54). But whereas the other kinds of resistance are all wasteful, this kind (called radiation resistance) represents the ability of an aerial to do its job.

The radiation resistance of an ordinary concentrated tuning circuit is generally very small compared with its loss resistance; at the other extreme, the loss resistance of a dipole, made perhaps of copper tubing, is small compared with its radiation resistance, which at resonance is about 70 Ω, measured at the centre, where the current is greatest. If therefore a current of, say, 2 A can be generated there, the power radiated is $I^2R_r = 2^2 \times 70 = 280$ W (R_r denoting radiation resistance).

EFFECTIVE HEIGHT

In general, the greater the radiation resistance of an aerial the more effective it will be for receiving as well as for sending. But a more useful piece of information about an aerial when it is used for receiving is what is called its *effective height*. It is the height which, when multiplied by the electric field strength, gives the e.m.f. generated in it. For example, if the wave from a sender has a strength of 2 mV per metre at a receiving station, and the effective height of the aerial is 5 metres, the signal voltage generated in the aerial will be 10 mV.

The effective height is less than the physical height. It can be calculated for a few simple shapes, such as a vertical wire rising from flat open ground, but usually has to be measured, or roughly estimated by experience.

CHAPTER 13

Detection

THE NEED FOR DETECTION

TURNING NOW to the reception end in Fig. 15, we see a number of boxes representing sections of a receiver. Although all of these sections are included in most receivers, they are not all absolutely essential. So we begin with the detector, because it is the one thing indispensable, for reasons now to be explained.

At the receiving aerial, the modulated carrier wave generates e.m.fs whose waveforms exactly match those of the currents in the sending aerial. The frequency of those currents, as we know (p. 31), is so high as to be inaudible. It has been chosen with a view to covering the desired range most economically (as discussed in the previous chapter), and bears no relationship to the frequencies of the sounds being transmitted. In order to reproduce those sounds, it is necessary to produce currents having the frequencies and waveforms of the sounds. For example, given Fig. 113c (or 131a), the problem is to obtain from it Fig. 113a. The device for doing so is the *detector*, or, as it is often called in America, the demodulator.

THE DETECTOR

The simplest method is to eliminate half of every cycle, giving the result shown in Fig. 131b. At first glance, this might not seem to differ fundamentally from a, for the original frequency appears to be still there, though at half-strength. It is quite true that the

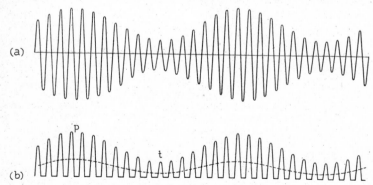

Fig. 131—(a) Sample of a modulated carrier wave, similar to Fig. 113 c. The average value of each cycle is zero; but if one half of each is eliminated (b) the average value of the other halves, shown dotted, fluctuates in the same manner as the modulating waveform (e.g., Fig. 113 a)

original frequency is there, and means have to be provided for getting rid of it. The fundamental difference is that whereas the average value of each cycle in *a* is zero (because the negative half cancels the positive half), in *b* it is proportional to the amplitude (at that moment) of the modulated carrier wave, which in turn is proportional to the instantaneous value of the a.f. modulating signal. The dotted line in Fig. 131*b* indicates the average level of the current, and it can be seen to vary at the same frequency and with the same waveform as Fig. 113*a*. There is admittedly some loss in amplitude, but (as we shall see) the types of detector in common use manage to avoid most of this loss and give an output almost equal to the peak values.

The process of suppressing half of each cycle, converting alternations of current into a series of pulses of unidirectional current, is called by the general term *rectification*. The detector usually consists essentially of a rectifier adapted to the particular purpose now in view, and may be taken to include such means as may be used for extracting the desired a.f. from a mixture like Fig. 131*b*. It should be noted that this rectified signal contains not only r.f. and a.f. components, but also a unidirectional component (d.c.). That is, the desired a.f. current does not alternate about zero, as in Fig. 113*a*, but about some steady positive or negative current (depending on which was eliminated by the rectifier). Although this d.c. is unnecessary and in fact undesirable for reproducing the original sounds, it has its uses as a by-product (p. 218).

RECTIFIERS

A perfect rectifier would be one that had no resistance to current flowing in one direction, and an infinite resistance to current in the opposite direction. It would, in fact, be equivalent to a switch, completing the circuit during all the positive half-cycles in Fig. 131*a*, thus enabling them to be passed completely, as in *b*; and interrupting it during all the negative half-cycles, suppressing them completely, as also shown in *b*. For very low-frequency alternating currents, such as 50 c/s, it is possible to construct such a switch (known as a vibrator rectifier); but any device involving mechanical motion is impracticable at radio frequencies.

A number of minerals, such as silicon, have a much lower contact resistance in one direction than the other, and in the early days of broadcasting they were very much used as detectors in *crystal receivers*. In improved form they are still used, for radar. Then the manufactured selenium and copper-oxide rectifiers used extensively for low-frequency rectification have been adapted for radio frequencies; and to them have been added rectifiers made of the rare element germanium. But the effect most commonly used is the one-way movement of electrons in a vacuum, of which the thermionic valve is the embodiment.

In considering resistance we began with the current/voltage graphs of ordinary conductors (Fig. 18), and noted that because

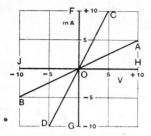

Fig. 132—Characteristic curves of various linear resistances. The line COD, by Ohm's Law, is seen to represent 500 Ω. If the resistance to negative voltages is different from that to positive, as shown for example by the line COB, the result is a partial rectifier

such graphs were straight lines the conductors described by them were called linear, and that since linear resistances were covered by the very simple relationship known as Ohm's Law there was really no need to spend any more time drawing their graphs. Then we came to valves, and again drew current/voltage graphs, such as Fig. 90, and found that they were curved, indicating non-linear characteristics, not conforming to Ohm's Law (except in the modified and limited sense of Fig. 97, and then only approximately). All non-linear conductors are capable of some degree of rectification, and all rectifiers are necessarily non-linear in the above sense; that is, their resistance depends on the voltage or current instead of being constant as in Ohm's Law.

Here now in Fig. 132 are some more current/voltage characteristics, the lines COD and AOB representing (as can be calculated from the current and voltage scales) 500 Ω and 2,000 Ω respectively. As we noticed before, the steeper the slope the lower the resistance. To go to extremes, the line FOG represents zero resistance, and HOJ infinite resistance; so FOJ is the graph of a perfect rectifier. COB is an example of a partial rectifier—a resistance of 500 Ω to positive currents and 2,000 Ω to negative currents. Now apply an alternating voltage to a circuit consisting of any of the foregoing imaginary resistances in series with a fixed resistance of 1,000 Ω (Fig. 133a). The voltage across the 1,000 Ω—call it the output voltage—is equal to the applied voltage only if R is zero. Both voltages are then indicated by the full line in Fig. 133b. If R were 500 Ω (COD), the output would be represented by the dotted line CD, and if 2,000 Ω by the dotted line AB.

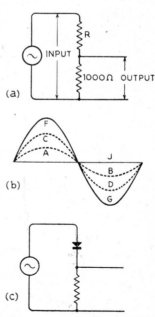

Fig. 133—The results of applying a sinusoidal voltage to a circuit (a) consisting of any of the resistances represented by Fig. 132 (denoted by R) in series with 1,000 Ω are indicated by b, which is lettered to correspond with the various characteristics in Fig. 132. When R is a rectifier it is represented by the symbol shown in c

171

If now a rectifier is substituted for R, the symbol being as shown in Fig. 133c, the positive and negative output voltages are unequal. For example, the perfect rectifier (FOJ) gives the output FJ in b; and the partial rectifier gives CB. The average voltage, taken over each whole cycle, is, of course, nil when R is not a rectifier. Using the perfect rectifier, the average of the positive half is 64% of the maximum (p. 78), while the negative is, of course, nil; so the average rectified current taken over a whole cycle is 32% of the peak value. Using the rectifier with the graph COB, the negative half-cycle (B in Fig. 133b) cancels out half of the positive half (C), which is two-thirds of the input; so the rectified result is less than 11% of the peak input.

LINEARITY OF RECTIFICATION

Whether complete or partial, however, the degree of rectification from rectifiers having characteristics like those in Fig. 132 would be independent of the amount of voltage, provided, of course, that the rectifier was arranged to work exactly at the sharp corner in its characteristic, whether that happened to correspond with zero voltage, as in Fig. 132, or not. So if we were to draw a graph showing the net or average or rectified voltage output against peak

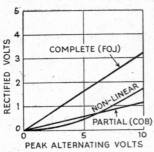

alternating voltage input to a rectifier of this kind we would get a straight line, such as the two examples in Fig. 134, corresponding to characteristics FOJ and COB in Fig. 132. These are therefore called linear rectifiers, it being understood that the term is in reference to a graph of this kind and not to one of the Fig. 132 kind.

It should be clear from Fig. 131b that it is necessary for the rectifier to be linear if the waveform of the modulation is not to be distorted. It is therefore unfortunate that in reality there is no such thing as a linear rectifier. The best one can do is to approach very close to perfection by intelligent use of the rectifiers available.

Fig. 134—The rectified outputs obtained by applying alternating voltages to various rectifiers are shown in these characteristic curves, lettered to correspond with Figs. 132 and 133

The weak feature of all of them is the more or less gradual transition from high to low resistance, exemplified by the typical " bottom bend " in Fig. 90, which causes weak signals to be rectified less completely than strong ones. Such a characteristic is represented in Fig. 134 by the curved line, and is explained in greater detail later (p. 182).

THE DIODE RECTIFIER

There were two reasons for the poor results of rectifier COB in Fig. 132 compared with FOJ. One was its *forward resistance*

(500 Ω), which absorbed one-third of the voltage, leaving only two-thirds for the 1,000 Ω load. The other was its finite *backward resistance* (2,000 Ω) which allowed current to pass during the negative half-cycles, so neutralizing another one-third of the voltage. With such a rectifier it would clearly be important to choose the load resistance carefully in order to lose as little as possible in these ways. As it happens, 1,000 Ω does give the largest output voltage in this case, the general formula being $\sqrt{R_F R_B}$, where R_F and R_B are respectively the forward and backward resistances of the rectifier.

The diode valve rectifier has one strong point in its favour. Although it may not be perfect in the forward direction, for it always has some resistance, it is practically perfect in the reverse direction; that is to say, it passes negligible reverse current, even when quite large voltages are applied. So even if the forward current were very small (due to a high forward resistance) the output voltage could, theoretically at least, be made to approach that given by a perfect rectifier, merely by choosing a sufficiently high load resistance.

Although, as we shall soon see, there are limits to the resistance that can be used in practice, the loss of rectification can usually be made insignificantly small. In fact, by a very simple elaboration of Fig. 133c—a capacitor in parallel with the load resistance—it is possible to approach a rectification efficiency of 100% instead of the 32% that is the maximum without it, and so do nearly three times better than our "perfect" rectifier. This point deserves closer consideration.

ACTION OF RESERVOIR CAPACITOR

The modified rectifier circuit is now basically as Fig. 135. Suppose, in order to get the utmost rectified voltage, we made the load resistance R infinitely great. The capacitor C would then be in series with the diode, with no resistor across it. To simplify consideration we shall apply a square wave instead of a sine wave; amplitude 100 V (Fig. 136a). We shall also assume that its frequency is 500 kc/s, so that each *half* cycle occupies exactly one millionth of a second (1 μsec). At the start C is uncharged, and therefore has no voltage across it. It can acquire a charge only by current flowing through the rectifier, which offers a certain amount of resistance, and so when the first positive half-cycle arrives its 100 V at first appears

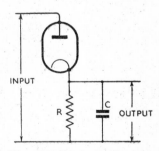

Fig. 135—Diode rectifier with the load resistance (R) shunted by a reservoir capacitance, C

wholly across that resistance, as shown by the full line in Fig. 136b.

The current driven by this voltage starts charging the capacitor, whose voltage thereby starts to rise towards 100 V, as shown by the

173

dotted line. It is clear that the voltages across rectifier and capacitor, being in series, must add up to give 100 V so long as that is the applied voltage; and Fig. 136*b* shows this to be so. The greater the resistance of the rectifier and the capacitance of the capacitor, the slower the rate of charge, just as with a very large balloon

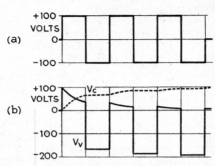

Fig. 136—Analysis of application of a square alternating voltage (*a*) to the circuit Fig. 135. The dotted line in *b* represents the voltage across C; the full line, that across the diode

inflated through a very narrow tube. As we noted in connection with Fig. 34, which showed another example of the same thing, the capacitance in microfarads multiplied by the resistance in megohms is the time constant—the number of seconds required for the capacitor voltage V_C to reach 63% of the applied voltage. Suppose that the rectifier resistance (assumed constant) is 0·01 MΩ and the capacitance 0·0001 μF. Then the time constant is 0·000001 second or 1 μsec. In this case that happens to be the time occupied by one half-cycle of the 500 kc/s applied voltage. So at the end of the first positive half-cycle V_C is 63, while V_V has dropped to 100 − 63 = 37. Then comes the negative half-cycle. The diode ceases to conduct, and while the capacitor therefore cannot charge up any more it likewise has no conducting path through which to discharge, and so remains at 63 V until the second positive half-cycle. Meanwhile, V_C (63 V) plus V_V must now be equal to the new applied voltage, − 100. The voltage across the rectifier must therefore be − 163.

The net voltage applied to the capacitor when the second positive half-cycle arrives is 100 − 63 = 37 V, so at the end of this half-cycle the voltage across the condenser will increase by 63% of 37, or 23 V, which, added to the 63 it already possessed, makes 86. The charge thus gradually approaches the peak signal voltage in successive cycles, while the average voltage across the rectifier falls by the same amount, as shown in Fig. 136*b*. The rectified output voltage therefore approaches 100% of the peak applied r.f. voltage. A similar result is obtained (but more slowly) with a sine wave signal.

Because C maintains the voltage during the half-cycles when the supply is cut off, it is called a *reservoir capacitor*.

CHOICE OF COMPONENT VALUES

This, of course, is excellent so far as an unmodulated carrier is concerned. When it is modulated, however, the amplitude alternately increases and decreases. The increases build up the

174

capacitor voltage still further; but the decreases are powerless to reduce it, for the capacitor has nothing to discharge through. To enable V_C to follow the modulation it is necessary to provide such a path, which may be in parallel with either the capacitor or the diode, so long as in the latter case there is a conducting path through the input to complete the discharge route.

Suppose, for example, the highest modulation frequency is 10,000 c/s. Then the time elapsing between a peak of modulation and a trough (p to t in Fig. 131b) is half a cycle, or 1/20,000th sec (50 μsec). If V_C is to follow that half-cycle of modulation to the extent of at least 63%, the time constant would have to be not more than 50 μsec.

Of the two things determining this time constant, the value of the resistance is to some extent already decided on other grounds, for it must be much higher than the diode forward resistance, or there will be loss of detector efficiency. Incidentally, there will also be damping of the tuned input circuit. In practice one may reckon, as a fair approximation, that the damping effect of a diode detector of the Fig. 135 type with a load resistance R is equivalent to connecting a resistance R/2 directly across the tuned circuit.* For these two reasons R is generally made not less than about 0·5 MΩ. The value of C is thereby fixed. If R is 0·5 MΩ and CR = 0·00005, then C must be 0·0001 μF (or 100 pF), which in fact is quite a usual figure.

Note that at modulation frequencies as high as 10,000 c/s, these values for C and R would result in quite an appreciable loss, for we were reckoning on V_C following the modulation to the extent of only 63%—rather less, in fact, because the rate of discharge is somewhat slowed by the presence of the carrier wave meanwhile. So from this point of view it would be better for CR to be still smaller.

Is there any limit to reducing C? The answer can be obtained by reconsidering Fig. 136 on the assumption that the time constant is very short. Instead of V_C remaining level during the negative half-cycles, as shown there, or declining slightly as it would with a moderate time constant, it would fall rapidly. So the reservoir action would largely fail; each positive half-cycle would have to start recharging C almost from scratch, and there would be a loss of detection efficiency—at all modulation frequencies. The correct choice of C is most difficult when the carrier-wave frequency is not many times greater than the top modulation frequency. If equal treatment of all modulation frequencies is reckoned more important than detection efficiency over all frequencies, then C should be kept low; and *vice versa.*

* This is quite easily proved. Denote the resistance which, if connected across the tuned circuit in place of the diode and its load resistance R and reservoir C, would be equivalent to them, by R'. Then assuming the resistance of the diode is negligible in comparison with R, C will charge up to the peak voltage $\sqrt{2}E$, E being the r.m.s. voltage developed across the tuned circuit. As R will be the only component dissipating power, the power dissipated (equal to the square of the voltage across R) divided by R is $2E^2/R$. But from the way in which we have defined R', this wattage must also equal E^2/R'. Therefore R' = R/2.

THE DIODE DETECTOR IN ACTION

As the action of the deceptively simple-looking circuit in Fig. 135 is not very easy to grasp, and is also most important, it will be worth spending some more time on it. Fig. 137 is a diagram which, compared with Fig. 136, is speeded up so as to show some modulation, and uses proper sine waves for the carrier. Also, the

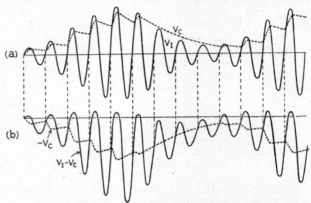

Fig. 137—In diagram *a*, V_I represents a modulated r.f. input voltage and V_c the resulting output voltage. The carrier frequency would normally be much higher relative to the modulation frequency, and this would permit a shorter time-constant ($= CR$) so that V_c could follow the peaks of V_I more closely. In diagram *b*, the full line shows $V_I — V_c$; i.e., the voltage across the diode

voltage V_C across the capacitor—which, of course, is the output voltage—is drawn together with the r.f. input voltage V_I at *a*. Notice that whenever V_I is more positive than V_O the diode conducts and C charges rapidly, because the time constant is CR_V*, and R_V (the resistance of the valve) is much less than R. Directly V_I drops below V_C, C discharges through the only path available (R) with the much longer time constant CR. It is too long in this case, because V_O loses contact with V_I altogether during the troughs, and its waveform is obviously a distorted version of the modulation envelope. But that is because for the sake of clearness the carrier frequency shown is excessively low for the modulation frequency.

Note too that in addition to the desired frequency, V_O has also a saw-tooth ripple at the carrier frequency, but much less of it than in Fig. 131*b*. Not only has C improved the rectification efficiency but it has also got rid of most of the unwanted r.f.

The third component making up V_O is a steady positive voltage (zero frequency), represented by the average height of the dotted line above the zero line. The voltage across the valve must, of course, be equal to V_I minus V_O (Fig. 137*b*). So it also contains

* Actually not quite, because R is at the same time a discharge path (like the old school problems about filling a tank with a hole in it!) but the error is usually unimportant.

the z.f. and a.f. voltages, and therefore could be used alternatively as the output voltage, but with the disadvantage of having nearly the full r.f. voltage along with it.

VARIETIES OF DIODE DETECTOR CIRCUIT

We have just seen that a diode detector circuit arranged as in Fig. 135 gives an output consisting of the desired a.f., plus a positive z.f., plus a much reduced r.f. This arrangement, repeated in Fig. 138a, is open to the objection that if a.c. is used for heating the cathode an appreciable fraction of its voltage may appear across R via the stray capacitance between heater and cathode. And in some receivers there is a need for a *negative* voltage proportional to the carrier amplitude. It can be obtained if the circuit is rearranged as in Fig. 138b, and at the same time the possible heater trouble is removed. This circuit is the one generally used when the input is tuned to a fixed frequency. But if it is necessary to use a variable tuning capacitor, it is often inconvenient to have both its terminals at varying potential. So if *a* is ruled out, *c* is an alternative, in

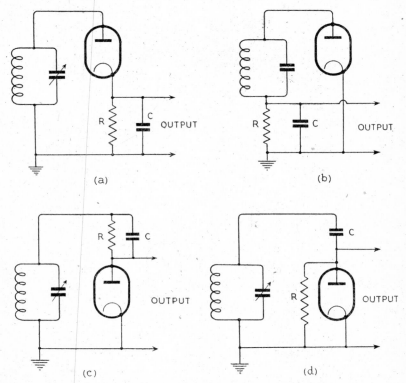

Fig. 138—The principal varieties of diode detector circuit

177

which the output is drawn from across the diode and so contains most of the original r.f. If, for reasons that will appear in Chapter 15, the tuned circuit is at a high positive potential, circuit c would apply this potential via R to the diode, taking it away from its effective rectifying point. To obviate this, R must be connected to the cathode side, as at d. Unlike the three other arrangements, in this one R is not by-passed by C, so it carries the r.f. a.c. as well as the d.c. and consequently loads the tuned circuit rather more heavily. The effective resistance is in fact approximately R/3 instead of R/2. As in c (but not a and b) the output contains a large proportion of r.f.

THE GRID DETECTOR

If any of the foregoing circuits were connected directly to a loudspeaker or a pair of headphones, the comparatively low resistance of such devices would completely upset the carefully-chosen detector circuit values, even if the amount of power available

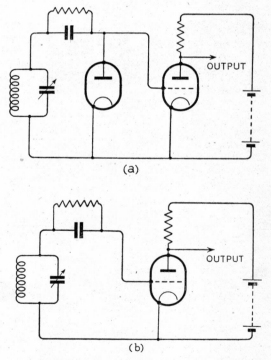

(a)

(b)

Fig. 139—If a diode detector (Fig. 138c variety) is connected straight to a triode amplifier (a), the grid-cathode path of the triode renders a separate diode unnecessary; this is what happens in the grid type of detector (b)

were sufficient to give useful results. So in practice a diode detector is followed by one or more stages of amplification.

Connecting the detector circuit of Fig. 138c, for example, straight to an amplifier, as shown in Fig. 139a, we find that the anode-cathode path of the diode is in parallel with the grid-cathode path of the triode. Since both the anode of the diode and the grid of the triode consist simply of an electrode close to an emitting cathode, there would seem to be no need to have them both. Experiment confirms this supposition; there is no change in the performance of the system if the diode is removed from its socket.

The simplified result, Fig. 139b, is the *grid detector*, in which the grid and cathode, acting as a diode, rectify just as in Fig. 138c. The resulting a.f. voltages at the grid then control the electron stream through the triode and so produce an amplified voltage at the anode in the way described on page 125.

In practice this apparently neat idea does not always work out very satisfactorily. As we have already noticed, the output of the type of diode circuit employed contains not only the desired a.f. but also a negative z.f. and a large amount of r.f. The negative z.f. may be useful, as a source of the necessary bias voltage for the triode (p. 129). But the r.f. is a nuisance, because it limits the amplitude of signal that can be handled without distortion to about half of what it could be if the r.f. were not there. Moreover, the amplified r.f. is liable to work round to the input through stray couplings and may even cause oscillation.

We shall soon see that restricting the detector input to not more than a volt or two of r.f. tends to introduce distortion in another way, and also limits the usefulness of the detector for auxiliary duties (p. 218). If, to escape this dilemma, the anode voltage of the triode is increased, it is found that the anode current runs up to an alarming figure, and even then may not satisfy the requirements in modern receivers, which often call for a rectified output of 20 V or more.

The apparent economy of this circuit therefore proves in most cases to be illusory. With the separate diode there is no restriction on the r.f. voltage, and the residue left in the output can be removed from the a.f. before it is passed on to the next stage.

FILTERS

Devices for separating currents of different frequencies are known as *filters*, and are a vast subject in themselves. Those used in detectors are usually of the very simplest types, however. All filters depend on the fact that inductive and capacitive impedances vary with frequency. The simple circuits of Figs. 60, 67, and 73 can all be used as filters.

Take Fig. 60—C and R in series. At very low frequencies, C offers a high impedance compared with R, and nearly all the voltage applied across them both appears across C. As the frequency rises, the impedance of C falls, until, at a very high frequency, most

179

of the voltage appears across R. The dividing frequency, at which the voltages across C and R are equal to one another (and to the input voltage divided by $\sqrt{2}$), is given by $X_0 = 1/2\pi fC = R$, so $f = 1/2\pi CR$.

Suppose the lowest carrier frequency to be handled by a detector is 150 kc/s, and the highest modulation frequency is 10 kc/s. One might make the dividing frequency 15 kc/s. Knowing R we can then find C, or *vice versa*. If the input voltage is to be derived straight from a diode detector, the impedance of the filter ought not to be too low, or C too high. Let us try 100 pF. Then, using c/s, μF and MΩ units, $R = 1/(2\pi \times 15,000 \times 0\cdot0001) =$ about $0\cdot1$ MΩ.

Fig. 140 shows a diode circuit (type Fig. 138d) with this filter incorporated, as R_1 and C_1. R, of course, is the load resistance.

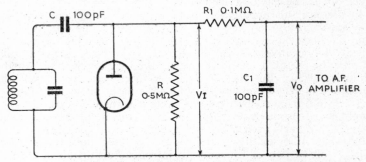

Fig. 140—To prevent the r.f. voltages left over after rectification being passed on to the a.f. amplifier, a simple filter, R_1 and C_1, is commonly used. The component values shown are typical

Having calculated the reactance of C_1 at various frequencies, one can easily work out the ratio of output voltage to input voltage, V_O/V_I, and plot it as a graph, Fig. 141. This shows clearly how a filter with the selected component values would cause negligible loss of modulation frequencies but would reduce the residual r.f. considerably. Admittedly this graph does not present an exact picture, because the filter is a shunt circuit to the load resistance and would affect the rectification somewhat; but with such high-impedance filter components it is broadly true.

The possibility of using the negative voltage resulting from rectification as a bias for the following amplifier valve has been mentioned. It is not always considered good to have a bias voltage that varies with amplitude of the r.f. reaching the detector, and a more usual policy is to exclude this voltage and apply a suitable bias to the amplifier in some other way. A filter to cut out a frequency lower than the desired frequencies—zero-frequency in this case—can be similar to the previous one, but with C and R interchanged. C in series definitely prohibits z.f., so is often called a blocking capacitor; but it must have sufficiently large

180

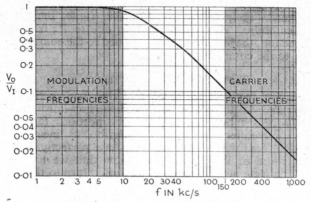

Fig. 141—The filtering action of $R_1 C_1$ in Fig. 140 is here shown
as a graph of V_o/V_I against frequency

capacitance to pass the lowest modulation frequency. If the
associated resistance is 1 MΩ, 0·01 μF or larger is usually
satisfactory.

A Typical Detector Circuit

This resistance, incidentally, is commonly used for volume
control in the manner shown in Fig. 142, which is a typical detector
circuit, developed from Fig. 138b. R_1 and C_1, as before, are the

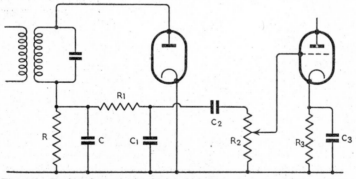

Fig. 142—Typical detector circuit, in which R is the load resistance, C the
reservoir, $R_1 C_1$ the r.f. filter, $R_2 C_2$ the z.f. filter, R_2 the volume control,
R_3 the biasing resistance, and C_3 its by-pass

r.f. filter, and R_2C_2 the z.f. filter, R_2 also serving as volume control.
This is the best place for it, because, as we shall see, distortion is
minimized by having the maximum possible signal amplitude at the
diode detector and the minimum going into the amplifier. The
purpose of R3 and C3 is to provide bias for the amplifier valve, as
explained on page 290.

181

Although for clearness separate valves are shown, in practice the diode is generally incorporated with the triode, making use of the same cathode. To prevent the bias due to R_3 from affecting the diode action, the lower end of R is joined to the common cathode instead of to the common negative line.

DETECTOR CHARACTERISTICS

In discussing rectifiers we noted that they had to be non-linear conductors in order to rectify, but that if the non-linearity consisted of a sharp corner between two straight portions (e.g., COB in Fig. 132), the rectifier itself could be described as linear (e.g., COB in Fig. 134). And that no real rectifiers have perfectly sharp bends, so all are more or less non-linear. Now that we have seen the details of complete detector circuits we shall return to this point and

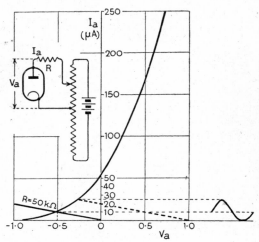

Fig. 143—The action of a detector can be examined in detail with the help of the load-line technique. When the foot of the load line (here shown at O) is moved to and fro horizontally to an extent representing the input voltage, the intersection of the load line with the valve curve traces out the corresponding variation in anode current, shown to the right for a 1 V-peak sinusoidal input

consider how to ensure that the non-linearity is less rather than more.

The various valve characteristic curves in Chapter 9 show that anode current begins gradually at first, and then the curve straightens out considerably. But this does not happen until the anode current is several milliamps. If we were to use a detector load resistance so low as to pass several milliamps, it would damp the tuned circuit excessively (p. 175). So for detector purposes the only part that concerns us is the microamp region, for which we need an enlarged view of the bottom bend (Fig. 143). Anode current (I_a) normally begins at an anode voltage (V_a) somewhere between 0 and -1 V. So if the anode were connected direct to the cathode with no load resistance, a current of about 50 μA (in this particular example) would flow.

182

When a load resistance is inserted, the drop in voltage across it due to current flowing through it makes the anode more negative. To find how much more, we adopt the load-line method explained on pages 124–5. For clearness let us take the rather low load of 50 kΩ, connected straight to cathode (zero volts). That means the load line must be drawn from the origin of the graph, 0, and of course 50 kΩ corresponds to 20 μA at 1 V. When so drawn, it cuts the valve curve at $-0\cdot5$ V, 10 μA, these being respectively V_a and I_a under the conditions assumed.

Now suppose a small alternating signal voltage is applied in series with R and the diode. Its effect can be represented on the diagram by making the load line vibrate horizontally to right and left of point 0 to the extent of the signal amplitude. The point of intersection with the valve curve will move up and down, indicating an alternating anode current. If first we suppose that the signal voltage is very small, say $\pm$ 0·01 V, then the tiny portion of curve actually used is practically straight, and there will be hardly any rectification. I_a will alternate slightly above and below 10 μA,

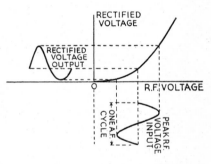

Fig. 144—As Fig. 143 shows, rectification is only partial even with as much as 1 V input. Here is a curve showing rectification plotted against r.f. voltage amplitude. It enables the distortion of the modulation to be ascertained for any r.f. amplitude and depth of modulation. The input curve here represents 50 per cent modulation

the negative half-cycle almost completely neutralizing the positive half. Small-signal detection is therefore very inefficient.

If the valve curve started up from zero at a sudden angle, even if only a slight one, we could improve matters by bringing our working point to it, either by applying a negative bias or by using a much higher load resistance. But magnifying the bottom part of the curve fails to reveal any sharp corner, so all we would do in our attempt to suppress the negative half-cycles would be to suppress the positive halves as well!

Now imagine that the signal voltage is increased to, say, 1 V peak. Moving the load line up to $+$ 1 V to represent the positive half-cycle brings the anode-current peak up to about 25 μA, a net peak value of $+$ 15 μA; whereas the negative half-cycle cannot be more than $-$ 10 μA at most; as shown at the extreme right. Averaged over the whole cycle, the anode current shows a small net positive value. In other words, there is some rectification, though still not very much.

It is obvious that further increases in signal voltage will all be net "profit" to I_a. To show the results with very large signal voltages it would be necessary to use an I_a–V_a diagram on such a scale that the gradual bend would look like a sharp corner, and rectification would approach the ideal.

Drawing a curve of rectified current, or rectified voltage due to this current passing through R, against signal voltage, we get a curve such as that in Fig. 144, showing poor detection of weak signals, improving with increase in signal.

DETECTOR DISTORTION

Consider now what happens when the signal is amplitude-modulated. The signal strength periodically waxes and wanes at the modulation frequency. The curve at the foot of Fig. 144 represents (on the r.f. voltage scale) one cycle of sinusoidal modulation to a depth of 50%. (It must not be confused with the individual r.f. cycles considered in connection with Fig. 143.) The negative half-cycles reduce the rectified voltage less than the positive half-cycles increase it, so the rectified waveform is distorted as shown to the left of the diagram. From the shape of the curve one can see that there would be some distortion at any depth of modulation, but the deeper the modulation the greater the distortion.

Further consideration of Fig. 144 will show that if the carrier wave is considerably stronger, enough to bring it on to the straight, then there will be no distortion so long as the depth of modulation is not enough to bring the signal strength down on to the bend. Modulation to a depth of 100% is bound to be distorted because it brings the signal strength at the negative peaks down to zero. The greater the carrier-wave voltage, the greater the depth of modulation before distortion begins, and the less the distortion at 100% modulation. That is one of the reasons why it is a good thing for the receiver to be designed so that the signal voltage at the detector is as large as possible, and at least not less than several volts.

In discussing Fig. 143, we assumed a load resistance with no reservoir capacitance. The effect of including the reservoir is to introduce a negative bias voltage proportional to the rectified current, pushing the initial working point lower down the curve. But since with most valves the degree of curvature anywhere on the bottom bend is very much the same, the general results are substantially as described above for the unshunted load resistor.

A great advantage of the diode detector over other types is that correct operation is mainly a matter of arranging that the input signal voltage is not too small. There is, however, a rather serious possible cause of distortion which is unaffected by signal strength. In the typical circuit shown in Fig. 142 the load resistance, so far as d.c. is concerned, is R. But a.c. at modulation frequency has another path in parallel, via C_2 to R_2. Since the impedance of C_2 is made relatively small, the a.c. load resistance is effectively R in parallel with $R_1 + R_2$, and therefore lower than the d.c. load resistance. Now Fig. 144 shows what happens when the peak alternating current exceeds the direct current—the negative peak is flattened out. If the resistance to a.c. is less than the resistance to d.c., and the modulation is anywhere near 100%, this condition is bound to happen. So to avoid distortion of deep modulation it is advisable to make $R_1 + R_2$ several times greater than R.

THE ANODE-BEND DETECTOR

We have given most attention to the diode detector because it is by far the commonest. The closely-related grid detector has also come under notice. There is one other type important enough to be described here.

We have seen that the I_a–V_g characteristics of a triode (Fig. 93) are very similar in shape to the I_a–V_a characteristics of a diode (Fig. 90). Both are one-way current devices and therefore rectifiers.

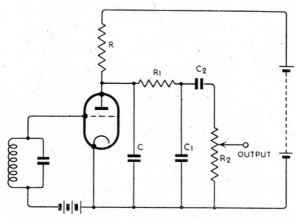

Fig. 145—Anode-bend detector circuit, which should be compared with Fig. 142

When using a triode for amplifying, one adjusts the negative grid bias to bring the working point on to the straightest part of the curve. But by increasing the bias so as nearly to cut off the anode current, we can use the valve as a detector, as in Fig. 145, where the components are marked to correspond with their equivalents in Fig. 142. This *anode-bend* detector has the advantage over the diode type that the input circuit is non-conducting—so long as the peaks of input voltage do not run into grid current. The power in the load resistance is supplied by the anode battery, instead of being taken from the tuned input circuit.

On the debit side, however, the bottom bend in the characteristic curve of a triode is generally more gradual than that of a diode, and the disadvantages described in the last two sections are consequently greater. Moreover, the remedy applicable to the diode—making

185

the input amplitude so large that the bend is relatively unimportant—does not work with the triode, because grid current would flow at the positive peaks, tending to rectify them in opposition to the negative rectification at the bend, as well as causing serious distortion.

Fig. 146 shows (top left) a typical triode I_a–V_g curve. If used as an amplifier it would be biased to about -2 V, so as to avoid the bend on the left and grid current on the right. As a detector it is here shown biased to -4 V, which reduces the anode current to about 0·2 mA. Below the V_g scale, the shading represents a carrier wave with its radio frequency too high to show each cycle individually. As in Fig. 144, its voltage dimension is horizontal, to fit the V_g scale; so the time dimension has to be vertical, from

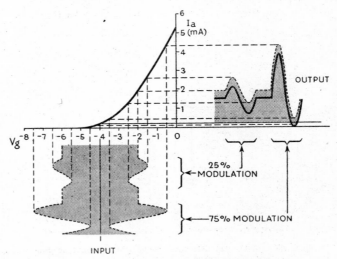

Fig. 146—Illustrating the action of the anode-bend detector with varying depth of modulation

top to bottom. It is shown first with an unmodulated amplitude of 2 V, swinging the grid from -6 V to -2 V and the anode current between 0 and nearly 2 mA, as shown to the right of the diagram. The heavy line, beginning at about 1·5 mA, indicates the d.c. level when the r.f. is smoothed out by C.

Next is shown one cycle of modulation to a depth of 25%, making the carrier wave vary between 1·5 V and 2·5 V, and causing corresponding variations in anode current. These variations occur over a steep and nearly straight part of the valve curve, so detection is efficient and nearly free from distortion. Lastly is shown a cycle of modulation at 75%. This brings the anode current down to the bend, cramping the negative half-cycle of output as shown on the extreme right. At 75% the positive peaks are at $-0·5$ V, in

186

the region where grid current starts; so 100% modulation even at this carrier voltage would not only accentuate the negative-peak distortion but would introduce positive-peak distortion as well. A greater carrier voltage would make matters worse, and a smaller carrier voltage would cause negative-peak distortion at less depth of modulation. For this and other reasons anode-bend detection is now seldom used except for special purposes.

CHAPTER 14

The Single-Valve Receiver : Reaction

THE CIRCUIT

BY NOW WE have covered enough ground to be able to discuss the behaviour of a simple type of receiver. In doing so we shall find ourselves making acquaintance with some of the incidental complications that arise when we have to deal with real circuits in place of circuits idealized to bring out their fundamental properties.

Fig. 147 shows the circuit of a single-valve receiver. The currents induced in the aerial by the wireless waves flow through the primary winding L_0, to which is inductively coupled the secondary winding L_1, this being tuned to the frequency of the desired signal by adjusting the variable capacitor C_1. The signal voltage developed across this tuned circuit is applied to the grid detector (p. 178) comprising C_2, R, and the valve. R, incidentally, is usually referred to as the *gridleak*. The detected and amplified signals in the anode circuit are passed through the headphones T and so made audible to the listener. The function of C_3 will be explained later (p. 193).

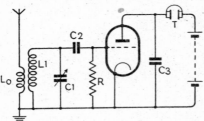

Fig. 147—Circuit of a single-valve receiver in which a triode valve is used as grid detector and amplifier of the detected signals

A separate diode detector would hardly be justified in a receiver of this kind, because the unamplified signals from the aerial would usually be less than 1 V. Moreover, we shall have a use for the r.f. part of the detector output (p. 194).

THE AERIAL COUPLING

We have already considered the problem of coupling a sender to its aerial (p. 152); now we have to couple the receiving aerial to the receiver. The same basic principles apply, and the various methods of coupling shown in Fig. 119 are used, but the aims are rather different. The main object with the sender, you may recall, was to get the maximum power into the aerial; and the purpose of the coupling was to transform the actual impedance of the aerial into the optimum load for the output valve.

At the receiving end we have the aerial picking up a small signal voltage and therefore acting as the generator. The load consists of the dynamic resistance of the tuning circuit, L_1C_1 in Fig. 147, in parallel with the detector. (The reactance of C_2 at r.f. is generally negligible.) We know how to calculate or measure the dynamic resistance (p. 110), and if we can assume that from the input side a grid detector is exactly the same as a diode detector of the Fig. 138d type we can regard its resistance as very nearly equal to $R/3$ (p. 178), and R is usually of the order of 1 MΩ. Actually, as we shall soon see, the input resistance of a grid detector may be appreciably less than $R/3$. Nevertheless, it is usually so high that the shunt path formed by the dynamic resistance of the tuning circuit is far from negligible as a load.

EFFECTS OF PRIMARY TURNS

One reasonable aim would be to develop the greatest possible voltage at the input to the detector; that is to say, across R and $L_1 C_1$. The importance of doing this came out in the previous chapter. The greatest voltage means also the greatest amount of power being delivered to R; and since in this case the " generator " e.m.f. is decidedly a " given " e.m.f., outside our control, the equal-resistance principle (p. 129) does apply. Denoting the aerial resistance by R_0 and the load resistance by R_L, we would design the coupling as a transformer having a $1 : \sqrt{(R_L/R_0)}$ turns ratio. For example, if R_0 were 0·8 kΩ and R_L were 80 kΩ, L_1 in Fig. 147 should have 10 times as many turns as L_0. L_1, being tuned, has to have the right number of turns to give it the inductance necessary to cover the wave band over which it is desired to tune; that leaves us with the primary turns as the sole variable.

But, as we noted in connection with senders (p. 153), this calculation is considerably modified in practice by the fact that in air-cored r.f. transformers the coupling is far from complete—not all the magnetic flux set up by the primary turns links all the secondary turns. The calculation with loose coupling is a good deal more involved, so at present we shall assume that conditions approximate to complete coupling. That being so, when the number of turns is adjusted to give the greatest voltage to the detector, half the aerial signal voltage is lost in the aerial resistance. The other half appears across the primary, and is multiplied by the step-up ratio (10 in our example). At the same time, the r.f. resistance of the tuning circuit is doubled by the coupling to it of the aerial resistance. This doubling can be simulated either by connecting a second resistance equal to R_L in parallel with the tuning circuit, or an equivalent resistance (p. 110) in series. Either way, the Q of the circuit is reduced to half what it would be with no aerial coupled. The selectivity (p. 105) is a half, too. The voltage appearing across the tuned circuit as the frequency of the signal is varied would under these conditions be shown by such a curve as Fig. 148a.

If the number of primary turns is reduced below the optimum amount just calculated, the voltage across L_0 is stepped up in a greater ratio, across L_1, but this benefit is more than offset by the reduction in the voltage across L_0 because its effective resistance is greatly reduced by the increase in step-up ratio and so most of the available voltage is lost in R_0. But the selectivity improves; see

189

Fig. 148*b*. On the other hand, if the primary turns are increased in number, the voltage across them increases slightly, but can never quite equal the aerial signal e.m.f., and this increase is more than offset across L_1 by the reduced step-up. Moreover, the effect of R_0 transferred to the secondary causes R to be shunted by a lower

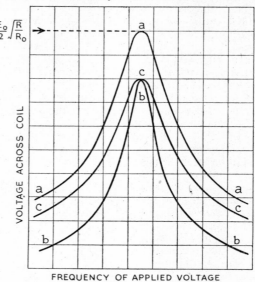

Fig. 148—(*a*) **A typical resonance curve for optimum number of primary turns in the aerial coupling transformer. If the number is reduced, signal strength at resonance is reduced, but selectivity increased (*b*). If above the optimum number, both sensitivity and selectivity are reduced (*c*)**

resistance, making the tuned circuit more heavily damped, or less selective, as shown by Fig. 148*c*.

In radio receivers, maximum signal voltage is not everything; it may be, and often is, worth sacrificing some of it in favour of selectivity. Increasing the number of primary turns above optimum, or coupling tightly, loses both signal voltage and selectivity, so has nothing in its favour; reducing it, or coupling more loosely, loses signal—not very much for a slight reduction—but gains selectivity, so is often adopted.

Another advantage of loose coupling is that less aerial reactance is transferred to the tuning circuit, and so the frequency to which this circuit resonates is less affected by the nature of the aerial used. This is particularly important when several circuits have to be simultaneously tuned by capacitors that are ganged (i.e., mounted on the same shaft).

Still another consideration is that when the capacitance is reduced in order to tune to a higher frequency, the dynamic resistance is increased, causing greater signal voltage, and the selectivity is reduced. Simultaneously, assuming the number of primary turns to be so small that in combination with the capacitance of the aerial it tunes to a higher frequency than any in the waveband covered by the tuning capacitor, the aerial circuit is brought nearer resonance, and so the signal voltage is greater for this reason also. When tuning to the lower frequency end of the band, the reverse takes place, and signal strength is relatively poor. To obtain a more uniform signal strength and selectivity over the waveband, the primary coil is often given a large enough number of turns to make it " peak " (i.e., resonate) beyond the *low*-frequency end of the band, to offset the falling dynamic resistance at that end. To prevent this from causing tremendous damping, the primary and secondary coils are placed so that only a small proportion of magnetic flux links both; thus the coupling is actually quite loose.

Lastly, an aerial, regarded as an impedance, is not just a simple fixed resistance, as we have conveniently assumed, nor are all aerials alike. The impedance of any one aerial varies greatly according to the frequency.

Taking all these matters into account, then, the practical design of the aerial coupling transformer is a complex problem.

TUNING RANGE

As you may remember (p. 107), the range of frequencies (or wavelengths) covered by a variable capacitor is equal to the square root of the capacitance range. So if we want to cover the European medium-wave broadcasting band, 525–1,605 kc/s, the capacitance variation must be $(1,605/525)^2 : 1$, or $9 \cdot 35 : 1$. If the variable part of the total tuning capacitance is, say, 500 pF, and C denotes the fixed part made up of the capacitance of the tuning capacitor at its minimum and the capacitances of the valve and its holder, the wiring, the terminals or tags to which the ends of L_1 are brought, and the capacitance transferred from the aerial through the primary L_0, then $(500 + C)/C$ must at least equal $9 \cdot 35$; that is, C must not exceed $500/8 \cdot 35 = 60$ pF. This can usually just be managed with a little care.

The value of L_1 can then be calculated as explained on page 107, and in this case works out at 164 μH.

MILLER EFFECT

In addition to the tuned-circuit damping due to the various items from aerial to valve grid that we lumped together as R_L, there is another effect, named after its discoverer, J. M. Miller, due to the voltages developed in the anode circuit and to the small capacitance between the anode and the grid of the valve. In Fig. 149— a conventional diagram of a valve used as an amplifier—the impedance in the anode circuit is represented by Z_a. This may be a resistance, a capacitance, or an inductance. C_{ga} represents the total capacitance between grid and anode, which is partly in the

191

valve electrodes themselves and their leads, and partly in the valve base, the valve holder, and the wiring.

Since the amplifying action of the valve produces a signal voltage at the anode, a small signal current flows through C_{ga} and the grid circuit to the cathode of the valve. In flowing through the components in the grid circuit, this current develops across them a voltage, and this voltage may have any phase relationship with the voltage already present due to the signal. If it were in phase with the original signal voltage the two would simply add, and the original voltage would be increased. If it were 180° out of phase, on the other hand, this new voltage would be in opposition to that already there, and the energy fed through C_{ga} would tend to damp out and reduce the signal voltage. In a third case the voltage fed back from the anode might be 90° out of phase with that already present, and would therefore neither help nor hinder it, but would produce the same effect as a reactance.

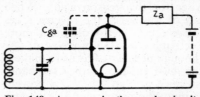

Fig. 149—Any a.c. in the anode circuit passes through the impedance Z_a and sets up alternating voltages at the anode. Current, due to these, passing through C_{ga} affects the grid circuit in varying ways according to the phase of Z_a

In general there will be a combination of this with one of the other two.

Let us first consider the case in which Z_a is a resistance, because we have already seen (p. 125) that the signal voltage at the anode of a resistance-coupled amplifier is opposite in polarity to that applied to the grid, and A times as great (where A denotes the stage amplification). Therefore every signal volt applied to the grid causes $A + 1$ volts between anode and grid. Consider Fig. 150a, in which C is a capacitor hidden in a box, in series with a special sort of meter that measures the charge passing into the capacitor when the switch is closed. As capacitance is equal to the charge required to raise the p.d. across it to 1 V (p. 57), we have here a means of measuring C. But suppose, b, that a demon in the box connects an A-volt battery in series with C whenever we connect our 1-volt battery. The charging voltage is $A + 1$ volts, and the meter indicates a charge $A + 1$ times as large as it would without the demoniacal activity. Knowing nothing of this, we conclude that the box contains a capacitor having a capacitance $A + 1$ times as large as C. So far as external electrical tests can tell, the boxes b and c are identical.

Thus the effect of the grid-to-anode capacitance C_{ga} is to make our resistance-coupled amplifier behave as if a capacitance $A + 1$ times as large as C_{ga} were connected across the tuned circuit L_1C_1. As A might be 50 or more, the result is serious.

If Z_a is an inductance, the energy fed back reinforces and increases the signal voltage on the grid, perhaps sufficiently to set up continuous oscillation, as in the T.A.T.G. oscillator (Fig. 107), which depends on this principle.

If Z_a is a capacitance, the fed-back energy tends to damp out the voltage already present. The damping effect on the grid circuit can be exactly imitated by reducing the value of R_L in our previous calculation. Since the whole effect depends on the alternating voltage at the anode, changes in magnitude of this will alter the value of the equivalent damping resistance R_L. The higher the impedance of Z_a (since we are considering the case where this is a capacitance, the lower the value of this capacitance) the higher will be the voltage developed, and hence the greater the damping effect in the grid circuit, represented by a low value of R_L.

The damping due to a small value for C_3 in Fig. 147 can be very serious indeed; with C_3 omitted altogether, so that the anode-circuit for r.f. currents consists only of the stray capacitances across valve, valve-holder, and phones, the energy fed back from anode to grid may be equivalent, for a signal at 1,000 kc/s, to connecting a resistance of as low a value as 5 kΩ between grid and cathode. Since the dynamic

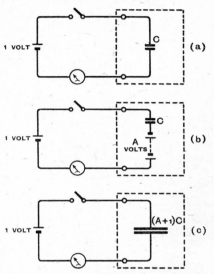

Fig. 150—Showing how the introduction of an extra voltage, such as that fed back from anode to grid in a valve, can be equivalent to a multiplied capacitance

resistance of the tuned circuit L_1C_1 will probably be twenty times as great as this, the effect of the damping in dropping signal strength and flattening tuning is catastrophic.

At very high frequencies, a similar result follows an entirely different cause—the appreciable time (relative to one cycle of r.f.) taken by electrons to cross the space inside the valve. The phase lag at the grid due to this *transit-time effect* is equivalent to a lowering of the valve's input resistance, causing increased damping.

THE ANODE BY-PASS

So C_3 in Fig. 147 is inserted as a low impedance to the r.f. currents, in order that the r.f. voltage developed at the anode may be as low as possible.

There is a limit to the reduction in damping that can be effected in this way, because although from the r.f. point of view the greater the capacitance of C_3 the better, we have to remember that there are audio-frequency voltages that we do want. Fortunately the reactance of C_3 is much greater at a.f., so they are not suppressed so effectively as the r.f. If we make C_3 about 0·001 μF, its reactance at 1,000 kc/s will be little more than 150 Ω, while at the higher a.f. (5 kc/s) it will rise to 30 kΩ, which will not be a very serious shunt to the phones, and so will not cause too great a diversion of high notes from their windings. Like almost every other item in a wireless set, the choice of a capacitance for C_3 is a compromise between conflicting requirements.

REACTION

Instead of striving to prevent all feed-back from the anode to the grid circuit, we can deliberately introduce it, so arranging matters that we have it completely under control. This can be done by inserting in the anode circuit a coil L_2, as in Fig. 151. As the diagram shows, this coil is close to L_1, in order to couple with it inductively, the arrow running through them indicating that their relative positions can be adjusted as required.

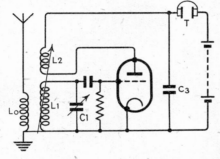

Fig. 151—Single-valve receiver as in Fig. 147, with the addition of adjustable reaction (L_2)

The r.f. current flowing in the anode circuit now passes through L_2 on its way to C_3. In doing so it sets up around L_2 a r.f. flux which, in passing also through L_1, induces a voltage in it. By connecting L_2 in the right direction this voltage can be made either to assist or to oppose the voltage already there, the effect in either case becoming more marked as L_2 is brought closer to L_1. We now have the reaction-coil oscillator circuit of Fig. 103. The fact that the grid circuit is tuned instead of the anode is a minor variation. The only essential difference is that now we are coupling too loosely to maintain oscillation.

We saw how tuned-circuit damping, or resistance, which causes oscillation to die out, can be completely neutralized by a sufficiently closely-coupled reaction coil, so that oscillation continues indefinitely and without any external source. That would not suit our purpose in a receiver, because we want the strength of oscillation in the tuned circuit to depend from moment to moment on what is coming in from the distant sender. What happens when the reaction coil is coupled in the direction that tends to cause continuous oscillation, but too loosely to do so, is that oscillations set up by the signals derived from the aerial build up more strongly (because they are reinforced by the induced voltage from the anode) and die away less quickly, just as if the series resistance of the tuned circuit were less, or (what is the same thing) its dynamic resistance greater.

194

Of course, reaction does not neutralize resistance in any literal physical sense. The essential characteristic of resistance is its absorption of power (p. 54), if, therefore, we supply synchronized power from the anode circuit of a valve, the circuit in which that resistance is located behaves as though it had lost some of its resistance. The valve is used as a source because it is only by making the voltage itself (in the grid circuit) control the power used to enhance it that the two can be locked unalterably together in the required phase.

In discussing tuned circuits (pp. 104–6) we saw that reduction of r.f. resistance increases both the magnification (Q) and the selectivity of a tuned circuit. With the aid of a valve to provide reaction we have the ability to adjust the resistance of the tuned circuit L_1C_1 to any value we want, simply by moving L_2 cautiously towards L_1 until the resistance has been reduced to the desired extent. As we do this the voltage developed by the signal across L_1C_1 steadily rises and the tuning becomes steadily sharper.

The effect on the tuned circuit can best be visualized with the aid of a series of resonance curves. In Fig. 152 the voltage across L_1C_1 is plotted against frequency for a number of values of Q.

A glance will show that as Q is increased by applying

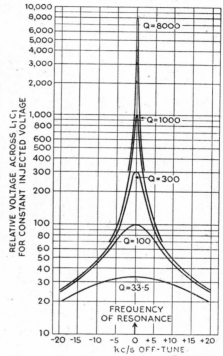

Fig. 152—Showing how r.f. voltage across a tuned circuit varies with frequency at different Q values, obtained by adjusting the reaction control

reaction the signal voltage rapidly rises* and the sharpness of tuning, as measured by the ratio of the voltage at resonance to that developed a few kilocycles off tune, becomes greater.

So great is the increase that it could not be shown on a curve sheet like those in Chapter 8; a logarithmic scale of relative voltage is necessary, and compared with Fig. 78 the rise is greater than it looks.

* The relative heights of the peaks are calculated on the basis of constant injected voltage. This ignores the reaction of L_1C_1 upon L_0, the aerial primary.

The lowest curve represents the behaviour of a tuned circuit of normal r.f. resistance connected to a detector. With the reaction coil out of use the circuit assumed has L = 155 μH, r = 10 Ω, and is supposed to be tuned to 1,000 kc/s. Detector damping across it is taken as 50 kΩ. For the tuned circuit alone, Q = 98, R = 95 kΩ; with detector damping in parallel the total dynamic resistance is reduced to 32·6 kΩ, making the equivalent r.f. resistance 29·2 Ω and reducing the effective Q to 33·5. The curve next in order (Q = 100) represents the same tuned circuit with the effects of detector damping almost exactly offset by the judicious application of reaction. Successive curves show the effect of more and more reaction, culminating in the extreme case where the magnification has been increased to 8,000, which is about the highest value known to have been reached, and held, by this means. It corresponds to the neutralization of all natural resistance of the circuit except for a small residue of about one-eighth of an ohm.

OVER-SHARP TUNING

At first sight it might appear that the reduction of circuit resistance to such low limits as this would be all to the good, since it would increase both the sensitivity and the selectivity of the receiver. If we had to receive only a simple carrier wave this conclusion would be true, but we must remember that the signal from a broadcasting station consists of a *modulated* carrier. As we have seen, the modulation consists of a variation in the amplitude of the carrier at the frequency of the musical note it is desired to transmit. We know also (p. 133) that if a tuned circuit had no resistance at all, any oscillation that might be set up in it would persist after the removal of the signal source, unchanged in amplitude, for ever. Such a circuit would evidently be quite incapable of following the rapid variations in amplitude of a modulated carrier.

It follows, therefore, that as we approach towards zero resistance by a greater and greater application of reaction, the voltage across the tuned circuit will be more and more sluggish in following the modulation. For the highest audible notes the r.f. voltage has to change in amplitude most rapidly; as the resistance of the tuned circuit is decreased these will therefore become weak and vanish at a value of resistance still high enough to enable the low notes, for which the variations in amplitude of the carrier are proportionately slower, to remain substantially unaffected.

The high, sharp peak of a very low-resistance circuit such as that giving the curve "Q = 8,000", therefore, tells us that high modulation-frequencies cannot be followed. On the other hand, the flatter curves such as that for Q = 100, indicate a resistance high enough for any current through the circuit to die away rapidly unless maintained by a driving voltage, thus enabling the voltage-variations across L_1C_1 to be a faithful copy of the signal as received from the aerial.

The Theory of Sidebands

By regarding the modulated wave from another point of view, the relationship between sharpness of tuning and the loss of high notes can be shown to be much closer than has been suggested. Strictly speaking, it is only an exactly recurrent phenomenon that can be said to possess a definite frequency. The continuous change in amplitude of the carrier wave in response to modulation makes the r.f. cycle of the modulated wave non-recurrent, so that in acquiring its amplitude variations it has lost its constancy of frequency.

A mathematical analysis shows that if a carrier of f_1 cycles per second is modulated at a frequency f_2 cycles per second the modulated wave is exactly the same as the result of adding together three separate waves of frequencies f_1, $(f_1 + f_2)$, and $(f_1 - f_2)$. It is not easy to perform the analysis of the modulated wave into its three components by a graphical process, but the corresponding synthesis,

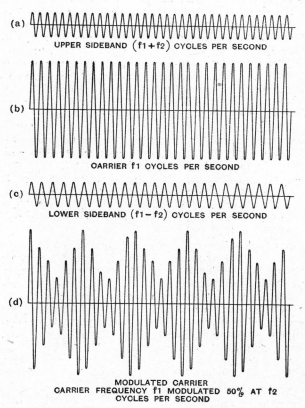

(a)

UPPER SIDEBAND $(f1+f2)$ CYCLES PER SECOND

(b)

CARRIER f1 CYCLES PER SECOND

(c)

LOWER SIDEBAND $(f1-f2)$ CYCLES PER SECOND

(d)

MODULATED CARRIER
CARRIER FREQUENCY f1 MODULATED 50% AT f2
CYCLES PER SECOND

Fig. 153—Showing that a modulated carrier wave (d) is identical with three unmodulated waves (a, b and c) added together

197

adding together three separate waves, requires nothing more than rather extensive patience.

Fig. 153 shows at a, b, and c three separate sine-wave trains, there being 35, 30, and 25 complete cycles, respectively, in the length of the diagram. By adding the heights of these curves point by point, the composite curve at d is obtained. There are in its length 30 peaks of varying amplitude, and the amplitude rises and falls five times in the period of time represented on the figure. If this is a thousandth part of a second, curve d represents what we have come to know as a 30 kc/s carrier amplitude-modulated at 5 kc/s. Fig. 153 shows it to be identical with three constant-amplitude wave-trains having frequencies of 30, 30 + 5, and 30 − 5 kc/s.

Thus a carrier modulated at a single frequency is equivalent to three simultaneous signals, the unmodulated carrier itself and two associated steady frequencies spaced away from the carrier on either side by the frequency of modulation. In a musical programme, in which a number of modulation frequencies are simultaneously present, the carrier is surrounded by a whole family of extra frequencies. Those representing the lowest musical notes are close to the carrier on either side, those bringing the middle notes are farther out, and the highest notes are the farthest removed from the carrier frequency. This *spectrum* of associated frequencies on each side of the carrier is called a *sideband*, and as a result of their presence a musical programme, nominally transmitted on a frequency of 1,000 kc/s, spreads over a band of frequencies extending from about 993 to 1,007 kc/s.

The same facts can be illustrated by a vector diagram. In such a diagram, as we know, a single unmodulated carrier-wave of frequency f is represented by a vector such as OP in Fig. 47, pivoted at one end (O) and rotating f times per second. The length of the vector represents (to some convenient scale) the peak voltage or current, and the vertical " projection " PQ represents the instantaneous value, which of course becomes alternately positive and negative once in each cycle.

If this were related to a waveform diagram such as Fig. 153, it should be clear that amplitude modulation would be represented by a gradual alternate lengthening and shortening of the vector as it rotated. Thus, modulation of a 600 kc/s carrier to a depth of 50% at a frequency of 1 kc/s would be represented by a vector revolving 600,000 times per second, and at the same time increasing and decreasing in length by 50% once during each 600 revolutions.

The attempt to visualize this rapid rotation makes one quite dizzy, so once we have granted the correctness of the vector representation we may forget about the rotation and focus our entire attention on how the alternate growing and dwindling can be brought about by vectorial means.

OP in Fig. 154a, then, is the original unmodulated-carrier vector, now stationary. Add to it two other vectors, each one quarter the length of OP. If they are both in the same direction as OP, they increase its length by 50%; if in the opposite direction they decrease it by 50%. The intermediate stages, corresponding to sinusoidal modulation, are represented by the two small vectors rotating *in opposite directions* at modulation frequency. Various stages in one cycle of modulation are shown at Fig. 154*b–j*, the total length

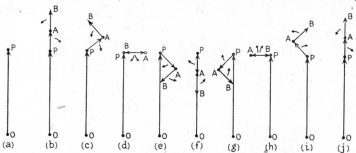

Fig. 154—Progressive series of vector diagrams, showing how adding a pair of oppositely-rotating vectors (PA and AB) alternately lengthens and shortens the original vector (OP) without affecting its phase

of all three vectors added together being OB in every case. Notice that in spite of the small vectors going through complete 360° cycles of phase relative to OP, the triple combination OB is always exactly in phase with OP. It therefore gives the true lengthening and shortening effect we wanted.

Having agreed about this, we can now set OP rotating at 600,000 r.p.s. again. In order to maintain the cycle of changes shown in Fig. 154 the little vector AB will therefore have to rotate at 600,000 r.p.s. plus once in every 600; that is, 601,000: while PA must rotate at 600,000 less once in every 600; 599,000.

Translated back into electrical terms, this confirms the statement that amplitude-modulating a carrier-wave of f_1 c/s at a frequency of f_2 c/s creates side-frequencies, $f_1 + f_2$ and $f_1 - f_2$. And Fig. 154 also shows that the amplitude of each of these side-waves relative to that of the carrier is *half* the percentage modulation.

We now have a direct relationship between the selectivity of a tuned circuit and its ability to receive the highest notes likely to be present as modulation on the carrier. If the resonance curve of the circuit is not substantially flat over a central portion wide enough to include the whole of the required sidebands, high notes will be attenuated—they will be quite literally tuned out owing to over-selectivity. In the curve for Q = 8,000, in Fig. 152, the sidebands corresponding to a modulation frequency of 5 kc/s are shown as being magnified only about 1·3% as much as the central carrier frequency. Lower notes are more fully preserved; higher notes even more greatly attenuated. The result is " woolly " and more or less unintelligible speech, and " boomy " music. For a tuned circuit in which Q = 100, however, 5 kc/s notes are passed at 70% of the carrier amplitude.

It is clear from these considerations that high selectivity is not an unmixed blessing, and that too much reaction sharpens tuning to such a point that the quality of the received programme suffers badly. Nevertheless reaction is useful for neutralizing the losses due to detector damping in a simple receiver of this kind, and may, without serious detriment to quality, be pressed far enough to halve or even quarter the natural resistance of a tuned circuit. But much greater amplification than this is needed for the successful reception of distant stations.

CHAPTER 15

Radio-Frequency Amplification: Screened Valves

INCREASING RANGE

IN OUR STUDY of detectors we noted that the effectiveness of all types deteriorated very rapidly as the r.f. voltage was reduced much below about 1 V. Signals picked up by the receiving aerial are seldom more than a few millivolts, and are more often only microvolts; so, even when magnified to some extent by the tuned circuit, they would be far too weak to operate a detector effectively—to say nothing of distortion.

Although the grid type of detector amplifies in addition to detecting, such amplification takes place after detection and therefore does nothing to improve the efficiency of the process. It can, however, be used to feed back amplified r.f. power to the tuned circuit, increasing its magnification and with it the r.f. voltage reaching the detector; but we have just seen that to bring weak signals up to a workable strength in this way discriminates undesirably between different modulation frequencies, and also demands very careful adjustment. For very wide-band modulation, such as television, even the unaided resonance peak may be too sharp and in need of flattening rather than further sharpening by reaction!

So the only real solution to the problem of providing sufficient input to operate the detector satisfactorily is to amplify *before* detection.

SIMPLE RESISTANCE COUPLING

At first it might seem that the desired result could be obtained by putting a resistance-coupled amplifier valve, as described on

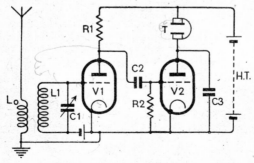

Fig. 155—This resistance-coupled amplifier is of little or no value for r.f. amplification

page 124, between the tuned circuit (L_1C_1 in Fig. 155) and the detector V_2. The r.f. voltage developed across L_1C_1 would be reproduced on an enlarged scale across R_1 (or so we were given to understand in Chapter 9), and would be passed to the detector (grid type or otherwise) by the capacitor C_2 which, as explained in connection with Fig. 138d, serves the double purpose of detector reservoir and of protecting the detector from the steady positive voltage at the anode of V_1.

If one tries this circuit in practice, the result is exceedingly disappointing. More likely than not, reception will be worse than it was without the amplifier. Yet it looks all right according to the book.

The snag, as in Miller effect, is one of the " invisible components " —this time the stray capacitance in parallel with the coupling resistance R_1. The valve V_1 itself contributes a quota—the capacitance between its anode and cathode. Although this may not look much as if it were in parallel with R_1, it is effectively so via the low-impedance path formed by the anode supply (or " h.t. ") battery. Similarly, the input capacitance of V_2 is added, via C_2. And then there is the wiring and the valve-holders. A typical total would be 40 pF, which, at say 1 Mc/s, is a reactance of about 4 kΩ. No matter how high a resistance may be chosen for R_1, the effective coupling impedance cannot exceed this figure. With so low a load, V_1 will not give very much amplification; a gain of about five times is as much as can be expected.

But this is not all. The anode load being, as we have just seen, predominantly capacitive, the Miller effect will be of the type which damps the input circuit heavily (p. 193). In the detector we reduced this damping to reasonable limits by connecting a capacitor direct from anode to cathode in order to reduce the r.f. voltage at the anode as nearly as possible to zero; we were then wanting only the rectified a.f. signals. Obviously we cannot do this to V_1, because even the stray capacitance is too much. In typical circumstances, the Miller damping with no intentional anode by-pass for V_1 would damp the r.f. grid voltage down to about one-twentieth.

With V_1 amplifying this reduced signal five times, the voltage finally delivered to V_2 would be a quarter of that developed across L_1C_1 unaided. On the whole, not a very successful amplifier.

THE TUNED-ANODE CIRCUIT

What is wanted now is some means of neutralizing the stray capacitance. As we know, inductance is such a means; so we connect in parallel with R_1 the amount of inductance to give a reactance equal (but opposite) to that of the stray capacitance. Since the coil used to provide this inductance will serve to bring the necessary positive voltage to the anode of V_1 more effectively even than R_1, the latter can be removed as superfluous. The inductance to provide a given neutralizing reactance depends on the frequency, as does also the reactance to be neutralized—in

202

the opposite way. An alternative to varying the inductance in order to tune to different signal frequencies is to vary the capacitance, as shown in Fig. 156.

The diagram shows that LC is connected, as a tuned rejector circuit, in place of the original coupling resistance. The stray capacitance in parallel now has no more effect than making it necessary to reduce C a little below the value at which resonance would be attained with no stray. At the frequency of resonance, LC behaves as a high resistance R—the dynamic resistance L/Cr of the circuit (p. 112). We have therefore achieved the equivalent (as regards signals of resonant frequency) of the unrealizable pure resistance-coupled arrangement of Fig. 155, with two advantages added. Of these, the minor advantage is avoiding the loss of anode supply voltage in the resistance R_1. The major advantage is to improve the selectivity, as will be discussed at length in the next chapter.

The amplification given by a tuned-anode stage is calculated by the simple formula $A = \mu R/(R + r_a)$ given on page 127 for a resistance-coupled stage, R being interpreted as the dynamic resistance of the anode tuning circuit.

We have found a remedy for loss of amplification due to stray capacitance from anode to earth (or equivalent parts of the circuit), for there is no difficulty at ordinary broadcast frequencies in obtaining a coupling impedance of the order of 100 kΩ by means of LC. The effect of the anode-to-grid capacitance remains to be seen, however.

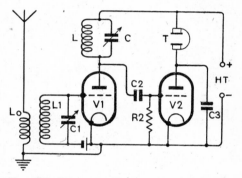

Fig. 156—The stray capacitances that rendered the Fig. 155 circuit ineffective can be tuned out by inductance, as in this tuned-anode circuit

GRID-ANODE CAPACITANCE

So long as the anode circuit is exactly tuned to the frequency of the signal being received, the anode circuit of the valve is purely resistive, and voltage fed back through C_{ga} (Fig. 157) neither assists nor damps down the voltage on the grid but merely makes it necessary to use less of C_1 for tuning to a given frequency. If the applied frequency (or alternatively the capacitance of C) is now increased, slightly more current flows through C than through L, so that the anode circuit becomes capacitive. The fed-back voltage will then, as we have seen, tend to damp out the signal.

If, on the other hand, the applied frequency (or alternatively the capacitance of C) is reduced, more current flows through L than

203

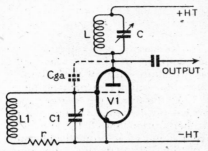

Fig. 157—The grid-to-anode capacitance of V1 (C_{ga}) causes difficulty in working the tuned-anode amplifier

through C, giving us an inductive anode circuit. Now the coupling provided by C_{ga} between the two tuned circuits will feed back energy that assists and builds up the voltage already present. We have, in all essentials, the tuned-anode tuned-grid circuit of Fig. 107.

INSTABILITY

Our amplifier circuit therefore turns out to be an oscillator circuit. That does not necessarily mean that it will actually oscillate. It will not do so unless the voltage fed back via C_{ga} is at least as great as that causing the anode voltage, and is in phase with it. In an amplifier of the type considered, the risk is so great as to be a certainty. The better the system is as an amplifier, the more likely it is to oscillate. Thus, if the stage gain is 50 times, it is necessary for only one-fiftieth of the anode voltage to find its way back to the grid in order to cause oscillation.

With coils of fairly good design (low r, or high dynamic resistance) and any ordinary triode, oscillation appears every time an attempt is made to bring L_1C_1 and LC into resonance with the same frequency. Although there is no tendency to oscillate at the exact frequency to which both circuits are tuned, at a very slightly lower frequency the conditions for oscillation exist.

In a receiver, oscillation results in a rushing noise, and in loud whistles and squeaks as the set is tuned. For practical purposes, therefore, the circuit of Fig. 157 is unusable.

When the triode was the only valve available, oscillation due to feed-back through C_{ga} was prevented by an elaboration of the circuit, whereby a r.f. voltage in opposite phase was fed to the grid through a small adjustable *neutralizing* capacitor. By this means the feed-back through the valve capacitance was cancelled out. But because neutralizing circuits need careful adjustment triodes have been superseded, for receivers at least, by valves in which the grid-anode capacitance has been practically eliminated by screening.

THE THEORY OF SCREENING

The capacitance between any two objects can be reduced to zero by placing between them as a screen an earthed metal sheet of sufficient size. The operation of such a screen can be understood by considering Fig. 158a, in which a stray capacitance is represented by two plates A and B separated from one another by an air-space. The a.c. generator E will therefore drive a current round the circuit

204

E a r t h—E—A—B—Z_1—
Earth. Across Z_1, which
is an impedance of some
kind between B and earth,
the current will develop a
potential difference, and
this p.d. will be the voltage
appearing on B as a result
of current passing through
the capacitance AB.

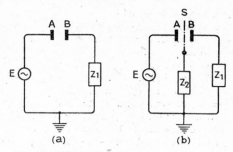

Fig. 158—Illustrating the theory of screening

At b a third plate S,
larger than either of the
two original plates, is
inserted between them in such a way that no part of either plate
can " see " any part of the other.   We now have no direct
capacitance between A and B, but we have instead two capacitances,
AS and SB, in series.   If an impedance Z_2 is connected between S
and earth the current round the circuit Earth—E—A—S—Z_2—Earth
will develop a p.d. across Z_2.   Since Z_2 is also included in the right-
hand circuit the voltage across it will drive a current round the
circuit Earth—Z_2—S—B—Z_1—Earth, and this will give rise to a
potential on B.   So far, S has not screened A from B;   there remains
an effective capacitance between them which, if Z_2 is infinitely large,
amounts to the capacitance equivalent to that of AS and SB in
series.   If S is thin this is practically equal to the original direct
capacitance between the two plates.

Now imagine Z_2 to be short-circuited.   Current will flow round
the first circuit, but since there is now no impedance common to
both there will be no driving voltage to produce a current in the
latter.   No matter what alternating voltages are applied to A, none
will appear on B, even though large currents may flow via S to
earth.   The effective capacitance between A and B has therefore
been reduced to zero, and B is completely screened from A.

It is very important to note that S is only effective as a screen if it
is definitely connected to earth either by a direct wire or through an
impedance Z_2 which is negligibly small.

THE SCREENED VALVE

This is the principle used in reducing the grid-anode capacitance
of a valve.   A screen is put between anode and grid within the
bulb, while capacitance between the wires running to grid and
anode is avoided by taking one or other of them out through the
top of the bulb.   Alternatively the screening is extended down to
and below the base, allowing both anode and grid to be brought
out at the same end.

Clearly, a solid metal sheet, while providing irreproachable
screening, would cut off the electron flow from cathode to anode.
The screen actually used therefore consists either of metal gauze
or a wire grid similar to the first or control grid.   The spaces

205

between the wires, while allowing electrons to pass freely, affect the screening remarkably little. In an unscreened valve, C_{ga} is usually of the order of 1 to 6 pF; with a screen as described, this is commonly reduced to less than 0·01 pF, and may even be less than 0·003 pF.

If the screen were earthed by connecting it straight to cathode, it would cut off the attraction of the positive anode; electrons near the grid would then not be drawn onwards, and the anode current would fall practically to zero. But since, as Fig. 158 shows, the requirements of screening can be met by making Z_2 negligibly small, we can connect a large capacitance between the screen grid and cathode of the valve, and then supply a suitable positive potential to the screen grid.

The portion of the valve comprising cathode, control grid, and screen grid is a triode, and could be used as one, the screen grid acting as an anode. The current through the valve is practically unaffected by whatever voltage may be connected to the real anode, because its electric field is screened off. But if, as is usual, the screen grid is given a potential of the order of + 100 V, the electrons from the cathode are accelerated towards it so rapidly that unless they chance to hit one of its wires they go right through. What happens to them then depends on the potential of the anode. If it is zero or less, practically all the electrons are attracted back to the screen grid, just as a ball thrown up into the air reverses and comes back. But if the anode is substantially positive it attracts and retains those electrons that come near it. Since the number that do so depends mainly on the potential of the screen grid and very little on the potential of the anode, increasing the positive anode voltage beyond a certain amount has very little effect on the anode current.

Thus, the total current through the valve (at a given control-grid voltage) is decided mainly by the screen-grid potential, but the way it is shared between screen-grid and anode depends also on the anode potential.

CHARACTERISTICS OF A SCREENED VALVE

This can be seen more clearly by looking at Fig. 159, which shows anode current plotted against anode voltage in an early type of screened *tetrode* (as a four-electrode valve is called). It would be as well at this point to take note of the standard system of referring to the electrodes, and their voltages and currents. In valves having, like this one, more than one grid, the grids are numbered, beginning with the one nearest the cathode. So the control-grid is called g_1 and the screen grid g_2. V_{g2} and I_{g2} mean respectively the voltage of the screen grid and the current collected by it—all voltages, as usual, being reckoned relative to the cathode, which is denoted by k. The standard symbols for the various kinds of valves are shown on page 319.

Looking now at the curves in Fig. 159, we see that the anode current is controlled by V_{g1}, just as in a triode. But the shape of each curve is quite different from the corresponding triode curves. Concentrate for the moment on the right-hand portions, where V_a is appreciably greater than V_{g2} (80 V in this case). The anode current increases only very slightly with increasing anode voltage.

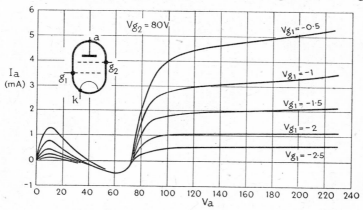

Fig. 159—Characteristic curves of a screened tetrode of the original type, which has now gone out of use

Another way of putting this is to say that r_a is far higher than in a comparable triode. For the curve $V_{g1} = -1.5$, the change of I_a by 0·2 mA for a 100-V change in V_a indicates $r_a = 100/0·2 = 500$ kΩ.

But a 1-V change in V_{g1} in this region alters I_a by about 2 mA, so g_m is 2 mA/V. Deriving μ in the usual way, (p. 122) we have $\mu = 500 \times 2 = 1,000$. So the introduction of the screen grid not only eliminates most of C_{ga} but also has quite a startling effect on the amplification factor and a.c. resistance. Besides being both much higher, they vary considerably more with the electrode voltages than in a triode, where they are determined mainly by the dimensions and spacing of the electrodes. The mutual conductance, however, is quite normal, since the influence of the control grid is almost unaffected by the division in the structure beyond it.

Although the right-hand portions of the curves in Fig. 159 agree with expectations, the left-hand portions certainly do not. What is the explanation of the strange hollow?

SECONDARY EMISSION

If the only effect of raising the anode voltage, beginning at zero, were to rob g_2 of more and more electrons, I_a–V_a curves would take forms such as that shown dotted in Fig. 160. But when electrons are made to bombard electrodes, they often dislodge electrons already there. This effect is called secondary emission.

207

Once liberated, these secondary electrons are free to be attracted by the most positively charged object in the neighbourhood, just as if they had been emitted in the regular way from a cathode. Secondary emission is not noticeable with a triode, because the only electrode to be bombarded violently enough is the anode, and, as it is the most positive electrode around, the secondary electrons all fall back on to it. But the situation is different in a tetrode.

As the anode voltage is raised from zero, the curve of I_a at first follows the dotted line (A). All the secondary emission from g_2 returns to it, and V_a is not high enough for secondary emission

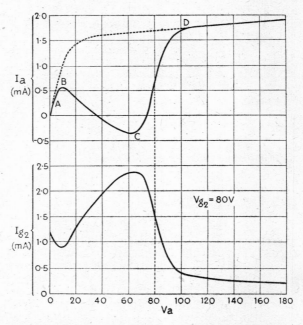

Fig. 160—The dotted line indicates the shape the anode-current curve would take but for secondary emission, which in tetrodes causes the curious departure BC. The corresponding variation in screen-grid current is graphed below

from the anode. At about point B, anode secondary emission begins; and as g_2 is so much more positive it collects it all. So secondary emission is a dead loss to the anode; hence the falling off in anode current. Increasing V_a has, as we know, little effect on the number of electrons arriving, but it increases the emission and hence the number leaving. So we have the paradoxical situation that increasing V_a reduces I_a. This is represented by the negative slope between B and C, and by the statement that r_a (over this range of V_a) is negative. Such a statement about a real ohmic resistance would, of course, be nonsense, but as we have seen (p. 119), r_a is just a convenient pretence.

Some types of electrode surface emit more than one secondary electron, on the average, for each primary electron, resulting in a negative anode current such as that indicated near C.

Beyond this point, as V_a approaches and then exceeds V_{g2}, increasing numbers of secondary electrons return to the anode, until finally none escape to g_2 and the valve curve rejoins the dotted line at D. Above this point, secondary emission has no effect on the net anode current.

The shape of the I_{g2} curve, shown below, is like the I_a curve upside down. If I_a and I_{g2} are added together, they come to nearly the same at all anode voltages, confirming the statement that the total " space " current in the valve is scarcely affected by V_a. I_{g2}, which is wasted, is made as small as possible by careful design of the valve electrodes.

THE SCREENED PENTODE

The secondary emission effects just described make a big hole in the useful range of anode voltage, for they render the valve unsuitable for amplification unless V_a is at all times substantially greater than V_{g2}. Not only is there some inconvenience in having to supply the two electrodes at different voltages, but if the valve is intended for handling a considerable signal voltage (say, to feed a diode detector) one must take care that the negative half-cycles do not bring the anode potential on to the steep slope, where the sudden change in r_a would cause distortion.

Several methods have been found for eliminating the secondary-emission " kink ", giving characteristic curves like the dotted line in Fig. 160. The most used of these is to insert between the screen grid and anode a third grid, called (for obvious reasons) the *suppressor grid*. Such a valve, having five electrodes, is called a *pentode*. The suppressor grid, g_3, is normally connected to cathode, so is at zero volts, and therefore prevents any secondary electrons from crossing between anode and g_2. The faster-moving primary electrons have sufficient momentum to carry them past g_3 into the zone of anode attraction.

In many types of pentode, g_3 is brought out to a separate connection instead of being connected internally to the cathode, and is thereby made available for certain special uses.

The addition of g_3, kept at constant zero potential, tends to reduce still further the influence of the anode voltage on the space current; in other words, the pentode has a higher r_a, and consequently a higher μ, than a corresponding tetrode. Since, in a r.f. amplifier, r_a acts as a shunt across the tuned circuit, the higher it is the less the damping.

Pentodes thus have several advantages over the type of tetrode described, which is now obsolete: a possible slight improvement in selectivity due to reduced damping; the availability for signal

209

handling of the whole range of anode voltage down to about 20 V; and the simplification of being able to supply V_a from the same source as V_{g2}.

KINKLESS TETRODES

An alternative method of preventing secondary electrons from being attracted to the screen grid is to increase the distance between it and the anode sufficiently for the negative space-charge (p. 118) of the stream of electrons flowing towards the anode to neutralize the positive attraction of the screen. This distance is critical because if too great the electrons will be turned back from the anode. So this type of valve is sometimes called the critical-distance tetrode.

In other types of tetrode the electrons passing through the control grid are constricted into definite beams, like rays of light passing through a grating, by the action of " beam-forming " plates connected to cathode; and the screen grid wires are aligned so as to come in the " shadows " of the control grid wires.

Both of these types of kinkless tetrode tend to show a slight advantage over the pentode if the utmost signal power is to be handled, by retaining the nearly flat top to the I_a–V_a curve down to a lower anode voltage, before falling down to zero; as one says, the curve has a sharper knee. There is no great call for this in a r.f. amplifier, but it is one of the primary aims in an a.f. output stage, as we shall see in Chapter 17. With the possible exception of the sharper knee, there is nothing to distinguish characteristics of kinkless tetrodes from those of pentodes. From now on, mention of pentodes should generally be understood to include tetrodes.

AMPLIFICATION USING SCREENED VALVES

The r.f. amplifier circuit of Fig. 156, which we found to be unworkable in practice owing to the back-coupling through the grid-anode capacitance of the triode being sufficient to make the amplifier oscillate, can be converted into a practical amplifier simply by substituting a screened valve for the triode and providing for g_2 to be maintained at a voltage recommended by the manufacturer. Some types are designed for V_{g2} to be the same as V_a, so that g_2 merely needs to be joined to the anode " h.t." supply; others work better with g_2 at a lower voltage, which is usually supplied through a resistor as shown in Fig. 161. (The value of I_{g2} at the specified V_{g2} is stated by the manufacturer, so the calculation of R is a simple exercise in Ohm's Law.) In either case a capacitor C, having not more than a few ohms reactance at the frequency to be amplified, should be connected as directly as possible between g_2 and cathode or earth, to keep the potential of g_2 steady.

We have already noted that the voltage gain given by a tuned-anode stage of amplification can be calculated by the same formula as for a resistance coupling, $A = \mu R/(R + r_a)$, R being the dynamic resistance of the tuned circuit, including the input resistance

210

of the next stage and any other things that are in parallel. But we have also noted that the μ and r_a of pentodes vary considerably with the conditions of use, and are both many times higher than for triodes. Typical values are: $\mu = 2,000$ and $r_a = 1\ M\Omega$. The value of R is rarely as much as one-tenth of r_a, and is often far less than that; so, taking into account the fact that the value of r_a is unlikely to be known within 10%, it is quite a good enough approximation to neglect R in comparison with r_a and say $A = \mu R/r_a$. But μ/r_a is g_m, so we can simplify the matter still further and say that $A = g_m R$. This is much simpler than the original formula; two rather variable valve parameters have been replaced by one—g_m—which for a given valve, is relatively constant. The most convenient units are: g_m in mA/V and R in $k\Omega$.

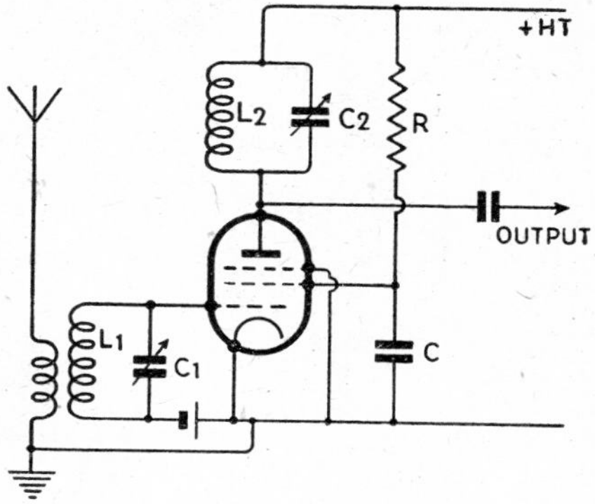

We see then that provided r_a is many times greater than R (as it almost invariably is

Fig. 161—Modification of Fig. 156 to convert it into a workable amplifier circuit by using a screened valve. Note the method of supplying the screen grid at a lower voltage than the anode, and at the same time avoiding signal-frequency variations in potential

in practice) the conditions for a high voltage gain with a screened valve are simply that we choose a valve with a high " slope ", working into a load having high dynamic resistance.

At television frequencies, in the region of 40–70 Mc/s, tuning circuits with dynamic resistances as high as those used for medium-frequency broadcasting (40–100 kΩ) are not practicable, and even if they were they would be reduced to a few kΩ by the low input impedance of the next valve at such high frequencies (p. 193); so it has been necessary to develop valves with very high g_m in order to get any useful gain. Values of 5–12 mA/V are usual in valves designed for television, compared with 1·5–3 mA/V for the lower frequencies.

At these lower radio frequencies it is possible to obtain a very high overall dynamic resistance, say 100 kΩ. It might seem that by using this in conjunction with a high-slope pentode, a gain of 500 or more could be obtained from a single stage. But it must be remembered that if the signal voltage at the anode is 500 times as great as the grid, it needs only 1/500th of it to work back to the grid, in phase with the signal there, to cause continuous oscillation. Even although the grid-anode capacitance in a screened valve is so small, it would usually be enough. To ensure that the amplifier is always stable (as it is called), a stage gain much higher than 150 is seldom attempted.

211

EXTERNAL SCREENING

The achievements of the valve designer in nearly abolishing C_{ga} can easily be nullified by injudicious construction of the rest of the amplifier. If the anode and grid leads from the valve were placed close together for several inches, the capacitance between them would be enough to make any reasonably effective r.f. amplifier unstable. So it is usual to lay them in opposite directions, and/or to screen one or both of them by an earthed metal covering or partition.

Having taken precautions against the amplifier behaving as a t.a.t.g. oscillator, one must also consider it as a possible reaction-coil oscillator (p. 135). There will, of course, be no intentional magnetic (or inductive) coupling, but accidental coupling is difficult to avoid when two tuning coils are mounted in the same unit. We have seen how a very minute capacitive coupling is enough to make a r.f. amplifier unstable, so it is not difficult to imagine that a very small stray induction has the same effect. Most radio apparatus is required to be compact, which means that the coils cannot be spaced far enough apart to avoid risk of instability. The larger the coils, the greater the risk, for two reasons: the magnetic field spreads out more, and the dynamic resistance tends to be higher.

If a coil is enclosed in a metal box or can, constructed so as to give a continuous low-resistance path parallel to the coil winding, the metal is in effect a transformer secondary winding with a single short-circuited turn. The currents induced in it by the tuning coil set up a magnetic field which opposes that due to the coil: so the resultant field outside this screen is greatly reduced.

If the coil is surrounded closely by the screen, its own self-inductance is largely neutralized, which means that more turns must be used to tune to a given frequency, and the r.f. resistance is greater. So it is desirable for the diameter of the screening can to be not less than twice that of the coil; and even then some allowance must be made in the design of the coil for the reduced inductance due to the screen.

Comparing magnetic (or inductive) screening with electric (or capacitive) screening, note that it necessitates low-resistance paths parallel to the coil winding but it need not be earthed, whereas capacitive screening need not provide closed circuits but must be effectively earthed or kept at some constant potential. Coils need both kinds of screening; the capacitance between them would be enough to by-pass the internal valve screening, quite apart from inductive coupling. Comprehensive screening is provided by enclosing them completely in metal cans in contact with the earthed part of the circuit.

TWO STAGES

For reception of the most distant stations, the gain—and the selectivity—given by a single stage of amplification is hardly adequate and it is desirable to add a second. This brings up, in

212

more acute form, the problem of instability, and experience shows that it is difficult to persuade two tuned-anode stages to refrain from self-oscillation.

Examining the two-stage tuned-anode amplifier of Fig. 162 we see that the tuned circuit 2, besides being in the anode circuit of V_1, serves as grid circuit for V_2, being connected between the grid of that valve and the h.t. line. This, being at zero potential so far as signals are concerned, counts as " earth " from the a.c. point of view. To keep the grid of V_2 at the right potential for amplification, grid bias is connected through a resistance high enough not to

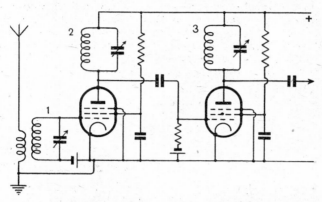

Fig. 162—Two-stage r.f. amplifier, using tuned-anode couplings

damp circuit 2 excessively. In its role of grid circuit to V_2, this tuned circuit is liable to have stray energy fed back to it from circuit 3, increasing its dynamic resistance above normal. It is this artificially-raised figure that must be taken when considering the stability of the first stage. We conclude that two stages, each individually stable, may oscillate if connected as in Fig. 162.

In addition, of course, the need for magnetic screening is more acute the greater the total amplification.

Feedback from the anode of V_1 to its grid can be reduced by cutting down the signal voltage at the anode. Naturally one dislikes sacrificing gain, so that one would like to maintain as high as possible the signal voltage eventually reaching the grid of V_2. This can be done by replacing each tuned circuit with a step-up r.f. transformer, something like that between aerial and first grid. The secondary winding is tuned in the usual way. The dynamic resistance, measured between the primary terminals, is less than that across the secondary, so the gain, measured at the anode, is correspondingly reduced, but this loss is partly made up by the voltage step-up of the transformer.

For reasons explained in Chapter 17, however, a somewhat different technique is usually adopted for obtaining a large amount

213

of amplification and selectivity before the detector, so it is not worth while pursuing the subject further just now.

CONTROL OF GAIN AND VOLUME

Two facts that must be duly considered in designing a receiver are: (1) the signal strengths picked up by the aerial differ very greatly according to the power and distance of the stations concerned, and (2) it is desirable, to say the least, to be able to control the loudness or volume of the programme. It would be possible to deal with both of these at once in some such simple way as that shown in Fig. 163, by which any desired proportion of the signal voltage in the aerial could be passed into the receiver.

In practice, such an arrangement would not give very satisfactory control over the enormous range between quiet reception of a local station and full volume from a distant one. Moreover the receiver would always be working at full gain, in which condition it is likely

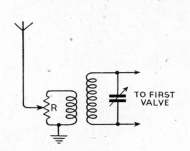

Fig. 163—One possible method— but not a good one—of controlling signal strength

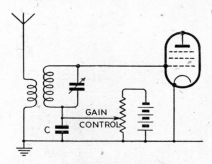

Fig. 164—Method of controlling the amplification (or gain) of a valve by adjusting its grid bias

to produce a certain amount of background noise (p. 301) which, while perhaps tolerable in listening to a distant station, must be avoided if possible while listening to a near one.

We know, too, that a diode detector works most efficiently and with least distortion when the signal amplitude is greatest. We shall soon see, however, that there is a limit to this, imposed by the signal voltage that the r.f. amplifier feeding the detector is able to handle. The ideal, then, is to provide sufficient r.f. amplification to bring the weakest worth-while signal nearly to the maximum the r.f. amplifier can handle (which should keep the detector happy), and arrange the a.f. amplification so as to give full volume from this. A control such as R_2 in Fig. 142, immediately following the detector, can then be used to adjust the volume to any desired level from maximum downwards. The remaining need is some method of reducing the r.f. gain appropriately whenever signal voltages stronger than the weakest are being received.

The objection to the Fig. 163 method of doing this can be overcome by controlling the gain of the r.f. amplifier itself. Since it is approximately equal to $g_m R$, we have the choice of varying either or both of these factors. The dynamic resistance, R, is a very awkward thing to control by a knob, but g_m is quite easy. We have not shown any I_a–V_{g1} curves for pentodes, because they are no different in character from those belonging to triodes, for which we have several samples (e.g., Fig. 94). Now g_m is the slope of a I_a–V_{g1} curve, and we see that by increasing the negative grid bias (V_{g1}) we can make the slope gradually less and less, right down to zero. All we need is a source of negative voltage with a potential divider to apply any desired proportion of it to the grid, in series with the signal source, as in Fig. 164. If there are several valves in the amplifier all their grids can be controlled simultaneously by this means. C is used to provide a low-impedance earth connection for the lower end of the tuned circuit.

DISTORTION IN THE R.F. AMPLIFIER

When receiving the weakest signals, this gain control would be turned up so as to apply only the least bias necessary to prevent the flow of grid current (p. 129). In these circumstances the working point is on a very nearly linear part of the valve characteristic, and as the signal voltage is very small the risk of distortion can be ignored.

But now suppose that a local station is tuned in. To keep the signal voltage from the last r.f. stage down to the same level as for the weak signal, it is necessary to reduce the gain, by applying more bias. This brings the working point down on the foot of the curve;* at the same time the input signal voltage is much greater, so the signal waves are considerably distorted—partly rectified in fact.

To make sure that we do not take too pessimistic a view of this situation, it may be as well to pause a moment to think what we mean by distortion here. Remember, it is the a.f. waveform, with which the r.f. carrier was modulated at the sender, that we are anxious to preserve. So long as this is done, it matters nothing what happens to the waveforms of the individual cycles of r.f. They could all be changed from sine waves into square waves, or any other shapes, but so long as they retained the same relative amplitudes they would still define the original a.f. envelope (p. 147). A perfect rectifier cuts off the negative half of every cycle, yet this drastic r.f. distortion introduces no distortion of the modulation. As we saw in connection with Fig. 144, it is the imperfect " curved " rectifier that distorts the modulation, by altering the relative proportions of the r.f. cycles; but unless the modulation is fairly deep it is surprising how little it is distorted by even a considerable curvature of the amplifying valve's characteristics.

* Although such valve curves are with fixed V_a, the effect on I_a of the variations in V_a due to the anode load are negligible in the case of a pentode.

CROSS-MODULATION

Distortion of the modulation waveform, however, is not the only thing that can happen as a result of non-linearity in the r.f. amplifier. There is what is known as *cross-modulation*, which makes its appearance in the misleading guise of lack of selectivity. Suppose a set with two r.f. stages and three tuned circuits is being used to receive a station 50 kc/s away from the local. We may be quite right in assuming that the overall selectivity of the three tuned circuits is enough to reduce the local station to inaudibility when they are all tuned 50 kc/s away from it. But the grid of the first valve is protected from it by only one tuned circuit, and may therefore receive quite a large voltage along with that of the weaker station to which the set is tuned.

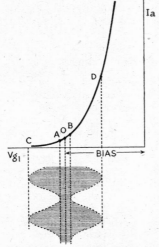

In Fig. 165 the I_a–V_{g1} curve is shown with a sample of the local station's modulated carrier wave (stood up on end) below. The r.f. cycles, being too close together to show individually, are represented by shading. The working point, set by the gain control bias, is marked 0.

Now consider what is happening to the wanted signal. It is being swung up and down the curve by the local station's carrier wave; between A and B during the troughs of local-station modulation, and between C and D during the crests. Owing to the curvature, the amplification it receives varies in a manner determined by the local-station modulation. On the average it is greater between C and D than between A and B. In other words, the wanted carrier wave is to some extent modulated by the modulation of the unwanted station.

Fig. 165—Showing how the average slope of the valve curve varies during each modulation cycle of a strong signal

So even although the unwanted carrier wave may be removed entirely by subsequent selectivity, it has left its mark indelibly on the wanted carrier, which, with its two-programme modulation, passes through the receiver, and both programmes are heard together.

If the transmission to which the set was tuned were switched off, the programme of the interfering station would disappear with it, proving that the interference was due to cross-modulation and not simply to insufficient selectivity.

To prevent cross-modulation it is necessary to reduce the curvature of the valve characteristic, if possible without sacrificing the ability to vary the gain.

VARIABLE-MU VALVES

The fault of the ordinary type of valve is that the slope of its I_a–V_{g1} characteristic changes very rapidly near the foot and much less so higher up. For the purpose of gain control this not only has the disadvantage of concentrating the curvature at the end that is used for local-station reception, and thereby causing distortion of those programmes for which it is least tolerable, but it also tends to unevenness of control. What is needed is a valve whose I_a–V_{g1} characteristic increases its slope steadily; if anything, less rapidly towards its foot.

This result is achieved very simply by winding the control grid with variable spacing as shown in Fig. 166b instead of evenly as in ordinary valves (a). So when the negative bias is gradually increased, current from the ends of the cathode is shut down first, while electrons can still pass through the centre part of the grid where there are relatively wide gaps between the negative wires; and it takes perhaps 30 or 40 volts to cut the current off everywhere. The

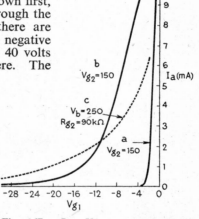

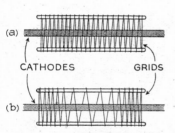

Fig. 166—Comparison between the grid of an ordinary valve (a) and a variable-mu valve (b)

Fig. 167— I_a — V_{g1} curves of (a) an ordinary screened pentode, (b) a variable-mu type, and (c) a variable-mu valve with g_2 fed through a resistor so that V_{g2} rises as —V_{g1} is increased

difference in characteristics is shown in Fig. 167, where curve a refers to a steep-slope pentode with sharp cut-off, and b to a comparable type having non-uniform grid spacing. It is known as a *variable-mu* valve; the name can be taken to mean that the mutual conductance is variable in a manner well suited to gain-control. How far this is successful can be better judged by plotting g_m in place of I_a, as in Fig. 168, which refers to the same valve and conditions as Fig. 167b. A logarithmic scale is used for g_m, not only for the sake of enabling a wide range of values to be shown clearly, but also because the ideal is for the gain to increase in the same *ratio* for equal changes in V_{g1}, and this ideal is represented on such a graph by a straight line. Fig. 168 therefore indicates a remarkably close approach to the ideal.

217

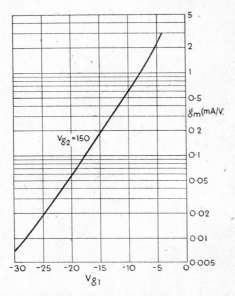

Fig. 168—**Mutual conductance plotted against** V_{g_1} **for the valve represented by** *b* **in Fig. 167**

It does show a slight tendency for g_m to increase too fast at the upper end, however, and this tendency is undesirable if only because it goes along with a rapid increase in I_a, which may cause difficulties in the supply of current. It can very easily be avoided by feeding g_2 through a suitable resistance (R in Fig. 161), which has the effect of reducing V_{g_2} as the negative bias is reduced. Increasing the bias reduces I_{g_2} as well as I_a and so reduces the voltage drop in R_1, and V_{g_2} rises, tending to prolong the range of control. This effect is illustrated by curve *c* in Fig. 167, where instead of feeding g_2 direct from 150 V it is fed from 250 V through 90 kΩ. By suitable choice of resistance and supply voltage, the gain-control characteristic can be varied by the designer to meet requirements.

AUTOMATIC GAIN CONTROL

In a perfect receiver, the adjustment of r.f. gain to compensate for the different strengths of incoming signals would take place automatically. All would then (for equal depth of modulation) be reproduced at the same loudness, determined by the listener's setting of the a.f. volume control. The ordinary listener does not want to be bothered with the purely technical task of ensuring that the r.f. gain is always such that the various stages of the receiver are working under the best available conditions.

Elsewhere (p. 177) we noted that there was a reason why diode detectors were generally connected in such a way that the steady voltage produced by the rectified carrier-wave was negative. That reason now emerges, for a negative voltage increasing with signal strength can be used as a gain-reducing bias—a device known as *automatic gain control* or a.g.c. (The name automatic volume control, a.v.c., still sometimes used, is obviously less appropriate.)

A simple system of a.g.c. is shown in Fig. 169. Although a more elaborate-looking section of receiver circuit than any hitherto, it is just a combination of Figs. 162 (modified for r.f. transformer coupling) and part of 142, together with one new feature—the a.g.c. connection from point P at the end of the diode load resistance, via

218

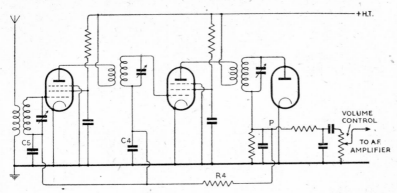

Fig. 169—Circuit diagram of the r.f. amplifier and detector portion of a receiver, showing automatic gain control

R_4, to the grids of the r.f. valves. During reception, the potential of P is affected in the Fig. 137b manner, which is a mixture of r.f., a.f., and negative z.f. The r.f. is filtered out before being passed on to the volume control, and the purpose of R_4, C_4 and C_5 is to filter out both r.f. and a.f. so that only the negative z.f. voltage reaches the grids as gain-control bias.

Obviously the signal level at the detector output must, in order to vary the gain, itself vary to some extent; so this system of a.g.c. is by no means perfect. But by various elaborations it can be made very nearly perfect. One of the commonest devices is to withhold the a.g.c. bias until the signal level at P has attained a working level. Details of such elaborations can be found in books on receiver design.

CHAPTER 16

Selectivity

SELECTIVITY COMPARISON

ALTHOUGH THE NEED for a considerable amount of selectivity has been mentioned incidentally (p. 106), it was the need for sensitivity that first drove us to consider r.f. amplification. Sensitivity, by the way, means smallness of signal input sufficient to yield a given output from a receiver. A set with a high sensitivity may therefore be expected to have a good range of reception. Selectivity, on the other hand, means ability to exclude unwanted stations.

By using reaction nearly to the limit at which continuous oscillation starts, one improves both sensitivity and selectivity; but we found that to obtain a large gain in this way not only demands very careful (and probably frequent) adjustment of the reaction control, but that the higher modulation frequencies receive only a small fraction of the gain, so that the quality of reception suffers very seriously. A single stage of r.f. amplification gives a gain of 100, or even more, without critical adjustment; two stages may give 10,000, and so on. Each stage introduces at least one extra tuned circuit; and the question now arises: may not these tuned circuits, by increasing the overall selectivity, lead to just the same loss of sidebands that made us reject reaction? To settle this question we shall have to go more thoroughly into the subject of selectivity.

What we need first of all is a standard method of comparing the selectivities of different tuned circuits, singly and in combination. It should exclude all matters that do not directly concern selectivity. Figs. 152 and 78 show resonance curves for single tuned circuits having different values of Q, and one can see at once that higher Q gives greater selectivity; but when presented in this way (with the same input voltage applied to each) the precise effect on selectivity is obscured by the effect on sensitivity. The method of Fig. 79, in which the input voltage to each circuit is adjusted to make the peaks coincide, levels out the sensitivity effect and directs attention to the way in which reception falls at frequencies on each side of resonance; so it is to be preferred.

Next, it is perhaps not very easy to compare the fractions, or even the percentages, which express the reception at off-tune frequencies relative to that at resonance; so we will turn the vertical scale upside down and make it indicate the number of " times down ". For example, instead of saying that the " $Q = 8,000$ " curve in Fig. 152 is 0.0067, or 0.67%, at 10 kc/s off tune, we would say it was $1/0.0067 = 150$ times down at that frequency. For convenience we will call the numbers on such a scale " S " values (since they concern selectivity). If, at a certain frequency, $S = 4$,

220

it means that the voltage at that frequency must be multiplied by 4 to equal that at resonance. To display a sufficiently wide range of S, it will be helpful to use a logarithmic scale.

CHANNEL SEPARATION

What about the horizontal scale? That it must be frequency, rather than wavelength, should be clear from our study of sidebands (p. 197). The " spread " of the sidebands on each side of the carrier wave is determined solely by the frequency of the modulation, and not at all by the frequency of the carrier wave. In broadcasting sound, the modulation frequencies are the audible frequencies, say 30–15,000 c/s; so the sidebands might spread up to 15 kc/s on each side of the carrier-wave frequency. Ideally, then, the carrier waves of different broadcasting stations should be spaced at intervals of at least 30 kc/s, plus a margin for selectivity, as suggested in Fig. 170a, where the dotted line is the ideal overall resonance curve of a receiver, embracing the whole of transmission A and completely rejecting transmission B.

Unfortunately the pressure of national demands for broadcasting " channels " has squeezed this ideal severely; the standard frequency

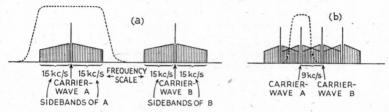

Fig. 170—At *a* is shown how broadcasting stations' carrier waves ought to be spaced on the frequency scale, in order to permit full reception of each without interference from others. How they actually are spaced is shown at *b*, explaining how interference is almost inevitable if full reception of sidebands is attempted

interval in Europe is only 9 kc/s. Obviously this faces receivers with an impossible task, for it brings 9 kc/s modulation of one station on to the same frequency as the carrier wave of the next and the 9 kc/s modulation of the next but one. Therefore few, if any, broadcasting stations on the medium and long wavebands actually radiate sidebands up to 15 kc/s; 8 kc/s is a more practical maximum. There is therefore some loss at the start. And even what is transmitted cannot be fully reproduced without interference, unless the transmission is so much stronger than those on adjacent frequencies as to drown them. So receivers for other than local-station reception must be designed to cut off at about 4·5 kc/s, sacrificing quality of reproduction in the interests of selectivity (Fig. 170b), and even then liable to some interference from adjacent-channel sidebands if they are strong enough. At very high frequencies there is less overcrowding; so sound transmitted on those frequencies (such as television sound) is not subject to the same degradation of quality.

The important point just now is that the spacing of carrier waves is necessarily on a frequency basis, not a wavelength basis. If a station transmits on 200 kc/s, the two nearest in frequency will be on 191 and 209 kc/s. The wavelengths corresponding to these frequencies (p. 31) are 1,571 1,500 and 1,435 metres, so the average wavelength spacing is 68 metres. Three consecutive carrier-wave frequencies higher in the scale are, according to the same 9 kc/s spacing, 1,502, 1,511 and 1,520 kc/s. The corresponding wavelengths are 199·7, 198·6, and 197·3 metres, so the wavelength spacing here is only 1·2 metres.

SELECTIVITY FACTOR

Whether we are concerned with programme separation or loss of sidebands, then, the basis of reckoning is " frequency off-tune ".

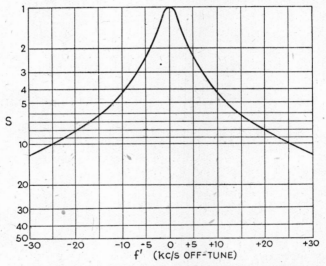

Fig. 171—Resonance curve for a tuned circuit having a Q of 200 at a frequency of 1,000 kc/s. S denotes the number of times the voltage developed across the tuned circuit by a constant input voltage is reduced when the input frequency is altered from 1,000 kc/s to the extent of f' kc/s

To distinguish this particular frequency from frequency in general, we shall denote it by f'. Fig. 171 is a specimen resonance curve plotted as S against f'. It shows that in this particular case adjacent carrier waves ($f' = +9$ and -9 kc/s) would be weakened by a factor of 3·7, and modulation frequencies of ± 5 kc/s by a factor of 2·2. Now we know that the sharpness of resonance, reckoned as the S for a given f', depends very largely on Q; does it depend on anything else? The answer is that for a single tuned circuit the only other thing is f_r, the resonant frequency. That is to say, if on

Fig. 171 we plotted resonance curves of a number of other tuned circuits all having the same Q, they would not be identical unless their resonant frequencies were identical. It happens that the curve actually shown on Fig. 171 refers to a circuit with a Q of 200 at a resonant frequency of 1,000 kc/s. If we plotted a curve for a circuit with the same Q but resonating at 500 kc/s, it would appear on this type of diagram to be twice as sharp. For example, S would be $3 \cdot 7$ at $f' = 4 \cdot 5$ kc/s instead of 9 kc/s. But if the Q of the 500 kc/s circuit were halved, its resonance curve would practically coincide with that in Fig. 171. So would a 100 kc/s circuit with a Q of 20, or a 2,500 kc/s circuit with a Q of 500. This principle applies generally; so we see that if in every case we were to divide Q by the resonant frequency, f_r, we would arrive at a factor defining the sharpness of resonance as seen on a diagram of S plotted against f'. Since in a simple tuned circuit $Q = 2\pi f_r L/r$ (p. 104), this factor simplifies to $2\pi L/r$. We can simplify it further by knocking out the 2π, because that is just a fixed number which would be the same in every case. So our selectivity factor is just L/r, the ratio of tuning-coil inductance to the series r.f. resistance (Fig. 84).

THE GENERALIZED RESONANCE CURVE

We can therefore draw a series of resonance curves for different values of L/r, and use it to find the value of L/r that best suits any particular requirement. Since the curve already in Fig. 171 applies to $Q = 200$ at $f_r = 1$ Mc/s, its L/r value, $Q/2\pi f_r$, is $200/(2\pi \times 1) = 32$ in μH and Ω units. The advantage of such a diagram over the Q type of resonance curves such as Fig. 152 is that it holds good for all resonant frequencies; not just for one.

Note that half of Fig. 171 is really unnecessary, because the curve is symmetrical, so that S is the same whether f' is positive or negative. Actually this is not perfectly true; but provided that f' is never more than a small fraction of f_r it is near enough for practical purposes, and we can omit the left-hand half.

One remaining disadvantage of our standard selectivity diagram is that the results with values of L/r intermediate between those for which the curves are plotted have to be judged by eye. But if the f' scale is also made logarithmic, the curves will all have the same shape, the only difference being that increasing L/r slides the curve bodily to the left. So if we modify the horizontal scale so as to take L/r into account as well as f', a single curve will tell the whole story, as in Fig. 172.

This curve can be used either to find the response at any off-tune frequency of a tuned circuit of given L/r, or to find the L/r required to fulfil given requirements. For example, suppose L/r is 10. To find the response at, say, 18 kc/s off tune it is only necessary to multiply 18 by 10 to get the right point on the horizontal scale, at which the curve shows S to be $2 \cdot 5$ times down. To take another example, suppose an adjacent-channel rejection of at least 5 times (per tuned circuit) is wanted. The curve shows that, for $S = 5$,

223

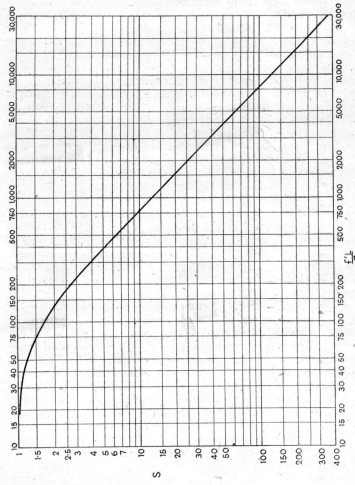

Fig. 172—Generalized resonance curve for any single tuned circuit. To make it refer to any particular circuit, multiply the numbers on the horizontal scale by r/L (or by $2\pi f_r/Q$) to convert them into a scale of f'

$f'L/r$ is 390. As f' is 9, L/r must be $390/9 = 43$, approximately. The response to, say, 4 kc/s modulation frequencies is seen by putting $f'L/r = 4 \times 43 = 172$, at which the curve shows $S =$ about 2·4.

It will have become abundantly clear by now that the sort of response curve that is really needed is one which remains level at $S = 1$ as far as the highest sideband frequency required, and then cuts steeply off to reject other transmissions. But what we have found is that the shape of the resonance curve of a single tuned circuit, drawn on a diagram of the most appropriate kind, is fixed by Nature and cannot be altered. Once we have decided on the response at any one off-tune frequency, the response at all others is thereby decided too, whether we like it or not.

More Than One Tuned Circuit

Now it is time to consider what happens when additional tuned circuits are used. If we can assume that these circuits do not react on one another, then it is simple. If the grid circuit of a r.f. amplifier reduces signals at a certain off-tune frequency 3 times (relative to the response at resonance), and the anode circuit is somewhat more lightly damped and reduces them 4 times, then obviously the total relative reduction is 12 times. If there is a second r.f. stage, and its anode circuit gives a further reduction of 3 times, the total is 36. In other words, this 2-stage amplifier amplifies this certain frequency 36 times less than it amplifies the frequency to which all three circuits are tuned.

If the problem is simplified by assuming all the circuits have the same L/r, then the curve in Fig. 172 is made to apply to a pair of circuits by squaring S; to three circuits by cubing it; and so on.

Comparison on Equal-Gain Basis

Comparison between one and several tuned circuits can be made in different ways. First of all we shall compare them on the basis of equal gain, in order to dispose finally of the question of reaction versus r.f. amplification. Taking some typical figures, suppose that the r.f. amplifier is a single stage giving a gain of 50 times, with input and output tuned circuits for which $L/r = 10$. Squaring the S values in Fig. 172, we get curve a in Fig. 173. To obtain equal gain by means of reaction, it would be necessary to apply enough of it to multiply Q by 50. This would multiply L/r by the same factor. So curve b is drawn for a single tuned circuit with $L/r = 500$. We see that the modulation frequency corresponding to a 5,000 c/s note is reduced 1·4 times by the r.f. amplifier; that is to say, it retains about 70% of its relative strength. But the reaction receiver reduces it 32 times, leaving only about 3%. True, it gives excellent selectivity; but it would take all the life out of music and make speech difficult to follow. At 9 kc/s off tune, or even 18 kc/s, the r.f. amplifier is very inselective. But, significantly, at the more remote frequencies its selectivity is beginning to overtake its rival.

H

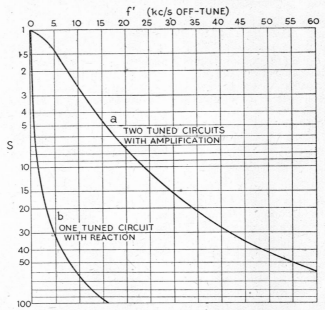

Fig. 173—Comparison of (a) two ordinary tuned circuits plus valve amplification (A = 50) with (b) a single tuned circuit made to give equal signal output at resonance by means of reaction, showing the poor selectivity of a and the sideband-cutting of b

Equal Selectivity

The excessive sharpness of b in Fig. 173 was a result of having to make the tuned circuit provide as much gain as a stage of amplification. But now let us disregard gain and compare one circuit with several on a basis of equal selectivity. Suppose the intention is to reduce signal voltages at two channels off-tune (18 kc/s) to one-hundredth of what they would be if exactly tuned in. Fig. 172 shows that the required L/r for a single circuit would be $8,000/18 = 445$. With two circuits, S for each would be 10, so $L/r = 800/18 = 44.5$. With four circuits, S would be $\sqrt{10}$, and $L/r = 13$. With six, S would be $\sqrt[3]{10}$, and $L/r = 8.4$. The overall response at other frequencies can be derived from Fig. 172 by taking S^2 for two circuits, S^4 for four, and S^6 for six. Plotting the results for one and six circuits on one graph, we get Fig. 174, which shows very clearly that a single tuned circuit, whether its extreme sharpness is necessitated by the requirements of gain or of selectivity, can fulfil these requirements only at the cost of drastic cutting of the wanted sidebands, and that a large number of relatively flat circuits is much to be preferred. One can see, too, that the selectivity at frequencies beyond the chosen reference point of 18 kc/s goes on increasing much more rapidly with many circuits than with few.

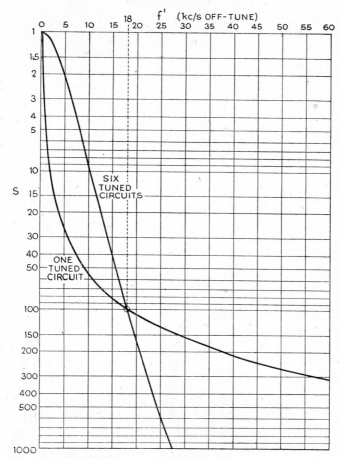

Fig. 174—Resonance curves for one tuned circuit and for six, the sharpness of resonance being adjusted in each case to give a 100-fold drop at 18 kc/s off-tune. They emphasize the value of using many flat circuits rather than one sharp one, for preserving sidebands

EQUAL QUALITY

Lastly, let us make the comparison on a basis of equal quality, as defined by equal preservation of sidebands up to a selected limit, say 5 kc/s. In Fig. 175 the L/r values have been chosen so that in each case the overall response is $1\frac{1}{2}$ times down; that is, a reduction of 5,000 c/s notes to two-thirds of their correct relative strength. This corresponds to a barely noticeable loss. Here we see that one tuned circuit gives hardly any useful adjacent-channel selectivity, and a station even three channels (27 kc/s) away is reduced only some six times. With six tuned circuits the corresponding figure is 140.

227

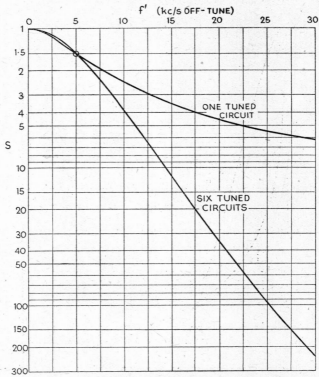

Fig. 175—Comparison of one tuned circuit with six circuits on a basis of equal sideband loss at 5 kc/s. This shows the greater selectivity of the six circuits

PRACTICAL COIL FIGURES

It is simple enough, on paper, to talk about choosing correct L/r ratios to provide the response-curves that we want. In practice it is not always easy, or even possible, to achieve them. Experience shows that a coil designed to be tuned, by means of the usual variable capacitor, over a range of frequencies, always has a lower resistance at the lower frequencies. In the ordinary small coils used in the modern receiver, the ratio L/r is found to vary from about 5 or 6 at 1,500 kc/s up to about 20 at 550 kc/s. If the coil has an iron-dust core and is wound with stranded wire in which the strands are insulated from one another ("Litzendraht") the 550-kc/s figure will probably rise to about 35, but the improvement at 1,500 kc/s is usually less.

The design of a coil for lowest attainable resistance requires the choice of correct wire-thickness, and the thickness required depends on the precise frequency for which the calculation is made. The figure given as representative for L/r can therefore be increased a little at either end of the waveband at the cost of a decrease at the other by designing the coil specifically for the frequency it is desired to favour. But the only really useful method of improving the L/r ratio is by making the coil larger; this is effective at all frequencies.

SELECTIVITY AND GAIN

It is an unfortunate feature of capacitance tuning that the more constant the selectivity over the frequency-band, the less constant will be the gain. Gain depends, as we have seen (p. 203), on the dynamic resistance $R = L/Cr$ (p. 112); as we reduce frequency by increasing C, r diminishes and tends to hold the product Cr constant, and with it the dynamic resistance, since L does not change. It is usually found that R has a maximum at about 1,250 kc/s, after which it falls steadily, till at 550 kc/s it is usually about half the maximum value.

If we did succeed in keeping r, and hence L/r, constant from 1,500 to 550 kc/s, we should get constant selectivity accompanied by a steady drop in R which, at 550 kc/s, would have less than one-sixth of its value at 1,500. Conversely, constant R would give us constant gain, but to get it r would have to decrease in the same ratio that C increases, making L/r over six times as great at 550 kc/s as at 1,500.

Tuning by varying L, keeping C constant, could theoretically avoid this difficulty, for then constant R would also mean constant L/r. But r shows no particular inclination to be strictly proportional to L in any variable-inductance tuner that has so far appeared.

CONCLUSIONS

Summing up the results of this chapter, we find it does much to blight the encouraging prospect of r.f. amplification opened up in the previous one. Using even six tuned circuits, the overall response curve is far from ideal, and seems unlikely to yield sufficient selectivity *and* good quality of reproduction, at any rate in the medium- and long-wave broadcasting frequencies. And whatever balance of selectivity and gain is chosen, with capacitance tuning it is bound to vary widely over the tuning range. Inductive tuning, though probably better in this respect, offers greater mechanical difficulties. And with any method of tuning, the problem of keeping, say, six separate circuits in tune over wide ranges of frequency is appalling from the designer's point of view.

So it is not surprising that all attempts to produce a really practical high-performance broadcast receiver on the lines of variable-frequency r.f. amplification have failed. The generally-accepted solution is the subject of the next chapter.

CHAPTER 17

The Superheterodyne Receiver

A DIFFICULT PROBLEM SOLVED

IF WE CONSIDER the difficulties listed at the end of the previous chapter we find that they all mainly result from having to tune over a wide range of frequency. Designing a receiver for one fixed frequency is comparatively easy. The variation of gain and selectivity with frequency does not, of course, arise at all. Nor do the mechanical problems of making one knob control a number of tuning circuits simultaneously; they can all be adjusted by skilled operators in the factory and fixed at that. So it would not be unreasonable to suggest having six or even more tuned circuits, thereby obtaining a better compromise between the conflicting requirements of selectivity and quality. In fact, as we shall see, it is practicable to use slightly more complicated tuning circuits, having response curves better suited to the purpose than the one shown in Fig. 172. Seeing, however, that the market for receivers capable of working on one frequency only is negligible, is it not just being rather tantalizing to imagine how easy it would be to design them?

Fortunately, a combination of the advantages of fixed-tuned selectivity with the ability to receive over a wide range of frequency is not so impossible as it might seem. The apparent miracle is actually accomplished in the great majority of present-day receivers, under the name of supersonic heterodyne—usually abbreviated to superheterodyne or just " superhet ". By means of a device called a frequency-changer it is possible to shift the carrier wave of any desired station, together with its sidebands, to whatever fixed frequency has been chosen for the selective circuits. This frequency—called the *intermediate frequency* (i.f.)—is usually in the region of 465 kc/s in receivers designed for the usual sound-broadcast wavelengths, because that falls between the medium and long wavebands and is a convenient frequency at which to amplify selectively. The frequencies of all incoming signals are shifted by the frequency-changer to the same extent. So if, for example, the original carrier-wave frequency of the wanted programme was 865 kc/s and it has been shifted to 465 kc/s, adjacent-channel carrier waves at 856 and 874 kc/s would be passed to the i.f. amplifier as 456 and 474 kc/s.

After the desired signal has been amplified at its new frequency and at the same time separated from those on neighbouring frequencies, it is passed into the detector in the usual way, and the remainder of the receiver is in no way different from a " straight " set.

Theory of the Frequency-Changer

The most important thing to grasp in this chapter is the principle on which the frequency-changer works. All else is mere detail.

Suppose a sample of the carrier wave coming from the desired station during one hundred-thousandth of a second to be represented by Fig. 176a. As it contains 10 cycles, the frequency must be 1,000 kc/s. Similarly b represents a sample of a continuous wave-train having a frequency of 1,450 kc/s, which is being generated by a small oscillator in the receiver. Now add the two together. Since the local oscillation alternately falls into and out of step with the incoming signal, it alternately reinforces and weakens it, with the result shown at c—waves varying in amplitude at a frequency of 450 kc/s. This part of the process is often referred to as b beating with a, and 450 kc/s in this case would be called the *beat frequency*. The same kind of thing takes place audibly when two musical notes of nearly the same pitch are sounded together.

Notice particularly that what is happening at 450 c/s is only a variation (or modulation) of waves of higher frequency. *No signal of 450 kc/s is present*, for each rise above the centre line is neutralized by an equal and opposite fall below the line. The average result, when applied to a circuit tuned to 450 kc/s, is practically nil. We have been up against this kind of thing already (see Fig. 131) and the solution is the same now as then—rectify it. After eliminating the negative

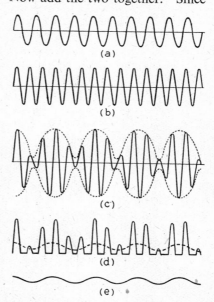

Fig. 176—Showing the action of a frequency changer. *a* represents a sample of incoming carrier-wave, and *b* an oscillation generated in the receiver. Adding the two together gives *c*, and rectifying *c* gives *d*. When the original frequencies have been tuned out, one is left with a signal (*e*) whose frequency is equal to the difference between the frequencies of *b* and *a*

half-cycles (*d*) the smoothed-out or averaged result of all the positive half-cycles (shown dotted) is a signal at 450 kc/s; that is to say, the difference between the frequencies of *a* and *b*. The mixture of 450 kc/s and the original frequencies is then passed to the i.f. circuits, which reject all except the 450 kc/s, shown now alone at *e*.

So far, the result is only a 450 kc/s carrier wave of constant amplitude, corresponding to the 1,000 kc/s carrier wave received from the aerial. But if this 1,000 kc/s wave has sidebands, due to modulation at the sender, these sidebands when added to the 1,450 kc/s oscillation and rectified give rise to frequencies which are sidebands to 450 kc/s. So far as the i.f. amplifier and the rest of the receiver are concerned, therefore, the position is the same as if they were a " straight " set receiving a programme on 450 kc/s.

Any readers who, in spite of Fig. 154, have difficulty in seeing amplitude modulation as sidebands, may find Fig. 177 helpful. This shows a rather longer sample of the carrier wave (a), the individual cycles being so numerous that they are hardly distinguish-

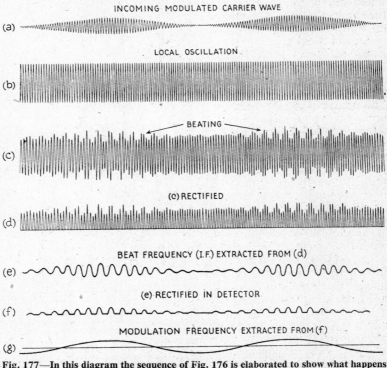

INCOMING MODULATED CARRIER WAVE

(a)

LOCAL OSCILLATION

(b)

BEATING

(c)

(c) RECTIFIED

(d)

BEAT FREQUENCY (I.F.) EXTRACTED FROM (d)

(e)

(e) RECTIFIED IN DETECTOR

(f)

MODULATION FREQUENCY EXTRACTED FROM (f)

(g)

Fig. 177—In this diagram the sequence of Fig. 176 is elaborated to show what happens when the incoming carrier wave is modulated. The additional lines, (f) and (g), show the extraction of the modulation frequency

able. And this time it is fully modulated; the sample is sufficient to show two whole cycles of modulation frequency. The local oscillation, which is certain to be much stronger, and of course is unmodulated, is shown at b. When a is added to it (c), nothing happens to it at the troughs of modulation, where a is zero, but elsewhere the cycles of a alternately strengthen and weaken those of b, causing its amplitude to vary at the beat frequency, in the manner shown. The amplitude of beating is proportional to the amplitude of a, and the frequency of beating is equal to the difference between the frequencies of *a* and *b*. The next picture, *d*, shows the result of rectifying *c*. We now have, in addition to other frequencies, an actual signal at the beat frequency (or i.f.), shown at *e* after it has been separated from the rest by the i.f. tuned circuits. The result of rectifying *e* in the detector is *f*; and after the remains of the i.f. have been removed by the detector filter the final result (*g*) has the same frequency and waveform as that used to modulate the original carrier wave.

Another way of looking at the frequency-changer is as a modulator, producing sidebands at frequencies above and below the original frequency. Until now we have only taken notice of the frequency *below* the original frequency, because it is clearly visible in a waveform diagram like Fig. 176 or 177. The fact that a frequency is produced, equal to that of the local oscillator *plus* that of the incoming signal, is not at all obvious. But it can be shown mathematically, and it also follows from our vector diagram, Fig. 154. Making the amplitude of a signal alternately greater and less (i.e., modulated) at a certain frequency (in this case the frequency of the oscillator) is equivalent to creating new frequencies equal to the original frequency plus and minus the frequency at which it is modulated.

When, in a superhet, the signal is passed into a rectifier along with the much stronger local oscillation, the oscillation modulates the signal by bringing it alternately on to low-resistance and high-resistance parts of the rectifier's characteristic. In theory, any sort of modulator would do.

The fact that both plus and minus frequencies are actually produced is easily proved in practice by tuning to both of them in turn. Either of these frequencies could be chosen as the i.f. in a superhet, but the lower or difference frequency is the one usually favoured, because it is easier to get the desired amplification and selectivity at a fairly low radio-frequency.

Types of Frequency-Changer

A frequency-changer therefore consists of two parts: an oscillator, and a device whereby the oscillation modulates or varies the amplitude of the incoming signal. This device is commonly called the mixer. If the word " mix " is understood in the sense a chemist would give it—just adding the two things together—then it is a very misleading word to use. Simply adding voltages or currents of different frequencies together creates no new frequencies, just as merely mixing oxygen and hydrogen together creates no new chemical substance. So from this point of view " combiner " would be a better name for the second part of a frequency-changer.

The oscillator presents no great difficulty; almost any of the circuits shown in Chapter 10 could be used. It is, of course, necessary to provide for varying the frequency over a suitable range, in order to make the difference between it and the frequency of the wanted station always equal to the fixed i.f.

233

In the theoretical explanation, we assumed that the i.f. signal was formed by passing both incoming signal and local oscillation together through a rectifier. That was actually the method used in early superhets, when the frequency-changer was called the " first detector ". It is still the method used in radar and other receivers working on frequencies higher than about 300 Mc/s, so is worth noting. Fig. 178 is the circuit in its essentials. The incoming signal and the local oscillation are fed in series into the rectifier, which may be a diode or a crystal. C_1 is used for tuning L_2 to the signal, so as to develop the greatest possible voltage at that frequency. There is, of course, no difficulty in obtaining a relatively large voltage from the local oscillator. C_2 serves the double purpose of tuning the transformer primary, L_5, to the intermediate frequency and of providing a low-impedance path for the two input frequencies.

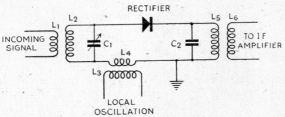

Fig. 178—Simple type of frequency changer, in which the incoming signal and the local oscillation are added together by connecting their sources in series, and then rectified

There are two reasons for choosing a simple crystal rectifier for radar receivers: (1) at the extremely high frequencies necessary for radar, valves fail because of transit-time effects (p. 193) and the capacitance and inductance of their electrodes; (2) i.f. amplification is not limited by considerations of expense, so the all-important sensitivity of the receiver is limited only by the amount of " noise " (p. 301) generated in the frequency-changer, and a crystal is better in this respect than multi-electrode valves.

But for broadcast receivers, which have to give the best performance at minimum cost, the simple Fig. 178 type leaves several things to be desired. The adjustment of C_1 is liable to affect the frequency of the local oscillator; and, conversely, the local oscillations are likely to find their way via L_2 and L_1 to the aerial, causing interference to other receivers in the neighbourhood. In other words, the signal and oscillator circuits interact, elsewhere than in the only proper direction—through the rectifier. Also the rectifier does not amplify. This last failing used to be made good by substituting a grid or anode type of detector, using a triode or pentode. But as the other defects were still experienced, especially on the short-wave band, special frequency-changer valves were developed.

234

FREQUENCY-CHANGER VALVES

The one feature common to all of these is that instead of applying the local oscillation along with the incoming signal to the same control electrode, it is made to modulate the signal indirectly, by applying it separately to another control electrode, screened off from the first. A typical example is the hexode, shown in Fig. 179. It can be regarded as a screened tetrode with the addition of one extra grid, g_3, for modulating the electron stream, and another, g_4, for screening g_3 from the anode. The incoming signal voltage is applied to g_1 in the usual way, just as if this were a r.f. amplifier valve and g_2 (to which g_4 is connected inside the valve) is held at a steady positive voltage. The local oscillator is connected to g_3, alternately raising and lowering the mutual conductance of the valve and so modulating the signal. The

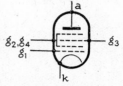

Fig. 179 — Conventional symbol for a hexode frequency-changer valve

anode current therefore contains a signal at the difference frequency, which is passed to the i.f. amplifier.

The local oscillation is usually generated by a triode; and for convenience this is often enclosed in the same bulb as the hexode, forming a triode-hexode. A typical circuit diagram, in simplified form, of this popular type of frequency-changer is shown as Fig. 180. The functions of most of the components are fairly obvious. C_1 tunes the control-grid circuit to the incoming signal frequency, f_s. Note that a.g.c. bias is applied just as in a r.f. amplifier (Fig. 169);

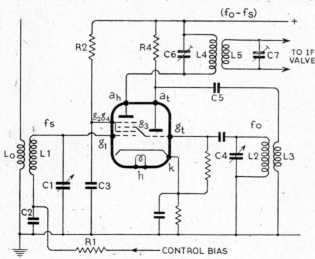

Fig. 180—The essentials of a typical frequency-changer circuit, using a triode-hexode valve

for one of the advantages of these special frequency-changer valves is that the signal-control grid can be given variable-mu characteristics, thereby increasing the effectiveness of the a.g.c. A by-passed cathode resistor provides a small amount of initial bias for g_1. The oscillator anode is fed in parallel with the reaction circuit (C_5L_3) via R_4, and the frequency of oscillation, f_o, is adjusted by C_4. The voltage at this frequency on the grid of the triode is applied to g_3 of the hexode via an internal connection. C_6 and C_7 are permanently set to tune the primary and secondary of the i.f. transformer L_4L_5 to the i.f. currents in the anode circuit.

A triode-heptode is a similar valve except that a fifth (suppressor) grid, between g_4 and a_h, is connected internally to the cathode. Such a heptode can be used with a separate triode; but there is another type of heptode which needs no separate oscillator. The first two grids act as grid and anode of the triode oscillator, modulating the electron stream *before* it reaches the signal-control grid, g_4. This is screened from oscillator and anode respectively by g_3 and g_5. This type of frequency-changer is generally less good than the triode-hexode or triode-heptode, at least at the higher frequencies (say over 20 Mc/s) for two reasons: the mutual conductance of the oscillator section may not be sufficient for easy oscillation, and there is more interaction between oscillator and signal sections.

CONVERSION CONDUCTANCE

The effectiveness of an ordinary amplifying or oscillating type of valve is, as we know, expressed as the mutual conductance, in milliamps of signal current in the anode circuit per volt of signal applied at the grid. In a frequency-changer valve, however, the anode current at signal-frequency is a waste product, to be rejected as soon as possible; what we are interested in is the milliamps of i.f. current per volt of signal-frequency. This is known as the *conversion conductance* of the valve, denoted by g_c. Obviously it does not depend on the valve alone but also on the oscillation voltage. If this is only a volt or two, it does not vary the mutual conductance over anything like its full range; consequently the signal current is modulated to only a fraction of its full amplitude, and the i.f. current is less than it need be. The conversion conductance reaches its maximum when the local oscillation is enough to bring the mutual conductance to zero during its negative half-cycles and to maximum during as much as possible of its positive half-cycles. The positive part of Fig. 177c is therefore reproduced with the full g_m of the valve, while the negative part is completely suppressed; the net result is the same as with a perfect rectifier, Fig. 177d. The incoming signal, however weak, is swept right round the bend by the oscillation. That explains why a superhet is sensitive to the feeblest signals, which, if applied straight to the detector, would make no perceptible impression (p. 183).

In Fig. 181a, a small sample of oscillation plus signal (such as Fig. 177c or 176c) is shown in relationship to the V_g scale of an

I_a–V_g valve curve. (The fact that in most modern frequency-changers the oscillation and signal are actually applied to different grids does not affect the essential principle.) Since the i.f. fluctuations are due to the signal alternately strengthening and weakening the local oscillation, their amplitude is, as we have seen, equal to that of the signal. Neglecting, as we generally can with these types of valve, the effect of the load in the anode circuit, corresponding fluctuations in anode-current half-cycles are practically equal to

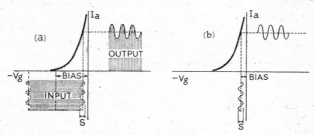

Fig. 181—Diagram showing how conversion conductance compares with mutual conductance

those that would be caused by an i.f. voltage of the same amplitude as the signal voltage amplified straightforwardly, as indicated at *b*. If the i.f. current amplitude in *a* were the same thing as the amplitude of the i.f. envelope, this would mean that the conversion conductance was practically equal to the mutual conductance. But, as is shown more clearly in Fig. 176*d*, the fluctuation in *mean* value of the half-cycles is $1/\pi$ or only about 32% of the peaks (p. 172). So g_c is only about one-third of g_m under ideal conditions, and in practice is between one-third and one-quarter.

In a r.f. tetrode or pentode the valve resistance is so much higher than any normal load resistance (R) that the voltage gain is approximately equal to $g_m R$ (p. 211). The corresponding quantity in a frequency-changer, the *conversion gain*, is equal to $g_c R$ and is the ratio of output i.f. voltage to input r.f. voltage. Even though it gives only about a quarter of the gain of a comparable r.f. amplifier, the frequency-changer makes a very welcome contribution to the gain of a receiver, in addition to its main function.

GANGING THE OSCILLATOR

We have seen that the intermediate frequency is equal to the difference between the signal frequency and the oscillator frequency. With an i.f. of 465 kc/s the oscillator must therefore be tuned to a frequency either 465 kc/s greater or 465 kc/s less than the signal. If the oscillator frequency f_o is higher than the signal frequency f_s the i.f. is $(f_o - f_s)$. If it is lower, the i.f. is $(f_s - f_o)$. It might seem to be a matter of indifference which of these alternatives was chosen. There are, however, marked practical advantages in making f_o higher than f_s.

237

Suppose the set is to tune from 525 to 1,605 kc/s. Then, if of higher frequency, the oscillator must run from (525 + 465) to (1,605 + 465), i.e., from 990 to 2,070 kc/s. If, on the other hand, the oscillator is of lower frequency than the signal, it must run from (525 − 465) to (1,605 − 465), or 60 to 1,140 kc/s. The former range gives 2·09, the latter 19 as the ratio between highest and lowest frequency. Since even the signal-circuit range of 3·06 is often quite difficult to achieve, owing to the minimum capacitance likely to be present in a finished set, the oscillator range from 990 to 2,070 kc/s would always be chosen in practice.

It is evident, since the frequency difference between signal and oscillator must be kept constant, that the oscillator must be tuned in a manner that is somewhat different from the tuning of the signal-frequency circuits. At first sight it might appear impossible to tune the oscillator with a capacitor section identical with those tuning the signal-frequency circuits, because the required ratio of maximum to minimum capacitance is different. This difference, however, can easily be adjusted by putting a fixed capacitance either in parallel with the oscillator capacitor to increase the minimum capacitance, or in series to reduce the maximum. The ratio of maximum to minimum having been corrected in either of these ways, correct choice of inductance

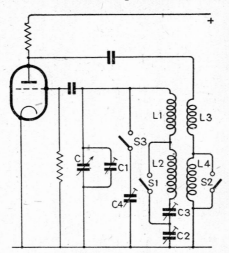

Fig. 182—Complete two-waveband oscillator circuit, showing arrangement of series ("padding") capacitors C₂ and C₃, and parallel ("trimming") capacitors C₁ and C₄. With correct values for these, ganging can be made practically perfect

for the oscillator coil will ensure that it tunes to the right frequency at the two ends of the tuning-scale.

In the middle, however, it will be widely out, but in opposite directions in the two cases. It is found that a judicious combination of the two methods, using a small parallel capacitor to increase the minimum a little, and a large series capacitor to decrease the maximum a little, will produce almost perfect "tracking" over the whole wave-band.

The resulting circuit is shown in Fig. 182. Here C is a section of an ordinary gang capacitor, and has at every dial reading the same capacitance as its companion sections tuning the signal-frequency circuits. With S_1 and S_2 closed, we have C_1 to increase

238

the minimum capacitance and C_2 to decrease the maximum, their values being critical for accurate ganging. Opening S_1 increases the inductance of the tuned circuit to enable the long-wave band to be covered by the set, at the same time decreasing the series capacitance to the resultant of C_2 and C_3. Simultaneously S_2 is opened to throw in the extra reaction winding L_4, and S_3 is closed to add C_4 to the minimum capacitance in the circuit.

The same principle can be adopted for any other wavebands that may be provided.

WHISTLES

Owing to the characteristics of the frequency-changer, a super-heterodyne is liable to certain types of interference from which an ordinary set is free.

The most noticeable result of these is a whistle, which changes in pitch as the tuning control is rotated, as when using a " straight " receiver in an oscillating condition, but generally less severe. There are many possible causes, some of which are quite hard to trace.

The best-known is *second-channel* or *image* interference. In the preceding section we have seen that it is usual for the oscillator to be adjusted to a frequency higher than that of the incoming signal. But if, while reception is being obtained in this way, another signal comes in on a frequency higher than that of the oscillator by an equal amount, an intermediate frequency is produced by it as well. If the frequency difference is not *exactly* the same, but differs by perhaps 1 kc/s, then two i.f. signals are produced, differing by 1 kc/s, and the second detector combines them to give a continuous note of 1 kc/s.

An example will make this clear; especially if for the i.f. we choose a round number, 100 kc/s. Suppose the station desired works on a frequency of 950 kc/s. When tuned to it, the oscillator is 100 kc/s higher, 1,050 kc/s, and yields a difference signal of 100 kc/s, to which the i.f. amplifier responds. So far all is well. But if a signal of 1,149 kc/s is also able to reach the frequency-changer it will combine with the oscillation to produce a difference signal of $1,149 - 1,050 = 99$ kc/s. This is too near 100 kc/s for the i.f. amplifier to reject, so both are amplified together by it and are presented to the detector, which produces a difference frequency, 1 kc/s, heard as a high-pitched whistle. Slightly altering the tuning control alters the pitch of the note, as shown in the table on the next page.

Since both stations give rise to carriers falling within the band to which the i.f. amplifier must be tuned to receive one of them, this part of the set can give no protection against interference of this sort. So the superhet principle does not allow one to do away entirely with selective circuits tuned to the original signal frequency. Such circuits are collectively called the *preselector*.

Another form of interference, much more serious if present, but fortunately easy to guard against, is that due to a station operating within the i.f. band itself. Clearly, if it is able to penetrate as far

Set tuned to:	Oscillator at:	IF signal due to 950 kc/s signal (wanted)	IF signal due to 1,149 kc/s signal (interfering)	Difference (pitch of whistle)
kc/s	kc/s	kc/s	kc/s	kc/s
945	1,045	95	104	9
946	1,046	96	103	7
947	1,047	97	102	5
948	1,048	98	101	3
949	1,049	99	100	1
$949\frac{1}{2}$	$1,049\frac{1}{2}$	$99\frac{1}{2}$	$99\frac{1}{2}$	0
950	1,050	100	99	1
951	1,051	101	98	3
952	1,052	102	97	5
953	1,053	103	96	7
954	1,054	104	95	9

An example of how second-channel interference is produced

as the i.f. tuning circuits it is amplified by them and causes a whistle on *every* station received. Again, a good preselector looks after this; but the 525 kc/s end of the medium waveband may be dangerously close to a 465 kc/s i.f. If so, a simple rejector circuit tuned to the i.f. and placed in series with the aerial does the trick.

The foregoing interferences are due to unwanted stations. But it is possible for the wanted station to interfere with itself! When its carrier arrives at the detector it is, of course, always at intermediate frequency. The detector, being a distorter, inevitably gives rise to harmonics of this frequency (p. 252); that is to say, currents of twice, thrice, etc., times the frequency. If, therefore, these harmonics are picked up at the aerial end of the receiver, and the frequency of one of then happens to be nearly the same as that of the station being received, the two combine to produce a whistle. It is easy to locate such a defect by tuning the set to two or three times the i.f. The cure is to by-pass all supersonic frequencies that appear at the detector output, preventing them from straying into other parts of the wiring and thence to the preselector circuits or aerial.

Oscillator harmonics are bound to be present, too; and are a possible cause of whistles. Suppose the receiver is tuned to 220 kc/s and the i.f. is 465. Then the oscillator frequency is 665, and that of its second harmonic is 1,330 kc/s. If now a powerful local station were to be operating within a few kc/s of 865, its carrier would combine with the harmonic to give a product beating at an audio frequency with the 465 kc/s signal derived from the 200 kc/s carrier. Such interference is likely to be perceptible only when the receiver combines poor preselector selectivity and excessive oscillator harmonics.

The exclusion of most of the varieties of interference peculiar to the superhet is fairly easy so long as there are no overwhelmingly strong signals. But if one lives under the shadow of a sender it is liable to cause whistles in a number of ways. Besides those already mentioned, an unwanted carrier strong enough to force its way as far as the frequency-changer may usurp the function of the local oscillator and introduce signals of intermediate frequency by combining with other unwanted carriers. Any two stations transmitting on frequencies whose sum or difference is nearly equal to the i.f. may cause interference of this kind. The designer guards against the danger by a suitable choice of i.f., provided that the frequencies of all pairs of stations that might be " local " are known. And, of course, preselector selectivity comes to the rescue once more.

The foregoing list of possible causes of interference is by no means exhaustive; but it is only in exceptional situations that whistles are conspicuous in a receiver of good design.

THE PRESELECTOR

As we have just seen, some selectivity is needed between the aerial and the frequency-changer. It is not called upon to deal with adjacent-channel interference, for we saw in the previous chapter that no reasonably small number of tuned circuits is capable of doing so without severely cutting sidebands. Leaving that task mainly to the i.f. amplifier, the preselector has to deal with second-channel interference, which is separated from the wanted channel by twice the i.f. At one time, an i.f. of about 110 kc/s was usual in broadcast receivers, and to exclude strong second-channel interference at least two preselector tuned circuits were necessary. The demand for cheap receivers (and therefore the fewest possible variable tuned circuits) led to the i.f. being raised to about 465 kc/s, giving a separation of nearly 1 Mc/s from the image frequency. Consequently, the majority of broadcast receivers now contain only a single preselector circuit. Except for such possible details as an i.f. trap, the circuit of a superhet of this kind, as far as the frequency-changer valve, is the same as the corresponding part of a " straight " circuit. It is reasonably satisfactory on the long and medium waves. At the higher frequencies of short waves, however, even 2 × 465 kc/s is only a few per cent off-tune, and it is usual to find that most short-wave stations can be received at two positions of the tuning knob.

Not only does the short-wave performance of such a receiver fall below that on the longer waves on account of image interference, but many of the short-wave signals are too weak to be heard without background noise caused by the frequency-changer valve (p. 302). Using at least one stage of r.f. amplification overcomes this disadvantage by strengthening the signals before they enter the frequency-changer, and at the same time the extra tuned circuit reduces the image interference. It also removes a fault that used to be characteristic of the early superhets in which signal and local

241

oscillation were fed together into the frequency-changer, and which is not unknown with modern types having only one preselector circuit—the radiation of energy from the oscillator. If this happens appreciably, one listener can interfere with another tuned to a station differing in frequency by the i.f. If he is on the long-wave band, say 200 kc/s, his oscillator on 665 kc/s will, if coupled to the aerial through stray capacitance or inductance, interfere with a neighbour tuned to, say, 668 kc/s on the medium band.

THE TASK OF THE I.F. AMPLIFIER

The i.f. amplifier is really a fixed-tuned r.f. amplifier that derives its signal, not from the aerial direct, but from the frequency-changer, since that is the point at which the i.f. currents first appear. The two great advantages obtained by frequency-changing are the fixed tuning and the fact that however high the signal frequencies may be the amplification is carried out at a reasonably low frequency. Tuning coils available at 465 kc/s have a higher L/r and consequently higher selectivity and gain than any at, say, 15 Mc/s. The fixed tuning means that the selectivity and gain are the same at all signal frequencies, and nearer the ideal than the best that would be practicable with variable tuning.

Fig. 175 showed us, however, that the combined effort of even six tuned circuits still falls quite a long way short of giving really good adjacent-channel selectivity in conjunction with well-preserved sidebands. The real limitation is the basic resonance curve of the simple tuned circuit, Fig. 172, because it has the wrong shape— quite different from the flat-topped, steep-sided ideal. And to have a valve in between every pair of tuned circuits is inconvenient and expensive, and gives unusably high gain. If you remember (p. 225), the reason for separating the tuned circuits by valves (apart from the desire for amplification) was to prevent the resonance curves of adjacent circuits from being distorted by the reactive coupling needed to transfer the signal from one to the other. Introducing such coupling makes it much more difficult to predict what sort of resonance curve will be obtained with any particular set of circuits. But although such reluctance to couple the circuits is natural enough when approaching the subject for the first time, it would be foolish to avoid it in practical design, because it can be shown (by a rather greater mathematical effort than is appropriate in a book of this kind) that such coupling not only saves valves but also gives a better-shaped resonance curve.

CRITICALLY-COUPLED TUNING CIRCUITS

There are many ways of coupling two tuned circuits; Fig. 183 shows some of them. The feature common to all is a certain amount of shared (or mutual) reactance. In type a it is capacitance, C_m; in b, self-inductance, L_m; and in c, mutual inductance, M. Fortunately for calculation, the result does not depend (at any

242

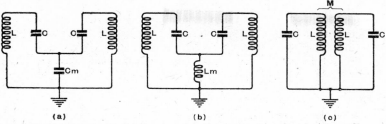

Fig. 183—Three methods of coupling two tuned circuits: (*a*) by capacitance common to both, C_M; (*b*) by common inductance, L_M; and (*c*) by mutual inductance, M

one frequency) on the kind of mutual reactance but only on its amount; so we can denote it simply by *x*. As a matter of fact, method *c* is nearly always used, because no extra component is needed and the coupling can be adjusted simply by varying the spacing of the two coils. Just as L/r is the factor determining the selectivity of a single tuned circuit, x/r determines the modifying effect of the coupling on the combined resonance curves of two similar circuits.

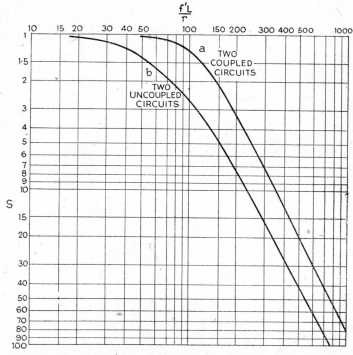

Fig. 184—Comparison between the overall resonance curve for a pair of similar tuned circuits, (*a*) uncoupled, and (*b*) " critically " coupled

This result can be shown most clearly in the form of the overall resonance curve for two circuits, (*a*) with no coupling, other than through a valve, and (*b*) with reactance coupling. The question at once arises: with how much? The shape of the curve is different for every value of *x*. Since the primary purpose of the coupling is to transfer the signal from one circuit to the other, a natural coupling to try for a start is the amount that transfers it most effectively. This is not, as might at first be supposed, the greatest possible coupling. It is actually (with low-loss circuits) quite small, being simply $x = r$.

For this value, called the *critical coupling*, the curve is Fig. 184*b*.

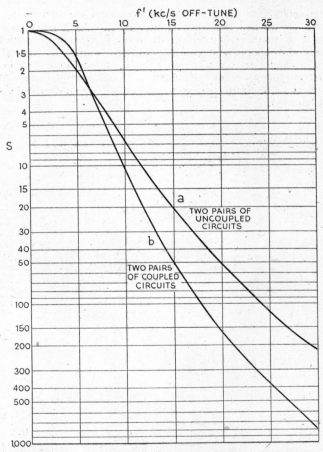

Fig. 185—In this comparison between coupled and uncoupled tuning circuits, two pairs are used, and the r.f. resistance of the coupled circuits (for which $L/r = 20$) is half that of the uncoupled circuits.
$$(L/r = 10)$$

244

The curve applies to a pair in which the two circuits have the same L/r; if there is any difference, an approximation can be made by taking the mean L/r. Curve *a*, for uncoupled circuits, is the same as Fig. 172 but with all the S figures squared. Although the difference in shape is not enormous, it is quite clear that the curve for the coupled circuits is considerably flatter-topped. It is also less selective. The advantage gained by the coupling is more obvious if the resistance of the coupled circuits is reduced to half that of the uncoupled circuits, as in Fig. 185. To relate the comparison more closely to practical broadcast reception, particular figures have been assumed for L/r, so that the horizontal scale can indicate actual frequency; and the curves have been drawn for (*a*) two pairs of coupled circuits, L/r = 20, and (*b*) four uncoupled circuits, L/r = 10. Although the coupled circuits retain sideband frequencies (up to over 6 kc/s) better than the uncoupled circuits, they also give substantially more selectivity.

EFFECTS OF VARYING THE COUPLING

Even so, an adjacent-channel selectivity of less than 8 is hardly an adequate protection against interference equal in strength to the wanted signal, still less against relatively strong interference. We may rightly ask whether any other degree of coupling than critical would give a still better shape; for, if so, any loss in signal transference caused thereby would be well worth while, as it could easily be made up by a little extra amplification. Fig. 186 has therefore been drawn to show what happens when the coupling between two tuned circuits is varied. Reducing the coupling below critical, by making *x* less than *r*, not only reduces the signal voltage across the second circuit but also sharpens the peak, so is

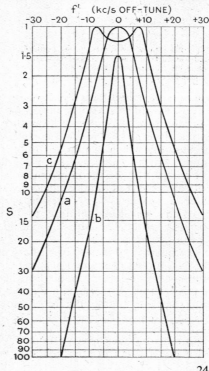

Fig. 186—Changes in resonance curve of a pair of coupled circuits caused by varying the coupling: curve *a* is for critical coupling; *b* is for less than critical; and *c* for more

wholly undesirable. Increasing the coupling splits the peak into two, each giving the same voltage as with the critical coupling at resonance; and the greater the coupling the farther they are apart in frequency. Here at last we have a means by which the selectivity can be increased by reducing the damping of the circuits, while maintaining sideband response at a maximum. Coupled pairs of circuits are one type of what are known, for obvious reasons, as *band-pass filters*. There is a limit, however, because if one goes too far with the selectivity one gets a result something like Fig. 187, in which a particular sideband

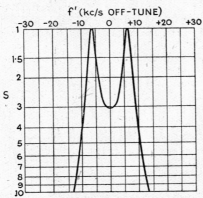

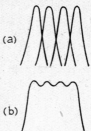

(a)

(b)

Fig. 187—The result of trying to maintain sidebands when using excessively selective coils in a bandpass filter—the twin peaks produced by over-coupling are too sharp

Fig. 188—" Stagger-tuning," in which the separate tuned circuits are set to " peak " at slightly different frequencies (as shown at (*a*)), so that the combined result (*b*) has a fairly flat top and sharp cut-off

frequency is accentuated excessively. Symmetrical twin peaks are in any case difficult to achieve in practice, and still more difficult to retain over a long period, because the tuning adjustments are so extremely critical. Moreover, they make the set difficult to tune, because one tends to tune it to the frequency that gives the loudest sound, which in this case is not the carrier frequency.

Perhaps the best compromise is to have one pair of circuits critically coupled, and sufficiently selective to cause appreciable sideband cutting; and the other pair slightly over-coupled, to give sufficient peak-splitting to compensate for the loss due to the first pair. The ultimate cut-off will then be very sharp and give excellent selectivity.

Owing to the difficulty of " lining up " the circuits (i.e., pre-setting the tuning) with sufficient accuracy to fulfil this plan, an alternative sometimes adopted, especially for the very wide television sidebands, is *stagger* tuning, in which a number of single or double circuits are peak-tuned to slightly different frequencies, as in Fig. 188.

A TYPICAL I.F. AMPLIFIER

In most broadcast receivers there is one stage of i.f. amplification, with one pair of coupled circuits between frequency-changer and i.f. valve and another pair between i.f. valve and detector. Television receivers have to retain sidebands up to 2·5 Mc/s or more, so a much higher i.f. must be used, and the circuits have to be flatly tuned. So their dynamic resistance, and therefore the gain obtainable per stage, must be small, making it necessary to use several stages.

To illustrate the orders of magnitude used in ordinary broadcast receivers, let us work out a simple example, in which the i.f. is 465 kc/s and both pairs of circuits are critically coupled. Fig. 184*b* can therefore be used to find the L/r needed to meet a given specification. Suppose we allow an overall loss of 50% at 4 kc/s. That makes the overall $S = 2$, so for one pair it must be $\sqrt{2}$. The corresponding $f'L/r$ is 112, and dividing this by 4 we get $L/r = 28$. Since the resonant frequency is 465 kc/s, $Q = 2\pi f_r L/r = 2\pi \times 0·465 \times 28 = 82$. (The fact that L is in *micro*henries is counterbalanced by expressing f_r in *mega*cycles per second.) Various combinations of L and C can be used to tune to 465 kc/s; and as the dynamic resistance is equal to QX_L (p. 112), the gain is greater the larger the value of L. The greatest would be obtained with no added capacitance, C consisting merely of the valve and circuit capacitances. Tuning could then be done by varying L, by screwing a plug of solidified iron dust in or out of the coil. But the tuning would be very sensitive to small variations in capacitance, due, say, to change of valve; so whether they are variable for tuning or not, capacitors are usually connected in parallel with the coils to bring the total capacitance up to some such value as 200pF. Assuming this figure, L must be 586 μH (p. 107). The dynamic resistance of each circuit separately is $QX_L = 82 \times 2\pi \times 0·465 \times 586 = 140,000$ Ω. As regards dynamic resistance and output voltage, a critically coupled pair is equivalent to a single circuit with r.f. resistance equal to $2r$—they are both halved. Supposing then that in our example the mutual conductance of the i.f. valve is 2 mA/V, the voltage gain of the stage is approximately $2 \times 140/2 = 140$ times, between the grid of the i.f. valve and the detector. It is assumed, of course, that the input resistance of the detector has been taken into account in the figure for L/r; in practice it might not be easy to achieve an overall figure of 28 for the secondary.

Taking 0·7 mA/V as a likely value for the conversion conductance, the gain due to the frequency-changer working into a similar coupled pair would be $0·7 \times 140/2 = 49$, making the total from grid of frequency-changer to detector $49 \times 140 = 6,860$. To deliver 10 V of i.f. to the detector, the r.f. input to the frequency-changer would have to be $10/6·86 = 1·46$ mV. Owing to the magnification of the pre-selector circuit, the input from the aerial, even without an r.f. amplifier, would normally be considerably less.

CHAPTER 18

Audio-Frequency Circuits

THE PURPOSE OF A.F. STAGES

IN ALL THE PARTS of receivers discussed until now the duty of each valve has been to supply the drive to the next valve; that is to say, the signal voltage to its grid. Because valves are voltage-operated devices—the current in the grid circuit normally being so small that the power is almost negligible—the output of each preceding valve has been considered in terms of voltage. But when we come to the last valve in the receiver—the output valve—we have to take into account the ultimate purpose of the receiver. In those used for receiving sound, it is usually to work a loudspeaker. To stir up a sufficiently loud sound, appreciable power is needed. The output valve has therefore to be of such a type, and so operated, that this audio-frequency power is available, without excessive distortion.

Like the others in the set, the output valve is voltage-operated. Its grid could therefore be connected direct to the output of the detector. This arrangement is sometimes adopted, but more often there is at least one stage of a.f. voltage amplification between the detector and the output stage. In view of the statement that the diode detector works best when the signal voltage it is required to handle is greatest, the use of a.f. amplification might seem illogical. Where it is used there are usually one or both of two reasons. Firstly, the amount of a.f. power required may sometimes call for a greater signal voltage at the grid of the output valve than the r.f. stage before the detector can supply without distortion. (" R.f." in this chapter must be understood to include " i.f." where applicable.) It must be remembered that each a.f. volt from the detector requires more than one r.f. volt into the detector, because there are losses in the detector and its filter, and because the depth of modulation is normally less than 100%. Secondly, if the receiver is required to be very sensitive the necessary amount of amplification may be difficult to obtain at a single frequency or even when divided between r.f. and i.f. It might amount to a voltage gain of 10,000,000 times, which would necessitate extraordinary screening to avoid all risk of oscillation (p. 213). The problem is greatly eased by dividing this total gain between several frequencies; for example, 50 at r.f., 4,000 at i.f. (including the frequency-changer) and 50 at a.f.

DISTORTION

A.f. amplification is the same in principle as r.f. amplification, but the emphasis is rather different. The problem of selectivity is removed, but the problem of distortion is greatly increased. So before going further into the methods adopted in the a.f. end of a receiver, we had better consider distortion in general.

There are two main kinds. The first is usually called frequency distortion, because it means that the gain or loss of the system varies with frequency, so that the audio frequencies present in the original sounds are not reproduced at the correct relative strengths. One example that we have already discussed is excessive selectivity in the tuned circuits, causing the high audio frequencies to be reduced relative to the low.

The other kind is non-linearity. It causes the amplitudes to be reproduced out of proportion. But that is putting it mildly. As we shall see, it sounds worse than such a bald description is likely to suggest.

FREQUENCY CHARACTERISTICS AND DECIBELS

Information about the frequency distortion in any piece of equipment can be presented very clearly and comprehensively by means of a graph in which gain (or loss) is plotted against frequency.

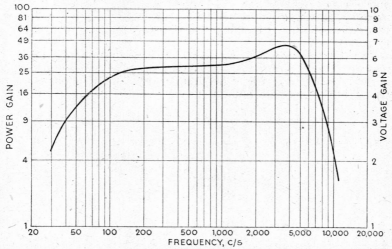

Fig. 189—A typical a.f. gain-frequency characteristic curve, with logarithmic scales in both directions

As perception of pitch (corresponding to audible frequency) is on a logarithmic basis the frequency scale is almost invariably logarithmic, usually running from 20 to 20,000 c/s in three 1 : 10 ranges. Perception of loudness also tends to be logarithmic; so the same type of scale is used for gain, amplitude, voltage, power, or whatever units are used for measuring the relative amounts at different frequencies.

For example, doubling the number of milliwatts going into the loudspeaker seems to represent about the same increase in loudness

249

whatever the initial loudness, whereas adding a certain number of milliwatts has a greater audible effect at low levels than at high.

Fig. 189 is a typical amplifier frequency characteristic. Note that if a power scale is used, its numbers are proportional to the *square* of the voltage (p. 54). The logarithmic scales, being non-uniform, are more difficult to interpolate (i.e., subdivide between the lines) than ordinary scales. Musicians have special units of frequency which are spaced uniformly on the logarithmic scale—octaves, divided into tones and semitones. Radio and sound engineers sometimes use these; but they almost always use a special unit for the vertical scale. As Fig. 189 shows, the distance on the power scale from 1 to 10 is the same as that from 10 to 100 or 4 to 40 or any other tenfold increase. So we could substitute a uniform scale of tenfold-increases. To avoid such a clumsy name for the unit, it has been called the bel; and because it is rather a large unit it has been divided into ten equal parts called decibels (abbreviation: db). If you divide the distance between 1 and 10 or 10 and 100 on a logarithmic power scale into ten equal parts, you will find each of them is a ratio of 1 to 1·259, or a 25·9% increase. In other words, ten 25·9% increases, each reckoned on the increasing total as in compound interest, is equal to one tenfold increase.

The voltage increase giving a 25·9% increase in power is 12·2%, *provided that the resistance is not altered.* The same applies to current (because $P = I^2R$). So although decibels are fundamentally power ratios, they are often applied to voltage or current ratios.

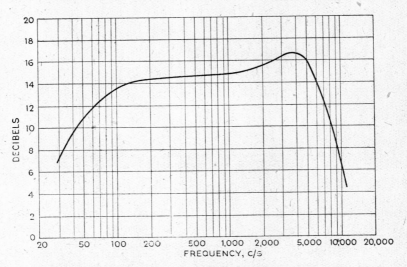

Fig. 190—This is exactly the same as Fig. 189 except that the gain scales have been replaced by a decibel scale, which has the advantage of being uniform yet logarithmically based

250

A table connecting decibels with power and voltage (or current) ratios is printed on page 320.

One important thing to realize is that decibels are not units of power, still less of voltage. So it means nothing to say that the output from a valve is 20 db, unless one has also specified a reference level, such as 0 db = 50 mW. Then 20 db, being 100 times the power, means 5,000 mW. The left-hand vertical scale in Fig. 189 is marked " Power Gain ", so " 16 " on the scale can only be taken to mean 16 mW output if we happen to know that the input was 1 mW. Unless the contrary is specified, zero on the db scale is usually understood to correspond to 1 on the gain scale, which of course means " no change ". This has been done in Fig. 190, which is exactly the same as Fig. 189 except that power and voltage gain scales have been replaced by a decibel scale.

Effects of Frequency Distortion

As a guide to interpreting frequency characteristics, it is worth noting that 1 db is about the smallest change in general level of sound that is perceptible. If the loss or gain is confined to a small part of the audible frequency range, several db may go unnoticed. So far as audible distortion is concerned, therefore, there is no sense in trying to " iron out " irregularities of a fraction of a decibel. A peak of one or two decibels, though unnoticeable as frequency distortion, may however cause non-linearity distortion by overloading the amplifier. An average fall of 10 db over all frequencies above, say, 1,000 c/s would be easily noticeable as very " plummy " indistinct reproduction. A rise of the same amount, or a falling off below 1,000 c/s, would be heard as thin shrill sound.

A cheerful side to the subject is that frequency distortion in one part of the apparatus can usually be compensated elsewhere. For example, if in the pursuit of selectivity some falling-off in top notes has resulted, it can be put right in the a.f. amplifier by deliberately introducing distortion of the opposite kind, re-emphasizing the weakened parts. But such methods should not be relied on more than is really necessary, because the more compensation is needed the greater the risk that slight changes in either it or the original distortion will be noticeable.

Arrangements whereby the listener can adjust the frequency characteristic to suit his taste are called *tone controls*.

Non-Linearity Distortion

Non-linearity (p. 41) can be expressed as a graph of output against input. A diagonal straight line passing through the origin, as in Fig. 18, represents perfect linearity, and means that any given percentage increase or decrease of input changes the output in exactly the same proportion. Valves are the chief examples of non-linearity, shown by curvature in their characteristics (Fig. 143, etc.). We have come up against this in connection with r.f.

251

amplifiers (p. 215) and detectors (p. 182), and noticed that distortion is avoided if the action of the valve is confined to those parts of its characteristics that are practically straight. The bad effects of unavoidable curvature can sometimes be reduced by " swamping " the non-linear resistance of the valve with linear resistance.

Judging from an output-input graph, the most obvious effect of non-linearity might seem to be that the volume of sound produced would not be in exact proportion to the original. It is true that reducing the signal strength at the detector to one-tenth is likely to reduce the a.f. output to far less than one-tenth, because of the " bottom bend " (p. 183). But that is about the least objectionable of the effects of non-linearity. What matters much more is the distortion of waveform. This has not bothered us very much until now, because we have been concerned mainly with the amplification of carrier waves, and the form of their individual cycles is unimportant (p. 215). Now that we have the a.f. waves, corresponding to those of the original sound waves, we must preserve their form with the utmost care. Otherwise we shall not be able to distinguish one musical instrument from another, or one person's voice from another (p. 26). If the waveform is sinusoidal, the sound has a round pure tone, like that of a flute blown softly. Fig. 8c shows samples of three sinusoidal waves, differing in frequency, and therefore heard with different pitch, but all having the same purity of tone. The fourth waveform is the result of combining the first three, and would be heard as a richer tone. Now if the first sample was an original waveform, as broadcast, and the fourth was the result emerging from the loudspeaker, distorted by non-linearity somewhere, then the reproduced sound would not be a true copy of the original. The thing to note is that the reproduction contains frequencies (namely, those of the second and third samples) not present in the original.

GENERATION OF HARMONICS

This point is so important that it is worth examining more closely. Fig. 191 is an example of a non-linear valve curve, and Fig. 192a is one cycle of a sine wave applied to it. The scale of grid voltage at its side enables us to plot the resulting wave of anode current (Fig. 192b). Obviously it is distorted; the positive half-cycle is somewhat pointed, and the negative half is flattened. At c this distorted wave is repeated for close comparison with a pure sine wave (shown dotted) having the same peak-to-peak voltage. The *difference* between the two (i.e., the result of distortion) is also plotted as a dotted line, and turns out to be a sine wave *of twice the frequency*. This double-frequency wave is called the *second harmonic* of the original wave, which is the first harmonic, more commonly called the *fundamental*. The peak-to-peak amplitude, or *swing*, of the second harmonic in this example is about 13 V, compared with about 100 V fundamental. The amplifier is therefore causing about 13% second-harmonic distortion.

252

Second-harmonic distortion is characteristic of the type of non-linearity shown in Fig. 191, in which the slope continually increases or decreases. The steeper slope in one direction gives that half-cycle a bigger peak, and the smaller slope in the other direction blunts the other half-cycle. Non-linearity of the kind shown in Fig. 193, working from point 0, would blunt both half-cycles, and is found to introduce a frequency three times that of the original— the third harmonic. Usually the characteristic curves of valves are less simple; one generally finds both second and third harmonic, accompanied by progressively weaker fourth, fifth, sixth, etc.

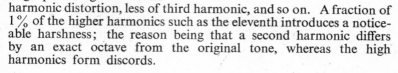

Fig. 191—Typical characteristic curve of a triode, showing non-linearity. If the working point is O (as a result of applying a grid bias of —30 V), a 30 V positive half-cycle of signal on the grid would increase the anode current by 62 mA, but an equal negative half-cycle would decrease it by only 37 mA; see Fig. 192

The ear tolerates a fairly large percentage of second-harmonic distortion, less of third harmonic, and so on. A fraction of 1 % of the higher harmonics such as the eleventh introduces a noticeable harshness; the reason being that a second harmonic differs by an exact octave from the original tone, whereas the high harmonics form discords.

INTERMODULATION

Although for simplicity the distortion of a pure sine wave has been shown, the more complicated waves corresponding to musical instruments and voices are similarly distorted. A most important principle, associated with the name of Fourier, is that all repetitive waveforms, no matter how complicated, can be analysed into pure sine waves, made up of a fundamental and its harmonics, which are all exact multiples of the fundamental frequency. So when one is dealing with waveforms other than sinusoidal it is usual to perform this analysis, and then tackle them separately on the basis of simple sine-wave theory; like the man in the fable who found it easier to break a bundle of faggots by undoing the string and attacking them one by one. Each harmonic current and voltage can be calculated as if it were the only one in the circuit—*provided that the circuit is linear*. But just now we are studying non-linear conditions, in which it is not true to say that two currents flowing at the same

253

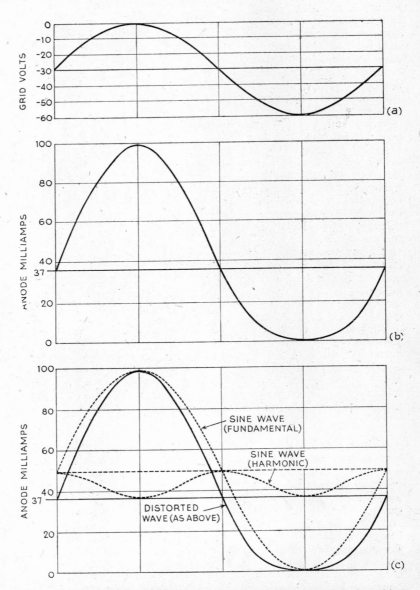

Fig. 192—Showing that the distorted output (b) resulting from applying the input (a) to the valve whose characteristics are given in Fig. 191 is equivalent to (c) the combination of an undistorted wave with its second harmonic

time have no effect on one another. If it were, then the frequency-changer would not work. We found (p. 233) that when two voltages of different frequency are applied together to a non-linear device such as a rectifier the resulting current contains not only the original frequencies but also two other frequencies, equal to the sum and difference of the original two. That is a very useful result in a frequency-changer or in a modulator, but extremely undesirable in an a.f. amplifier. It means that all the frequencies present in the original sound—and there may be a great many of them when a full orchestra is playing—interact or *intermodulate* to produce new

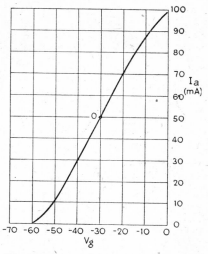

Fig. 193—Non-linearity of this kind does not cause second-harmonic distortion, for the half-cycles of anode current resulting from equal half-cycles of grid voltage are also equal; but it does introduce third-harmonic distortion

frequencies; and, unlike the lower harmonics, these frequencies are generally discordant. Even such a harmonious sound as the common chord (C, E, G) is marred by the introduction of discordant tones approximating to D and F. When non-linearity distortion is severe, these intermodulation or combination tones make the reproduction blurred, tinny, harsh, rattling, and generally unpleasant. And once they have been introduced it is quite impracticable to remove them.

ALLOWABLE LIMITS OF NON-LINEARITY

Whenever one attempts to get the greatest possible power from a valve, one comes up against non-linearity. It is, in fact, what limits the power obtainable. So naturally the problem is most acute in the output stage. If the signal amplitude is reduced, so that it operates over the most nearly linear parts of the valve characteristics, the distortion can be made very small, but then the output will be uneconomically small in relation to the power being put into the valve. It is not a question of adjusting matters until distortion is altogether banished, because that could be done only by reducing the output to nil. It is necessary to decide how much distortion is tolerable, and then adjust for maximum output without exceeding that limit.

Fixing such a limit is no simple matter, because it should (in reproduction of music, etc.) be based on the resulting unpleasantness

255

judged by the listener. Different listeners have different ideas about this, and their ideas vary according to the nature of the programme. And, as has just been pointed out, the amount of distortion that can be heard depends on the order of the harmonic (second, third, etc.)

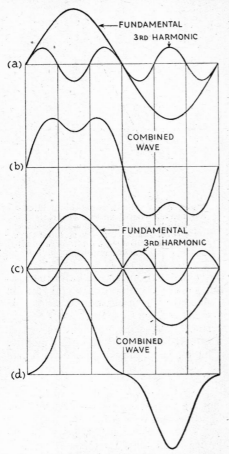

or intermodulation tones, as well as on the percentage present.

Various schemes for specifying the degree of distortion in terms that can be measured have been proposed, but the nearer they approach to a fair judgment the more complicated they are; so the admittedly unsatisfactory basis of percentage harmonic content is still generally used. The strongest harmonic only is included, usually second or third; and the most commonly accepted limit is 5 or 10%.

We shall see later how the percentage harmonic distortion can be found, at least approximately, from the valve curves.

PHASE DISTORTION

The main result of passing a signal through any sort of filter, even if it is only a resistance and a reactance in series, is to alter the amplitudes of different frequencies to different extents (p. 179). If it discriminates appreciably between frequencies within the a.f. band it introduces frequency distortion, which, of course, may be intentional or otherwise. It also shifts

Fig. 194—The waveform resulting from adding together the fundamental and third harmonic seen at *a* is shown at *b*. The fundamental and harmonic at *c* have the same amplitudes and frequencies as at *a*, and differ only in relative phase, but the waveform of the combination (*d*) is quite different from *b*

the phases to a differing extent. If the signal is a pure sine wave, the phase shift has no effect on the waveform; but few people spend their time listening to continuous pure sine waves.

To take a very slightly more complex example, a pure wave is combined with a third harmonic, shown separately in Fig. 194a. The waveform of this combination, obtained by adding these two together, tends towards squareness, as shown at b. Suppose now that after passing through various circuits the relative phases of the component waves have been altered, as at c. Adding these together, we see the resulting waveform, d, which is quite different from b. Yet oddly enough the ear, which is so sensitive to some changes of waveform (such as those caused by the introduction of new frequencies), seems quite incapable of detecting the difference between d and b, or indeed any differences due to phase shifts in continuous waves.

One has to be much more careful about phases when dealing with television signals, however, because the result is judged by the eye, to which form is of paramount importance. Phase distortion such as that shown in Fig. 194 would be very objectionable.

Generally, it can be said that if care is taken to avoid phase distortion, frequency distortion will take care of itself.

DISTORTION IN RESISTANCE-COUPLED AMPLIFIERS

Coming now to apply this general information about distortion to actual amplifiers, we begin with a.f. voltage amplification, of which the typical example is the stage between detector and output valve in a receiver. Almost invariably resistance coupling is used, and we have already (in Chapter 9) discussed this method fairly fully, at least as regards stage gain and choice of load resistance. The question of distortion now arises.

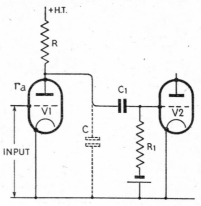

Fig. 195—Simple form of resistance-coupled amplifier. C denotes the unavoidable stray capacitance

In most sets the voltage needed to drive the output valve fully is not more than about 10 V, so the a.f. amplifier does not have to work very hard, and there is seldom any difficulty in keeping non-linearity within tolerable limits. This kind of distortion will therefore be considered in connection with the output stage, where it is the main problem. We shall concentrate now on frequency distortion.

Fig. 195 shows the essentials of a resistance-coupled stage, from its own grid to the grid of the next valve, V_2 (usually the output valve). The total stray capacitance in parallel with R (p. 202) is indicated by C. It was this C that we found made the method unsuitable for radio frequencies by offering a low-impedance by-pass to R (p. 202). At audio frequencies its impedance is, of course, much higher; all the same, it is as well to take it into account when choosing the value of R. A typical value for C is 30 pF, and the table below shows its reactance at various frequencies, calculated from $X_c = 1/2\pi f C$.

f, in c/s	X_c in kΩ
100	53,000
1,000	5,300
10,000	530
100,000	53

At 100 c/s its reactance is 53 MΩ, so has quite a negligible effect. Even at 1,000 c/s it is not likely to do more than slightly shift the phase. But if, with the object of getting a high stage gain, we were to use a fairly high value of R in conjunction with a pentode, there might be an appreciable loss at 10 kc/s, due to a reduction in the effective coupling impedance.

We know (p. 127) that the stage gain A is $\mu R/(r_a + R)$, and that $\mu = g_m r_a$ (p. 122). Combining these we get $A = g_m r_a R/(r_a + R)$; that is to say, A is proportional to the resistance of R in parallel with r_a (p. 45). But if this resistance combination is shunted by an equal reactance, the total impedance is reduced to $1/\sqrt{2}$ or 70·7% of what it was (p. 97), and the gain is reduced accordingly. So it follows that high notes of frequency f are reduced to 70·7% of their correct voltage—a 3-db loss—when $1/2\pi f C = R r_a/(R + r_a)$;

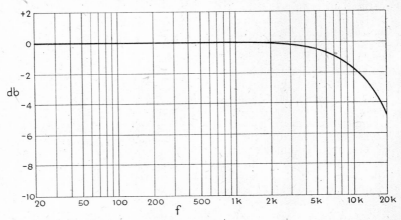

Fig. 196—Frequency curve of the amplifier of Fig. 195 when r_a of V1 is 1·5 MΩ, R and R_1 in parallel is 0·5 MΩ, and C is 30 pF, showing falling-off (in decibels) at the top audio frequencies due to C. It has been necessary to assume an abnormally high value for R in order to show appreciable loss in this frequency band

that is to say, when the reactance of the stray capacitance is equal to the anode resistance of the valve in parallel with the load resistance.

On the assumption that the r_a of the pentode is 1·5 MΩ and R with R_1 in parallel is 0·5 MΩ, Fig. 196 is the frequency character- istic curve (compare Fig. 141). Any reduction in reactance (increase in capacitance) or increase in R or r_a leads to greater proportionate loss of high notes. The curve is not altered in shape thereby; it is merely shifted to the left. It will be clear that where a high capaci- tance is inevitable (as in long screened lines to a distant amplifier), or the frequency is very high, choosing a valve of low anode resistance, with a coupling resistance of low value, helps to keep the loss of higher frequencies within reasonable bounds. A better method for special purposes is described on page 272.

In television, vision-frequency (v.f.) amplifiers are required to cover all frequencies from zero to several Mc/s; and it is necessary to use very low coupling resistance, in conjunction with specially high-slope valves.

The grid capacitor and leak, C_1 and R_1 in Fig. 195, form a potential divider across the source of amplified voltage (anode of valve to earth; remembering that " + H.T." counts as earth so far as signals are concerned). Only the signal voltage appearing across R_1 reaches the grid of the next valve. This time it is the lowest frequencies that are reduced, by C_1 acting as an impedance in series. (Compare the filter R_2C_2 in Fig. 142.) The shape of the frequency characteristic is exactly the same as that in Fig. 195, except for being reversed, left to right. And again the position of the 70·7% point ($= -3$ db) can be found, by putting $R_1 = 1/2\pi fC_1$. With page 63 in mind, another way of stating the same condition is to say that the time constant, C_1R_1, is $1/2\pi f$—roughly one-sixth of the time period of one cycle of the voltage.

Since the -3 db point can be regarded as marking the frequency where the loss begins to be noticeable, this " reactance = resistance " criterion is a very useful one to remember for both low- and high- note loss.

A usual combination is $C_1 = 0·01$ μF, $R_1 = 0·5$ MΩ, with which the -3 db frequency is about 32 c/s.

TRANSFORMER COUPLING

Resistance coupling is cheap and compact, and by suitable choice of components can easily be made to have negligible frequency distortion over the useful a.f. band; but the mean anode voltage is inevitably less than that of the h.t. source because of the drop in the resistance R, and this reduces the signal output obtainable within the limits of reasonable non-linearity. Where it is needed, a higher output voltage can be obtained by transformer coupling (Fig. 197), not only because the resistance of the primary is relatively low, but also because a voltage step-up is possible.

A full discussion of transformer coupling would be rather involved, so we shall omit the finer points and assume that the transformer is perfect, except perhaps for a certain amount of self-capacitance in the windings, which adds to the valve and circuit stray. Unfortunately, the capacitance across the secondary is equivalent to n^2 times as much across the primary, where n is the step-up ratio (p. 100). So C in Fig. 197, which includes what is transferred from the secondary, is likely to be considerably greater than in Fig. 195.

We can regard the primary winding as taking the place of R in Fig. 195, so what we are interested in is again the signal voltage at the anode. (On our perfect-transformer assumption, the voltage delivered to the next grid will differ only in being n times as much.) The anode load of the amplifier valve is really a rejector circuit, consisting of the inductance of the primary winding with C effectively in parallel.

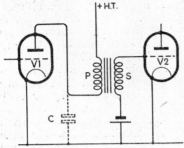

Fig. 197 — Simplest transformer - coupled amplifier circuit, C again representing the total stray capacitance (most of it transferred from the secondary, S) in parallel with the load of V1

This, of course, will resonate at a certain frequency, at which the coupling impedance will be very high, falling off at lower and higher frequencies. If a pentode were used, so that the gain was approximately proportional to the coupling impedance, the prospect of avoiding frequency distortion would be very poor. But the full-line curve in Fig. 98 shows that when the coupling resistance is much greater than the valve resistance it can vary over quite a wide range without much influence on the gain. The same applies to coupling impedance in general. So by using a low-resistance valve—a triode—and taking care to keep the reactance of both L_p and C relatively high at all the frequencies to be amplified, frequency distortion need not be excessive.

It is generally arranged that the resonant frequency is somewhere in the middle of the a.f. band. The high-note loss can be calculated in the same way as for resistance coupling, but rather more simply, because at such frequencies the transformer impedance can be regarded as infinite, and the $-$ 3-db criterion is just $1/2\pi f C = r_a$. The higher the step-up ratio, the greater is C; so high stage-gain goes along with severe top-note loss.

At the low end of the frequency range, C can be neglected, and the controlling factor is the inductive reactance of the transformer primary. A 3-db loss occurs when it is equal to r_a. This can easily be proved by noting that the equivalent circuit is Fig. 97 with L_p substituted for R (compare Fig. 67) and making use of the appropriate vector diagram, Fig. 68. So if one attempts to increase the stage-gain by reducing the primary turns, the primary inductance will be too low to avoid low-note loss. If, for example, the valve

260

has a resistance of 10,000 Ω, and it is intended that the 3-db point should be at 30 c/s, then $2\pi \times 30\,L = 10,000$; so L must be 53 H.

It is important to note that the necessary value for the primary inductance is that which holds in actual use, with the steady anode current of the valve passing through the winding. The permeability of the iron core, on which the inductance depends, falls off very severely when the magnetizing force due to the current in the coil exceeds a certain amount. This is described as magnetic saturation. So a large initial anode current reduces the range of frequencies that are adequately reproduced.

This effect can be allowed for by making sure that the minimum value of L_p prescribed by the formula is reached even with the steady current passing through the winding, or alternatively by diverting the steady current through another path, as in Fig. 198. This is a combination of resistance- and transformer-coupling, in which the benefit of a step-up is obtained; but the voltage drop in R is not avoided. Since R is effectively in parallel with the transformer primary, it tends to keep the gain more uniform by damping down the resonance peak.

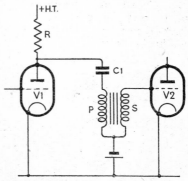

Fig. 198—Shunt-fed transformer-coupled amplifier, for avoiding loss of primary inductance due to anode feed current in the transformer primary

THE OUTPUT STAGE

As a load, a loudspeaker can be regarded (very approximately) as a low resistance, usually between 1 and 20 Ω, with a certain amount of inductance in series. If it were connected directly in the anode circuit of even the lowest-resistance valve, the system (considered as an equivalent-generator circuit, Fig. 97) would be very inefficient, because nearly all the power would be wasted in the resistance of the valve. So its impedance is matched to the valve (p. 100) by means of a transformer—the output transformer. We can therefore assume that the load can be made to have any resistance to suit the output valve. The primary of the transformer, as we have seen in connection with a.f. amplification, introduces a parallel inductance, so the output stage as a whole, connected as in Fig. 199a, is roughly equivalent to Fig. 199b, in which the resistance and inductance L_s and R_s are n^2 times the actual resistance and inductance of the loudspeaker.

Next to giving it the correct ratio, the most important thing about the transformer is to make sure that the inductance of its primary (L_p) is high enough not to by-pass the signal current at the lower frequencies. On the principle we have already noted for intervalve

261

reactances (p. 260), it is usual to make the reactance of L_p equal to R_s at the lowest wanted frequency; i.e., $2\pi f L_p = R_s$.

The effect of L_s is negligible at low frequencies, and at high frequencies depends somewhat on r_a, but in general it causes high-note loss.

The main problem, however, is to find the best value for R_s (in practice, the best transformer ratio) for any given valve. On page 129 we found theoretically that, for a given fixed signal voltage on the grid, the greatest power was obtained in the load by making the load resistance equal to the generator resistance. But that was on the assumption that the valve was a perfect linear generator, which it certainly is not. In practice this general law has to be modified to allow for the bends and curves of the valve characteristics. The usual way of doing this is by making use of the actual valve characteristic diagram, fitting a load line to it, as explained on page 124. To avoid awkward complications it is assumed that the frequency is neither so low nor so high that L_p or L_s need be taken into account, and therefore that the load is a pure resistance and so can be represented on the diagram as a straight line.

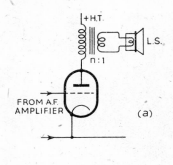

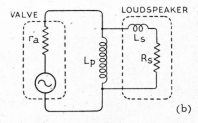

Fig. 199—(*a*) Circuit of output stage in its simplest form. Electrically this can be approximately represented by the generator circuit (*b*)

There is one modification to be made to the method as originally explained. Then we were dealing with a resistance load directly in series with the valve, so that the steady feed current as well as the alternating signal caused a voltage drop, bringing the mean voltage at the anode well below that of the source. Now we are feeding the valve through a transformer winding, having a resistance so low that for approximate purposes it can be neglected, and the a.c. resistance is what is transferred into it from the secondary by transformer action. This difference in conditions is represented by making the initial or working point start at a value of V_a equal to the h.t. source voltage, as shown in Fig. 200. Here R_d is the load line for a directly-connected load, with one end pivoted at the h.t. voltage, as in Fig. 96. The working point, O_d, is normally about half-way along the line, reckoned in terms of grid voltage, so that the cycles of input signal voltage swing the grid up to $V_g = 0$

and down to anode-current cut-off. A purely a.c. load, such as a resistance connected by a perfect transformer, is represented by a load line such as R_a; and it is easy to see how avoiding the d.c. voltage drop enables a much larger output voltage and current to

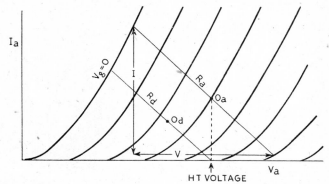

Fig. 200—R_d is a typical load line for a resistance load as in Fig. 96. R_a represents a load having negligible resistance to d.c. and the same resistance to a.c. as R_d

be obtained from a given valve and h.t. voltage. The peak-to-peak signal voltage across the load is marked V, and the corresponding current I; and we found (p. 142) that the power output is VI/8. The problem is so to place the load line that the maximum power is obtained, provided that:

(1) the working point is not beyond the maximum rated anode voltage and current;
(2) the top end does not run into grid current;
(3) the bottom end does not more than cut off anode current;
(4) the specified non-linearity is not exceeded.

OPTIMUM LOAD RESISTANCE

The first three conditions are easy to observe: it is No. 4 that is the trouble. The usual procedure is to mark the working point O_a at the maximum allowable (or available) V_a and I_a. The necessary grid bias is indicated at once if O_a happens to fall on one of the curves; otherwise it must be estimated from the nearest curves on each side. Then the load line is rotated about O_a until equal grid voltages measured from O_a up and down the line reach the start of grid current at the top end (roughly $V_g = 0$, but actually a volt or so negative) and slightly above $I_a = 0$ at the other.

Then comes the tricky job of deciding whether the result is within the tolerable limits of distortion. With typical triode characteristics, the positive peaks of output current turn out larger than the negative, as we saw when looking at Fig. 192. Assuming, as we generally can with such characteristics, that the distortion is predominantly second-harmonic, we can see from a closer look at

263

Fig. 192c (repeated here as Fig. 201) that the amount by which the distortion increases the positive half-cycle is equal to twice the peak

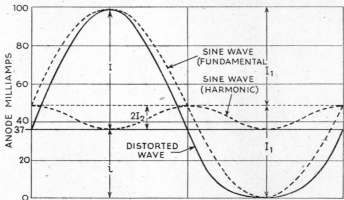

Fig. 201—Fig. 192 c again, with symbols added for convenience in deriving a formula for percentage second-harmonic distortion. I_1 is the peak value of the fundamental current, and I_2 of the harmonic; I is the peak current of the larger half-cycle of the distorted current, and i the smaller

current of the harmonic, and that the negative half-cycle is reduced by the same amount. In the symbols of Fig. 201:

$$I = I_1 + 2 I_2$$
$$\text{and } i = I_1 - 2 I_2$$

Subtracting the second from the first:

$$I - i = 4 I_2$$

And adding them:

$$I + i = 2 I_1$$

Dividing I_2 by I_1 thus obtained, we have:

$$\frac{I_2}{I_1} = \frac{I - i}{2(I + i)}$$

Multiplied by 100, this is the percentage second harmonic. This result leads to a simple method of finding the percentage harmonic distortion from the valve curve sheet. An example will help to make it all clearer.

Suppose the valve characteristics are as in Fig. 202 and that the maximum rated anode voltage and current are 250 V and 37 mA. The working point (O) is marked at this rating, and at once shows the necessary grid bias to be − 30 V. In the absence of any guidance in the matter, let us try to find the best load resistance. To meet condition 2, the peak signal voltage should be + 30 V or slightly less; and to meet condition 3 the equal negative peak should arrive at or slightly above zero I_a. We rotate a straight load line about O until it complies with these conditions, as it does in the

264

position BOC. The slope of this line shows it to represent a load resistance of just over 2 kΩ. It is, in fact, the load line from which Fig. 192 was derived.* But we saw that the output waveform resulting from an input of 30 V peak was very noticeably distorted, and calculated that the second-harmonic distortion was about 13%. We can now do this more easily direct from Fig. 202. I, the positive peak of anode current, represented by the height of B above O, is 99 − 37 = 62 mA; and i, the negative peak, represented by the height of O above C, is 37 − 0 = 37 mA. So the percentage second-harmonic distortion, 100 $(I − i)/2 (I + i)$, is 50 × 25/99 = 12·6.

If we want to restrict the distortion to 5%, then we put $50(I − i)/(I + i) = 5$, which by a little algebra yields $I/i = 11/9$. So it is necessary to see that the amplitudes of the output half-cycles (for equal input half-cycles) are in a ratio not exceeding 11 to 9. With the load resistance represented by BOC, the greatest input within this restriction is about 15 V, giving a total output swing

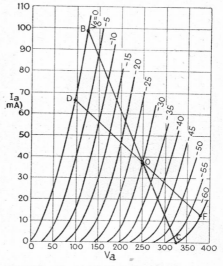

Fig. 202—Two trial load lines drawn on a curve sheet relating to a triode output valve. With load line BOC the distortion is excessive (see Fig. 192, which was derived from this). The higher resistance represented by DOF is better

of 110 V and current swing 53 mA, the output power therefore being 110 × 53/8 = 730 mW only. The fact that the signal amplitude has to be so much restricted in order to keep within the 5% limit shows that the load resistance was incorrectly chosen. Going through the same process of drawing load-line, investigating permissible grid-swing before the distortion limit is reached, and calculating from the current and voltage swings the power delivered to the speaker, enables us to find the power that can be delivered into each of a series of loads of different resistance. The results are given as a curve in Fig. 203.

The *optimum load*, being that into which the greatest power can be delivered, is evidently about 5·2 kΩ. The corresponding load-line is drawn as DOF on Fig. 202. To achieve this power the grid requires a signal that swings it from 0 to − 60 V, giving a swing in anode current from 12½ to 67 mA The two excursions

---

* Fig. 192 is therefore what is called a *dynamic* characteristic curve; that is to say, a curve in which account is taken of the load resistance as well as r_a.

265

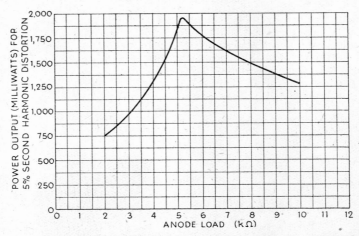

Fig. 203—The results of calculating the output power at 5 per cent second-harmonic distortion in Fig. 202 for various values of load resistance

from O are n the ratio 9 to 11, showing that 5% second-harmonic distortion has just been reached. The power available for the loudspeaker is now

$$\frac{(67 - 12\frac{1}{2}) \times (378 - 94)}{8} = \frac{54\frac{1}{2} \times 284}{8} = 1,935 \text{ mW.}$$

This result, it must be remembered, applies only to point O, representing maximum voltage and current ratings for the valve. At other points, the optimum load is likely to be different.

In general, the user of a valve is not obliged to go through this elaborate examination of valve curves, for the makers' recommendations as to anode voltage and current, grid bias and optimum load, are set forth in the instruction slip accompanying each valve. This is just as well, because actually, although there is a middle range of frequencies over which a loudspeaker is an approximately resistive load, at the extreme frequencies the reactance predominates, and this makes the matter too complex to deal with here. The resistive load line is, all the same, a useful guide.

In providing the optimum load the user can do no more than ask the maker of his chosen loudspeaker to supply it with a transformer suited to the valve he proposes to use. The ratio of the transformer (p. 100) should be $\sqrt{(R_p/R_s)}$ where R_p and R_s are respectively the optimum load and the mean impedance of the moving coil.

THE OUTPUT PENTODE

The ordinary tetrode is not suitable as an output valve owing to the distortion that would occur when the signal swung the voltage at the anode close to or below that of the screen grid (p. 207). But

266

a pentode, or a kinkless tetrode (which in what follows will be regarded as the same thing—p. 210) is suitable for use as an output valve.

Compared with the triode, the pentode offers the two advantages of being more *efficient*, in the sense that a greater proportion of the power drawn by its anode circuit from the h.t. supply is converted into a.c. power for operating the speaker; and of being more *sensitive*, in that a volt of signal applied to its grid produces a larger output. For these two reasons the pentode has largely supplanted the triode as output valve.

An output pentode differs from a screened pentode in details of design, resulting from the fact that the second grid is less important as a screen and more important for altering the shapes of the valve curves.

In Fig. 204 are reproduced the curves of a typical output pentode. We see again the high anode resistance (curves nearly horizontal) typical of valves using a constant-voltage grid between control grid and anode.

The optimum load resistance for a triode is nearly always greater than its anode resistance, but for the tetrode or pentode is generally much less than the anode resistance. At the working point O ($V_a = 250$ V, $V_{g1} = -10$ V, $I_a = 31$ mA) the resistance of the valve is some 125 kΩ. XOY is a load-line representing 250 kΩ drawn through O. Towards X it cuts the curves for $V_{g1} = -8$ to $V_{g1} = 0$ in very rapid succession, while towards Y it is far from reaching the curves for $V_{g1} = -12$ to $V_{g1} = -20$. With a load such as this, the application of a signal swinging the grid from 0 to -20 would very evidently result in the most appalling non-linearity distortion, together with amazingly high a.f. voltages at the anode.

If we were to fly to the other extreme and draw a load line (X′OY′) representing a very low load, distortion would again result, owing to the line now cutting the curves for high bias in rapid succession, while the intercepts with the low-bias curves are widely spaced. Since these two types of distortion, for high and low load resistances respectively, occur at opposite ends of the grid-swing, it is reasonable to expect some intermediate load to be best.

We are led to the same conclusion if we consider the power developed (still for the grid-swing 0 to -20 V) in the two loads. XOY offers high voltages and negligible current, while X′OY′ provides high current but negligible voltage. For both voltage and current to be reasonably large an intermediate value of load is required.

Let us investigate an 8 kΩ load, indicated by the line AOC. The power delivered to this load when a signal swings the grid from 0 V to -20 V can be obtained, as with a triode, from the voltages and currents at the points A and C; it is

$$(424 - 56) \times (56 - 9)/8 = 368 \times 47/8 = 2{,}160 \text{ mW.}$$

267

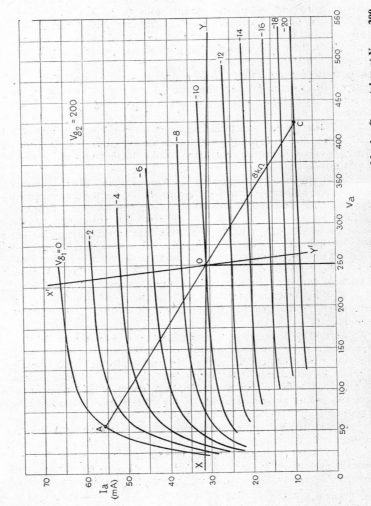

Fig. 204—Typical output-pentode curves. The line AOC represents a usual load. Curves taken at $V_{g_2} = 200$

HARMONIC DISTORTION IN THE PENTODE

How about distortion? With the triode, as we have seen, second-harmonic distortion predominates. With the pentode we have to take into account distortion resulting in both second and third harmonics of the original signal.

A load resistance can generally be found which makes the positive and negative half-cycles equal, so that second harmonic is almost or entirely absent; third harmonic then predominates, and can be calculated by a method somewhat similar to that described on page 264 for second harmonic. This is not necessarily the best load resistance, however; and the calculation or measurement of distortion when there are two or more harmonics at the same time is beyond the scope of this book. Fig. 205 gives some of the results,

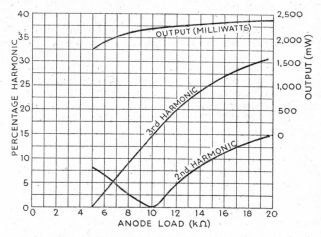

Fig. 205—Output and harmonic distortion related to load resistance for the pentode of Fig. 204. Working point O; input signal 10 V peak

showing how the output power and the percentage of second and third harmonic vary with load resistance, given a fixed input (grid) voltage.

That there is a medium load resistance making the second-harmonic distortion zero is very clearly brought out by this diagram. With load resistances that are either higher or lower, the second harmonic rises fairly steeply. The third harmonic increases steadily with increasing resistance, as does also the power delivered. Bearing in mind that third-harmonic distortion is more unpleasant than second, one would be disposed to recommend a load of about 6 kΩ in this case. It must be remembered, however, that this graph applies to only one particular working point, and that the optimum load resistance varies according to the working point

269

selected. It is after comparing the curves for a number of alternative working points that the final operating data for a valve are
determined by its designer.

An important general conclusion for the user to note is that with
pentodes there is less latitude in the choice of load resistance than
with triodes; so the fact that the impedance of a loudspeaker
load varies considerably with frequency is more likely to result in
distortion when the output valve is a pentode.

NEGATIVE FEEDBACK

This and other disadvantages of the pentode offset to some
extent its advantages—its relatively high gain and high power
efficiency. If a reduction in the gain of the valve can be tolerated,
however, it is possible to decrease the proportion of harmonics in
the output very considerably without decreasing the power available. This is done by feeding back into the grid circuit some of the
amplified voltage present at the anode, in the opposite polarity to
that required to maintain oscillation. It is therefore called *negative*
feedback.

If A denotes, as before, the gain of the stage (i.e., ratio of anode
voltage swing to grid swing) without negative feedback, and B is
the fraction fed back in series with the input, then for every signal
volt applied between cathode and grid, $-$ A volts appear at the
anode, and $-$ AB volts are fed back. The input source is now
required to supply, not 1 volt, but $1 + $ AB volts to produce the
same output. The gain of the stage with negative feedback (which
we might call A$'$) is thus A$/(1 + $ AB).

Taking as an example the load-line AOC in Fig. 204, we have
A = anode-swing/grid-swing = 368/20 = 18·4. If one-fifth of this
is fed back, B = 1/5, AB = 3·68. AB $+$ 1 is 4·68, so the preceding
stage must deliver 4·68 times as much signal voltage as if there were
no negative feedback, and A$'$ = 18·4/4·68 = 3·93. Since the
signal applied between grid and cathode is as before (the increase
being solely on account of having to balance out the fed-back
voltage), the valve does not actually handle any increased signal and
so requires only its normal bias.

Provided that the drop in gain from A to A$'$ in the output stage
is made good by a sufficiently increased input signal, there need be
no drop in output power. But consider now what happens to
harmonics or any other superfluous features generated within the
output stage itself. The effect of feeding them back negatively is
to reduce them in exactly the same proportion as the signal proper,
but since they are not present in the input signal the increase in the
input does nothing to restore them. So negative feedback reduces
harmonic distortion in the same ratio as it reduces the gain of
the stage.

It also reduces frequency distortion. Suppose, in the example
just considered, that at the highest signal frequency the output stage
gain (A) was reduced 25% (from 18·4 to 13·8) by stray capacitance

270

or some other cause. Then A′ at this frequency would be 13·8/
$(1 + 13·8/5) = 3·67$, which is only $6\frac{1}{2}\%$ less than the normal A′ (3·93).

There are various practical methods of introducing negative
feedback; the circuit shown in Fig. 206 is perhaps as good as any
for illustrating the principle. R_1R_2 is a potential divider for
tapping off a fraction of the output signal voltage of the valve.
C is a blocking capacitor to
shut off the h.t. voltage; it
should have a sufficiently large
capacitance to offer negligible
impedance, relative to $R_1 + R_2$,
to currents of any signal frequency. B is then equal to
$R_2/(R_1 + R_2)$. To avoid wasting
an appreciable amount of the
output power, $R_1 + R_2$ should
be not less than about ten times
the load resistance.

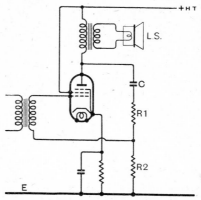

Provided that the step-down
is not too great for feedback
purposes, a much better method
is to feed back the secondary
voltage of the output transformer. This renders C unnecessary; and R_1 and R_2
also, if the whole voltage is fed
back; it counteracts distortion
due to the output transformer

Fig. 206—One circuit arrangement for
negative feedback in an output stage.
R_1 and R_2 form a potential divider across
the output, the voltage developed across
R_2 being fed back into the grid circuit in
series with the transformer secondary

as well as that in the rest of the stage; and it reduces hum due to
an imperfectly-smoothed h.t. supply (p. 283), instead of increasing it
as the Fig. 206 circuit does.

Care must be taken that the increased " drive " demanded by the
grid of the output valve when negative feedback is used does not
overload any preceding stage. Pentodes are available giving the
output of that illustrated in Fig. 204 with only about one-third of the
drive, and so are particularly suitable for negative feedback.

Another way of avoiding the risk of overloading the drive stage,
and at the same time extending the benefits of feedback, is to feed
the output back over more than one stage. If this is done, there is
another risk, that at a certain frequency (usually right outside
the band of signal frequencies) the total phase-shift inside the stages
embraced by feedback will amount to 180°, converting negative
feedback into positive feedback, sufficient perhaps to set up continuous oscillation. This problem of *stability* in negative-feedback
amplifiers receives much attention in radio textbooks.

There is one other very important effect of negative feedback.
Depending on whether the voltage fed back is arranged so as to be
proportional to the output voltage or the output current, the
apparent resistance of the output valve is either reduced or increased.

271

When, as is usual, this valve is a pentode, it is very desirable for its resistance to be reduced. The reason is that loudspeakers inevitably resonate or " ring " at certain frequencies, accentuating sounds of those frequencies unnaturally, as well as prolonging them beyond their duration in the original. By shunting the loudspeaker with a low resistance, such resonance can be damped down just as in any tuned circuit. The usual resistance of a triode output valve—a fraction of the load resistance—is low enough to serve this purpose, but a pentode is not, and an appreciable part of the poor quality of reproduction associated with pentodes can be traced to speaker resonances.

From the point of view of the load, the resistance of an output valve with negative voltage feedback appears to be

$$r_a' = \frac{r_a}{1 + \mu B}$$

instead of r_a as it would be without feedback. Note that this reduction is greater than the reduction of gain and distortion, because μ is greater than A—very much greater if the valve is a pentode. In our example (Fig. 204), r_a is about 120 kΩ and μ 360 at the working point O, so the apparent resistance r_a' when B = 1/5 is 1·65 kΩ; which is, if anything, lower than the resistance of a triode that would be used for a load of, say, 6–8 kΩ.

So, by applying negative feedback to a pentode, the low distortion and effective damping of a triode can be combined with the high power efficiency and small bias voltage of the pentode. The degree of feedback normally used brings the sensitivity of the pentode about level with the triode.

THE CATHODE FOLLOWER

In all valve circuits we have considered up to this point, the load has been between anode and + h.t. If, instead, it is connected between cathode and − h.t. we get an extreme case of negative feedback, in which the whole of the output voltage is fed back. In its simplest form the circuit is as Fig. 207.

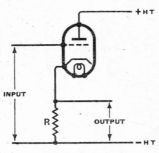

Fig. 207—Simplest form of cathode-follower circuit

Suppose a signal of 1 volt to be applied between grid and cathode. This causes A signal volts to appear across R. When the grid swings positive, it causes more anode current to flow, increasing the voltage drop across R, and therefore making the cathode more positive too. The A volts across R are therefore in series with the 1 volt between grid and cathode, making a total of 1 + A volts to be supplied by the driving source: 1 volt actually to

272

drive the valve and A volts to oppose the A volts fed back across R.

This brief consideration reveals several features of the arrangement. The first is that since the input is $1 + A$ volts and the output is A volts, the voltage amplification of the stage as a whole must be less than 1, no matter what the characteristics of the valve and the value of R. The value of B in the formula given on page 270 is 1, so the " gain " is $A/(1 + A)$ as just found.

If A is made large by using a high-μ valve and high R, the output is very nearly as much as the input, but never quite as much. A stage that gives out a less voltage than is put in may not appear worthy of further attention; but it is too soon to jump to such a conclusion.

The next point is that as the " live " side of the output—the cathode—goes more positive when the grid is made more positive (and *vice versa*), the output is not an inversion of the input as in the anode-coupled amplifier, but is in the same phase.

A third result follows from this; namely, that as the cathode signal voltage is normally very nearly the same as that on the grid, the signal voltage between them is small in relation to the input. It is this that earns for the device the name *cathode follower*; the cathode follows the changes of grid voltage. This is just the opposite of the demoniacal intervention explained with the aid of Fig. 150, in which the input capacitance of the valve is inconveniently multiplied. The demon is a friendly one this time, connecting the A-volt battery the opposite way round so as to reduce the charging current and *divide* the effective grid-to-cathode capacitance (C_{gc}) by $A + 1$. On the anode side, the Miller effect is eliminated because the anode is at a fixed potential, so the grid-to-anode capacitance (C_{ga}) is just normal. The contrast can be illustrated by an example. Suppose the real C_{ga} and C_{gc} are each 5 pF and the amplification A is 40. Then with the load resistance in the anode side C_{ga} becomes multiplied by 41, making 205 pF, while C_{gc} is still 5 pF (because the cathode potential is fixed). The total input capacitance is thus 210 pF. With the resistance transferred to the cathode side, C_{ga} remains 5 pF, and C_{gc} is divided by 41, giving 0·12 pF. Total, 5·12 pF. This feature is of great value when amplifying signals having a wide range of frequencies (such as in television) from a high-impedance source, as any substantial input capacitance in the next stage would provide a low-impedance shunt at the high frequencies, cutting them down in relation to the low.

A fourth feature is the extreme reduction in apparent internal resistance of the valve. The formula given on the previous page stated that this resistance is equal to $r_a/(1 + \mu B)$ in a valve with negative feedback. In the cathode follower B is 1, so we are left with $r_a/(1 + \mu)$, which is approximately equal to $1/g_m$. For instance, if g_m is 5 mA/V, which is 0·005 A/V, the valve resistance is $1/0·005 = 200 \ \Omega$.

Another way of looking at this is to consider what happens when

273

the load impedance is much reduced, say by feeding into some low impedance. If r_a is very large, as in a simple pentode amplifier, the output voltage falls almost in proportion with the fall in load impedance. But in the cathode follower such fall in voltage reduces the voltage fed back, so that more of the input voltage is available for driving the valve, thus increasing the output. There is thus a strong compensating action tending to keep the output steady regardless of changes in load impedance; which is just what is implied by the very low effective valve resistance mentioned above.

This, too, is a valuable feature when amplifying a wide range of frequencies and feeding them to some distant point via a line, which inevitably has a considerable amount of shunt capacitance. If the source had much internal resistance, this would cause the higher frequencies to be discriminated against; but the resistance of a cathode follower is so low that the circuit it feeds into has little effect unless its impedance is lower still.

We have, then, a very useful device for feeding a low-impedance load from a high-impedance source. The fact that there is a slight loss in voltage is outweighed by the great step-up in current. Compared with the cathode follower, a transformer is an impedance-changing device that sacrifices far more voltage in yielding a current step-up, is difficult to design for handling a very wide range of frequencies, and is much more liable to distort and to introduce stray coupling.

It is obvious that R in Fig. 207 incidentally provides grid bias (p. 290). If less bias is needed, it can be tapped off through a resistance too high to divert an appreciable proportion of the signal, as shown in Fig. 208. The grid capacitor is to prevent a conductive input circuit from shorting out the effect of this bias connection. A very large capacitance is commonly connected across the anode supply as shown, to help keep the anode potential constant.

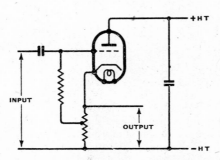

Fig. 208—A more practical form of cathode-follower, in which provision is made for reduced grid bias, and for keeping the anode at a steady voltage

A point worth noting is that if a pentode is used in a cathode-follower circuit it is converted into a triode, because the second grid and the anode are necessarily at the same signal-frequency potential relative to the cathode.

VALVES IN PARALLEL AND IN PUSH-PULL

If more power is wanted than can be provided by a single output valve, two (or more) may be used. By simply adding a second

274

valve in parallel with the first, connecting grid to grid and anode to anode, the swings of voltage at the anode are left unchanged, but the current swings are doubled. So, therefore, is the power, while the load resistance needed for two valves is half that needed for one. The performance of the whole output stage can be deduced from the $V_a - I_a$ curves of one of the valves merely by multiplying the figures on the anode-current scale by the number of valves it is proposed to use. In practice it is necessary to be careful to choose valves with closely similar characteristics.

Alternatively, the valves may be connected in *push-pull*, as shown in Fig. 209. Here the output valves are driven from a transformer

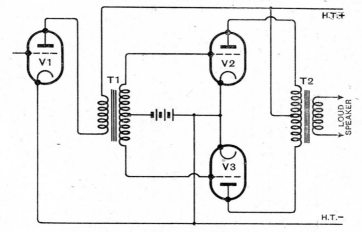

Fig. 209—Two output valves, V₂ and V₃, in push-pull

T_1, in which the mid-point, instead of one end, of the secondary is earthed. At an instant when, with the normal connection, the " live " end of the secondary would be at (say) + 20 V, the other (earthed) end being zero potential, the centre-point of the winding would be at + 10 V. With the push-pull arrangement this centre-point is brought to earth potential, the two ends, therefore, being respectively + 10 V and − 10 V. Thus each valve receives half the available voltage, the two halves always being in opposite phase.

The resulting opposite-phase anode currents, which would cancel one another if passed in the same direction through a transformer, are made to add by causing them to flow through separate halves of a centre-tapped primary, T_2. The voltage induced in the secondary, and hence the current flowing in the loudspeaker, is due to the combined currents of the two valves.

This mode of connection has several advantages over the more obvious parallel arrangement. These are:—

(1) The steady anode currents, since they pass in opposite

275

directions through their respective half-primaries, cancel one another so far as saturation of the core of the transformer is concerned (p. 261). A smaller transformer can therefore be used for two valves in push-pull than for the same two valves in parallel.

(2) Signals fed through the common h.t. connection cancel; valves in push-pull therefore do not feed magnified signals into the h.t. line of a set, and so are less likely to cause undesired feedback. Conversely, disturbances on the h.t. line (hum, etc.) cancel in the two valves.

(3) *Second*-harmonic distortion produced by either valve is cancelled by equal and opposite distortion from the other. Two *triodes* in push-pull, therefore, give a greater undistorted output than if connected in parallel.

Third-harmonic distortion does not cancel in this way. Pentodes, whose output is limited by third harmonics, therefore do not share in this advantage, though they do benefit by (1) and (2).

PHASE SPLITTERS

Owing to the difficulty of designing transformers to handle the very low and very high audio frequencies without distortion, and their high cost, and liability (as will be seen later) to pick up hum, the idea of using resistance coupling to drive a push-pull stage is very attractive.

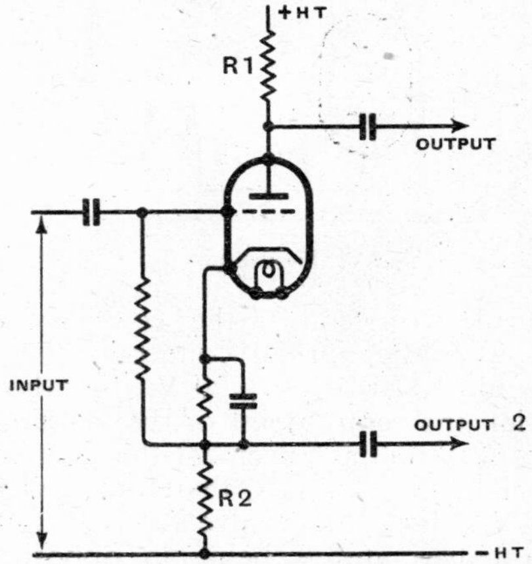

Fig. 210—The " concertina " phase-splitter circuit as an alternative to the transformer T_1 in Fig. 209, for providing two equal outputs in opposite phase for driving a push-pull stage

Several circuits have been designed to carry this idea into effect, of which one example will now be given.

In the ordinary resistance-coupled amplifier the resistor is on the anode side and the inverted output is taken from the anode. In the cathode-follower the resistor is on the cathode side, and the output taken from the cathode is " right way up ". If we had both of these outputs simultaneously they would be in opposite phase and therefore suitable for driving a push-pull pair. There is no reason why we should not have them, simply by splitting the coupling resistance into two equal parts and putting one on the anode side and the other on the cathode, as in Fig. 210.

Because the same signal current passes through R_1 and R_2, making these resistances equal ensures that the two outputs are equal, or balanced—a matter of great importance in a push-pull

276

system. To facilitate matching these resistances, the grid biasing arrangement (which will be dealt with in the next chapter) is independent, and made so by shorting out the bias resistor to signal currents by means of a high-capacitance shunt capacitor.

It will be seen that half the total output is fed back to the grid circuit, and therefore each of the two outputs is slightly less in voltage than the input (p. 273).

Looking at the circuit diagram, and imagining the two output points moving in and out in potential, the aptness of the name " concertina " circuit is clear.

The Loudspeaker

As the commonest type of load in the output stage of a receiver is the loudspeaker, we shall end this chapter with a glance at how it works.

A great many types have been devised, but the only one in general use to-day is the moving-coil. As the name suggests, it works on essentially the same principle as the moving-coil meter (p. 67). The object, of course, is to convert the electrical power delivered to it from the output stage into acoustical power having as nearly as possible the same waveforms. The mechanical force needed to stir up air waves is obtained by making use of the interaction between two magnetic fields (p. 66). One of the fields is provided by a powerful permanent or electro-magnet, and the other is developed by passing the signal currents through a coil of wire.

Fig. 211 shows a cross-section of a speaker in which the steady magnetization is obtained by passing d.c. through the coil A surrounding an iron core, B. Alternatively, a powerful permanent magnet, usually made of an alloy of nickel and aluminium, may be used instead of the electromagnet. In either case, the magnetic

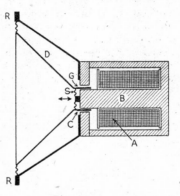

Fig. 211—Cross-section of a moving-coil loudspeaker

path is completed, except for a small circular gap at G, with iron. The high permeability of the iron results in a very intense concentrated flux across the gap. In this gap is suspended the moving coil C, through which the alternating signal currents from the secondary of the output transformer are passed. The mechanical force is proportional to both the flux density in the gap (which is large and constant) and the current in the moving coil. As the latter is alternating, the force is alternating, acting along the directions of the double-headed arrow in Fig. 211 and so tending to move the coil to and fro in the gap. The coil is attached to a

277

conical diaphragm D, which is flexibly supported at its centre by a " spider " S and at its circumference by a ring R, so the vibrations of the coil are communicated to the diaphragm and hence to the air.

It is more difficult to avoid distortion due to the loudspeaker than any other in the whole system. As already mentioned (p. 272) the moving system as a whole has its own resonant frequency, usually in the region of 80 c/s; its bad effects can be alleviated by a low output-stage resistance. To reproduce the lowest frequencies fully, it is necessary to move a large volume of air. If this is done by permitting a large amplitude of movement, either a very large magnet system is needed, or there is non-linearity due to the coil moving beyond the uniform magnetic field in the gap. If it is obtained by using a very large cone, this makes it impossible for the cone to vibrate as a whole at the high audio frequencies, and they are badly reproduced. The design is therefore a compromise. For the highest quality of reproduction it is usual to have two or more loudspeakers, each reproducing a part of the whole a.f. band.

It will be evident that at an instant when the diaphragm in Fig. 211 is moving to the left, there will be compressed air in front of it and rarefied air behind it. If the period of one cycle of movement of the diaphragm is long enough to give the resulting air wave time to travel round its edge from front to back, these pressures will equalize and not much sound will be sent out. To prevent this loss, evidently worst at the lowest frequencies, the loudspeaker is mounted so that it " speaks " through a hole in a *baffle*. This consists of a piece of wood, flat or in the form of a cabinet, designed to lengthen the air-path from front to back of the diaphragm and so to ensure that the bass is adequately radiated.

CHAPTER 19

Power Supplies

THE POWER REQUIRED

THE POWER THAT has to be fed to sender and receiver valves can be divided into three classes: cathode-heating, anode (including screen-grid) supplies, and grid bias.

So far as cathode heating is concerned, it is purely a matter of convenience that it is done electrically. In principle there is no reason why it could not be done by a bunsen burner or by focusing the sun on it with a lens. But there are overwhelming practical advantages in electric heating.

Cathode heating power has to be supplied all the time the valves are required to work, whether or not they happen to be drawing any other power at the moment; and since it is a substantial part of the total power fed to a sender or receiver, many attempts have been made to produce a " cold " valve, hitherto with very limited success.

Power supplied to the anode is more directly useful, in that a part of it is converted into the r.f. or a.f. output of the valve. This is generally not true of power taken by auxiliary electrodes, so valves are designed to reduce that to a minimum.

Not all valves need any grid bias; and, of those that do, not all have to be provided with it from a special supply. And only in large sending valves is any substantial grid power consumed, the reason being that with this exception care is taken to keep grid current as nearly as possible down to nil (p. 129).

BATTERIES

A battery consists of a number of *cells*, and although a single cell is commonly called a battery it is no more correct to do so than to call a single gun a battery.

A cell consists of two different sorts of conducting plates or electrodes separated by an " exciting " fluid or *electrolyte*. The e.m.f. depends solely on the materials used, not on their size, and cannot greatly exceed 2 V. The only way of obtaining higher voltage is to connect a number of cells in series to form a battery.

Other things being equal, a small cell has a higher internal resistance than a large one, so the amount of current that can be drawn from it without reducing its terminal voltage seriously is small. To obtain a large current a number of cells of equal voltage must be connected in parallel, or (preferably) larger cells used.

Many types of cells have been devised, but only two are commonly used for radio. They represent the two main classes of batteries— primary and secondary.

Primary cells cease to provide current when the chemical constituents are exhausted; whereas secondary cells, generally called *accumulators*, can be " recharged " by passing a current back through them by means of a source of greater e.m.f.

The most commonly used primary batteries are the so-called dry batteries—a badly chosen term, because any really dry battery would not work. The name refers to cells in which the electrolyte is in the form of a paste instead of a free liquid. The essential ingredient is ammonium chloride or " sal-ammoniac ", and the plates are zinc (−) and carbon (+). The e.m.f. is about 1·4 V per cell. When current is drawn, each coulomb causes a certain quantity of the zinc and electrolyte to be chemically changed. Towards the end of its life, the e.m.f. falls and internal resistance rises. Ideally, the cell would last indefinitely when not in use, but in practice a certain amount of " local action " goes on inside, causing it to deteriorate; and its " shelf life " is generally only a few months.

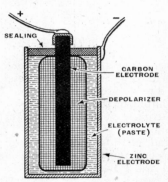

If only the ingredients named above were included in a dry cell, its voltage would drop rapidly when supplying current, and recover after a period of rest, due to the formation and dispersal of a layer of hydrogen bubbles on the surface of the carbon. To reduce this layer a *depolarizer* is used, consisting largely of manganese dioxide around the carbon electrode. Fig. 212 gives an idea of the usual construction of dry cells.

Fig. 212—Cross-section of a dry cell, showing the essential parts

The most commonly used secondary cell is the lead-acid type, in which the plates consist of lead frames or grids filled with different compounds of lead, and the electrolyte is dilute sulphuric acid. Accumulators have an e.m.f. of 2 V per cell and possess the great advantages of very low internal resistance and of being rechargeable. Against this there are certain drawbacks. The acid is very corrosive, and liable to cause much damage if it leaks out or " creeps " up to the terminals. If the cell is allowed to stand for many weeks, even if unused, it becomes discharged, and if left in that condition it " sulphates ", that is to say, the plates become coated with lead sulphate which cannot readily be removed and which permanently reduces the number of ampere-hours the cell can yield on one charge.

If the terminals are short-circuited, the resistance of the accumulator is so low that a very heavy current—possibly hundreds of amps—flows and is liable to cause permanent damage. Some accumulators, such as those used in motor cars, are designed to supply heavy currents for short periods. Others, called " block " or " mass " batteries, are intended to give small currents for long periods, and are suitable for certain wireless purposes.

CATHODE HEATING

As stated in Chapter 9, the cathode of a valve may be either directly or indirectly heated. The power for either type can be obtained from a battery, but in practice directly-heated valves are used because they require only about one-tenth of the power needed by the indirectly-heated types, and therefore a given battery will run them for much longer, or alternatively a much smaller battery can

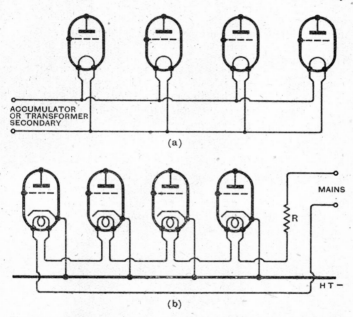

Fig. 213—Diagram *a* shows the usual method of connecting the filaments of battery valves or heaters of a.c. valves, namely, in parallel. To run heaters from d.c. mains, they are connected in series, as at *b*. Note that in spite of the different potentials of the heaters all cathodes can be joined to — h.t.

be used. These points are important, because battery power is far more expensive than that drawn from the mains, and high-power batteries are very heavy. Seeing then that the chief use of batteries is to enable the set to be carried about, it is desirable for the power required to be as small as possible.

The vast majority of public electricity supplies are a.c. of about 230 V at a frequency of 50 c/s, which can be stepped down to any convenient voltage for valve heating by means of a transformer. If an attempt were made to run directly-heated valves in this way it would be unsuccessful, because the slight variation in temperature

281

between peak and zero of the a.c. cycle, and also the variations of potential between grid and filament from the same cause, would produce a 50 c/s variation in anode current, which would be amplified by the following stages and cause a loud low-pitched hum. An occasional exception is a carefully arranged output stage, which of course is not followed by any amplification.

The temperature of the relatively bulky indirectly-heated cathode changes too slowly to be affected by 50 c/s alternations, and as it carries none of the a.c. its potential is the same all over. Incidentally this improves the valve characteristics, and so does its larger area compared with a filament. Further, its greater rigidity allows the grid to be mounted closer to it; resulting in still greater mutual conductance. One may therefore expect a mains-driven set to be more sensitive than a battery set with the same number of valves.

The most usual rating for a.c. receiver valve heaters is 6·3 V. This voltage is to enable these valves to be used alternatively in cars, whose batteries average 6·3 V (or 12·6 V) when on charge. They are usually connected in parallel, like battery valves, as in Fig. 213a, but if they are all designed to take the same current, so that they can be run in series (Fig. 213b) the voltage may be anything from 6·3 to 40 according to type. These are intended chiefly for d.c. mains.

Anode Current from A.C. Mains

The cost of power from the mains is, at most, not more than about one-fortieth that of power from h.t. batteries. So one can afford in a mains-driven set to use plenty of anode current; which means, in turn, a more ample output and less need to run the output stage on the verge of distortion.

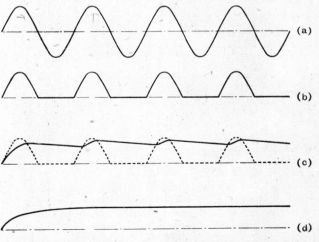

Fig. 214—(a) Original a.c.; (b) after rectification; (c) the effect of a reservoir capacitor; (d) after passing through a smoothing filter

The power is there; the problem lies in making use of it. Obviously the a.c. cannot be used as it is, because during one half of each cycle the anodes would be negative and the valves would be inoperative. Before we can use it, we have to convert the current from alternating to direct.

We have already seen, in Chapter 13, how to convert a.c. into d.c. The first requirement is a rectifier. If the a.c. is of sine waveform it can be represented by Fig. 214a. The result of connecting a rectifier in series is to abolish half of every cycle, as shown at b.

The average of this is only about one-third of the peak alternating current (p. 172), and in any case would be useless for running radio sets because it is not continuous. By using a reservoir capacitor (p. 173) this defect can be removed and at the same time the average is brought almost up to the full peak voltage. The conditions are not quite the same as in a detector, because there the load resistance is usually quite high, whereas a typical receiver taking about 62 mA at 250 V is a load resistance of 4 kΩ. Unless the reservoir condenser is enormous, therefore, it has time for the discharge to cause an appreciable loss of voltage between one half-cycle and the next, causing the current supply to vary, as in Fig. 214c.

This is described as d.c. with a ripple, or unsmoothed d.c.; and would cause a hum if used to feed a receiver. The third requirement is a smoothing circuit, which is a filter (p. 179) designed to impede the a.c. ripple while permitting the d.c. to pass freely. If the filter is effective, the result is as in Fig. 214d, practically indistinguishable from current supplied by a battery.

TYPES OF RECTIFIER

The simple diode valve (p. 118) is an obvious rectifier, and is perhaps the most commonly used of any. Power rectifiers differ from diode detectors in having larger cathodes to supply the much greater emission needed, and larger anodes to dissipate the greater heat. A typical rectifier for a receiver has a 4-V 2-A heater and is capable of supplying 120 mA at 350 V.

High-power rectifiers are made for supplying up to several amps at tens of thousands of volts. To stand the high reverse voltage when the diode is not passing current, the anode must be spaced some distance from the cathode. Then during the other half-cycle, when a very heavy current is flowing, the space-charge (p. 118) is bound to be large, requiring a large voltage between anode and cathode during the conductive half-cycle to neutralize it. This voltage is deducted from the output and thereby lost, merely causing an undesirable amount of heat at the anode.

A very interesting way has been found of overcoming this disadvantage. You will remember that in discussing screen-grid tetrodes we came across the phenomenon of secondary emission, caused by the original electrons from the cathode adding to their numbers by knocking out others from the anode, or from anything else they might strike. Much the same thing happens in the space

283

between if a small quantity of gas or vapour is present there. Provided that the electrons are travelling at a certain minimum speed, they are capable of knocking electrons out of the vapour molecules. Molecules with electrons missing are positively-charged ions (p. 38), which therefore neutralize the negative space charge of an equal number of electrons. Although the ions are naturally attracted to the negative cathode, they are far heavier than electrons and move comparatively slowly. Each one remains in the space for a length of time sufficient for hundreds of electrons to cross it, and so neutralizes the space charge not only of its own electron but also of many of those emitted from the cathode. In effect, the whole of the space (except for a thin layer close to the cathode, where the emitted electrons are getting up enough speed to split the gas molecules) is converted into a good conductor, like a metal; so the voltage drop between cathode and anode is greatly reduced.

The anode-voltage/anode-current characteristic of this type of valve, known as a soft valve, or gas-filled valve, is therefore quite different from that of a high-vacuum or hard valve (compare Fig. 215 with Fig. 90). As the anode voltage is gradually applied, a very small anode current flows, until the voltage is sufficient to move the electrons fast enough to *ionize* the gas. When once that starts, the space charge is reduced, causing the anode voltage to be more concentrated, increasing the ionization; and so on, until the slope resistance of the valve is nil and the current is limited only by the external circuit resistance. The point at which the current begins to increase without limit is called the *striking voltage*. This is the voltage drop across the valve, almost regardless of the current passed, and depends mainly on the type of gas or vapour. With mercury vapour it is only about 12–15 V, even though several amps of current may be flowing. The power lost in the rectifier is therefore very small compared with that available at the output, and a rectifier no bigger than a receiving valve can handle an output of a kilowatt.

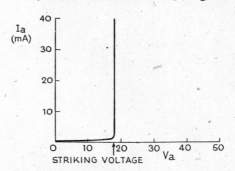

Fig. 215—Characteristic curve of a " soft " diode. When it is passing current the voltage across it is nearly constant, and r_a is therefore nil

The conventional symbols for soft valves are distinguished from those of the corresponding hard types by a black spot, or sometimes by shading.

Quite a different sort of rectifier is made of alternate disks of copper oxide and copper, and called a metal rectifier. The disks

284

are clamped together in contact and require no heater. They are suitable for heavy currents, and although they are sometimes employed to rectify thousands of volts they are more outstandingly useful for low voltages such as are needed for charging batteries. Provided that they are not overheated by passing more than their rated current, they are extremely reliable and robust.

Very similar is the selenium rectifier, which is capable of standing a higher temperature.

Summarizing: the hard diode is most suitable for moderate or small currents at moderate or large voltages; the soft diode is better for heavy currents at all except very low voltages; and the metal or selenium rectifier is best for any current at low voltages.

RECTIFIER CIRCUITS

There are various ways in which rectifiers can be connected in power unit circuits, and the simplest is indicated in Fig. 216a. A transformer T is shown for stepping the mains voltage up or down as required, and a single rectifier—the symbol denotes any type—is connected in series with it and a reservoir C_1. A simple filter circuit consisting of a choke L and capacitor C_2 completes the apparatus.

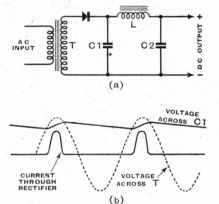

This is called a *half-wave* rectifier circuit, because only one-half of each a.c. cycle is utilized, the other being suppressed (Fig. 214b). If, as is desirable, C_1 is large enough for the voltage not to drop much between half-cycles, the proportion of each cycle during which the alternating voltage ex-

Fig. 216—The voltages and rectifier current in a simple half-wave rectifier power-unit circuit (a) are shown in diagram b

ceeds it is very small; and, as the recharging of C_1 has to take place during these brief moments, the rectifier is obliged to pass a current many times greater than that drawn off steadily at the output (Fig. 216b). If a large output current is needed, then the reservoir capacitance must be very large, the rectifier must be able to pass very heavy peak currents, and there are difficulties in designing the transformer to work under these conditions. So this circuit is confined mainly to low-current high-voltage applications.

Fig. 217 compares this half-wave circuit (a) with the more elaborate arrangements; and for comparison the transformer is assumed to supply the same peak voltage in all of them.

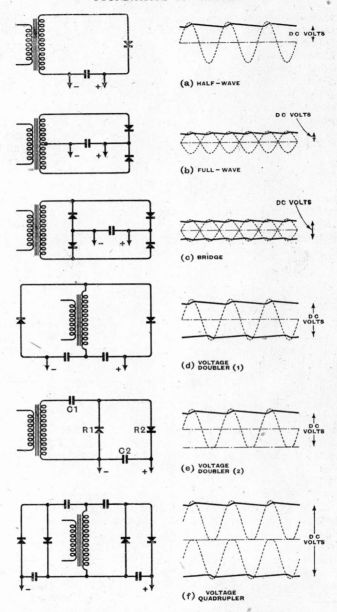

Fig. 217—Comparison of various rectifier circuits, the voltage supplied from the transformer being the same in all. Note the comparative output voltages

(a) *Half-wave*. The no-load output voltage (i.e., the voltage when no current is being drawn) is very nearly equal to the peak input voltage; but, for the reasons given above, the voltage tends to drop considerably on load.

(b) *Full-wave*. By centre-tapping the transformer secondary, two type *a* circuits can be arranged, in series with the a.c. source, to feed the load in parallel. For the same voltage from the whole secondary, the output voltage is halved; but for a given rectifier rating the current is doubled, and at the same time is steadier, because each rectifier takes it in turn to replenish the reservoir. The resulting ripple, being at twice the a.c. frequency, is easier for the filter to smooth out. The rectifier cathodes are " common ", and, as one is always out of use while the other is working, a single cathode can serve both anodes without any increase in emission being needed.

This is sometimes described as a 2-phase circuit (the transformer gives two phases 180° apart); and, though less suitable than *a* for high voltage, is better for large current. It is commonly used with valve rectifiers in receivers.

(c) *Bridge*. Circuit *b* yields a terminal which is either positive or negative with respect to the centre tap by a voltage slightly less than half the total transformer peak voltage. By connecting a second pair of rectifiers in parallel with the same transformer winding, but in the opposite polarity, a terminal of opposite polarity is obtained. The total voltage between these two terminals is therefore twice that between one of them and the centre tap; i.e., it is nearly equal to the peak voltage across the whole transformer. The outputs of the two pairs of rectifiers are effectively in series. Unless a half-voltage point is wanted, the centre-tap can be omitted.

This arrangement gives approximately the same no-load output voltage as *a*, but with the advantages of full-wave rectification. Unfortunately three separate cathodes are needed, so the circuit is not commonly used with valve rectifiers; it is, however, quite usual with metal rectifiers, especially for low voltages.

(d) *Voltage Doubler: first method*. In contrast to *b*, the rectifiers are fed in parallel off the source to give outputs in series. As compared with *a*, the voltage is doubled and the ripple is twice the frequency. The voltage drop on load tends to be large, because each reservoir is replenished only once per cycle.

Like *c* (with centre tap), this circuit gives two supplies, one positive and one negative, from one transformer winding.

This circuit is the commonest for obtaining receiver h.t. with metal rectifiers.

(e) *Voltage Doubler: second method*. R_1 and C_1 act, as explained in connection with Fig. 136, to bring the negative peaks (say) to earth potential, so that the positive peaks are twice as great a voltage with respect to earth. R_2 and C_2 employ this as the input of a type *a* system, giving an output which, on no-load at least, rises to almost twice the transformer secondary peak voltage.

Compared with *d*, one output terminal is common to the source, which may be convenient for some purposes. As R_2C_2 is a half-wave rectifier this system suffers from the disadvantages of that type, as well as the losses in R_1, so is confined to high-voltage low-current power units.

(*f*) *Voltage Quadrupler*. By connecting a second type *e* circuit in parallel with the transformer, to give an equal voltage output of opposite polarity, the total output voltage tends towards four times the peak of the supply. The conversion of *e* to *f* is analogous to the conversion of *a* to *d*.

FILTERS

We have already used a simple filter circuit (R_1 and C_1 in Fig. 140) to smooth out the unwanted r.f. left over from the rectification process. The same circuit is used in some low-current power units, but to avoid the voltage drop in R_1 an iron-cored choke coil is more usual. This has to be carefully designed if the core is not to be saturated by the d.c., which reduces the inductance and therefore the effectiveness of the coil for smoothing.

A typical smoothing choke for a broadcast receiver might have an inductance of 20 H at 60 mA. It is a common practice to save a component by making the magnetizing coil of the loudspeaker (p. 277) serve also as a smoothing choke.

The capacitor ought to have a very low reactance at ripple frequency, so is generally made large—8 to 16 μF, or even more; usually of the electrolytic type.

Fig. 218 shows a complete h.t. power supply of the type that has become almost standardized for radio purposes. It consists of a

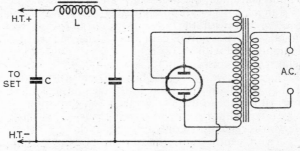

Fig. 218—Full-wave rectifier circuit (*b* in Fig. 217) fitted with smoothing filter, LC

transformer, with one secondary to heat the cathode of the full-wave rectifier V, and the other to supply the 2-phase voltage to its anodes. One can recognize Fig. 217*b* here. The output feeds into a reservoir capacitor and then through the filter LC. The transformer is generally furnished with at least one other secondary, to heat the cathodes of the receiver valves. A separate one is needed, because those cathodes are at a greatly different potential from the rectifier cathode. Even if the cathodes are indirectly heated, the slender insulation between them and the heaters cannot stand high voltages as well as high temperatures.

DECOUPLERS

Unless the smoothing capacitor is uneconomically large, its impedance to signal-frequency currents, looking from the load end, is a good deal higher than that of a battery in good condition. Therefore the varying (signal) currents in each valve fed by the power unit set up across it a corresponding voltage, which is passed on to all the other valves fed from the same supply, and may seriously upset the working, possibly even causing continuous oscillation. We have, in fact, a form of feedback.

To obviate such an undesirable state of things, *decoupling* is used. It is simply an individual filter for those valves liable to be seriously affected. As those valves are generally the preliminary stages in a receiver, taking only a small proportion of the total anode current, a resistor having sufficient impedance at the frequencies concerned can be used. The loss in voltage may actually be desirable, as these stages are often required to be run at lower voltages than the power output stage; in which case a single cheap component is made to serve the double purpose of a voltage-dropping resistance and (in conjunction with a capacitor) a decoupler. Of such is the essence of good commercial design.

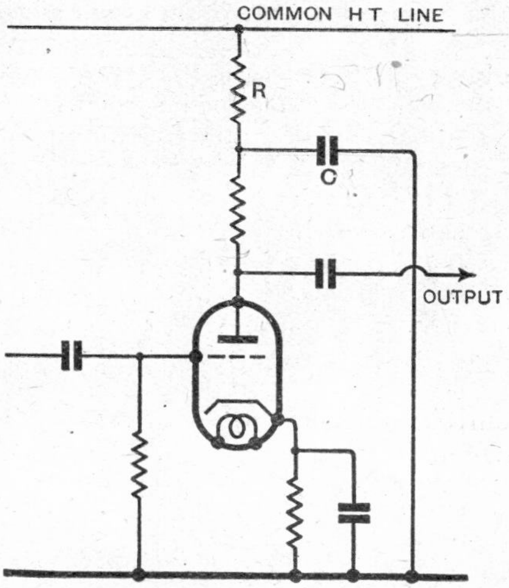

Fig. 219—Decoupling a valve from the h.t. line is performed by inserting R to block signal currents, and providing C to give them a path back to earth

These decoupling components are shown as R and C in Fig. 219. The signal currents tend to take the easy path, through C, back to the cathode, rather than through R and the h.t. source. The larger the electrical values of C and R, the more complete the decoupling.

Similar arrangements are used for keeping screens and such auxiliary electrodes at the necessary constant potentials.

It is the extensive use of decoupling and filtering that renders multi-valve circuit diagrams so alarming for the novice to contemplate. But once their purpose has been grasped it is easy to sort them out from the main signal circuits.

J

GRID BIAS

The most obvious way of applying grid bias is by means of a battery in series with the circuit between grid and cathode; exemplified in Fig. 103. A slight modification is the parallel-feed system, shown in Fig. 104, where R is a resistance so high that it causes negligible loss of the signal applied through C_g. A suitable choke coil is sometimes used instead of R; for example, if there is a likelihood of grid current and it is not desired to alter the effective bias by a substantial voltage drop across R.

Quite obviously it would be possible to replace a bias battery by a mains power unit designed to give the correct voltage. Except for high power apparatus such as senders this is hardly ever done, because the power involved is so small and there are more convenient alternatives.

We came across one of these alternatives in Fig. 142, where a resistor R_3 inserted between the cathode of an amplifying valve and the common negative line was described as a biasing resistor. The space current (i.e., the whole current passing through the valve, to anode, and screen grid if any) causes a voltage drop across it, positive at the cathode end so that relative to the cathode the grid is biased negatively. The required amount of bias is obtained by choice of resistance.

One advantage of this method is that it is to some extent self-adjusting. If for any reason the valve passes more than the normal current, it thereby increases its bias, which tends to correct the condition. Another advantage is that it simplifies the providing of each valve in a set with its most suitable bias.

If only a simple cathode resistor is used, it carries not only the steady (or z.f.) component of anode current but also the signal current, which produces a voltage in opposition to the grid input. We have, in fact, negative feedback (p. 270). If that is wanted, well and good; but if not, then something has to be done to provide a path of relatively negligible impedance for the signal currents, without disturbing the z.f. resistance. A by-pass capacitor, C_3 in Fig. 142, serves the purpose; for r.f. a value of $0 \cdot 1$ μF or even less is enough, but for the lowest audio frequencies nothing less than 25 or 50 μF will do.

This individual cathode bias system is inapplicable to battery sets in which all the filaments are connected in parallel. In such sets an alternative method is to connect a resistor between the filament battery and — h.t., and to tap off from it the required bias to each grid circuit.

The principle of still another biasing method emerged when we considered Fig. 137b. All that is needed is a grid capacitor and leak having a time constant that is long relative to one signal cycle (p. 175). The peculiarity of the method is that the bias voltage is approximately equal to the peak value of the signal reaching the grid. This is unsuitable for some purposes, and just what is wanted for others—such as oscillators. If the positive feedback in the oscillator is very large and the time constant equal to the duration of many cycles, the first burst of oscillation may generate such a large bias that anode current is cut off, so quenching the oscillation, which cannot resume until some of the negative charge has had time to leak off the grid. Oscillation then restarts, is again quenched, and so on. This phenomenon of intermittent oscillation is known as *squegging*, and is sometimes usefully employed. Elsewhere, it is a nuisance, which can be cured by reducing the positive feedback and/or the time constant of the grid circuit.

Both the gridleak and the cathode resistor methods of developing grid bias are referred to as automatic grid bias or *auto-bias*.

CHAPTER 20

Cathode-Ray Tubes

DESCRIPTION OF CATHODE-RAY TUBE

THE PRECEDING CHAPTERS have covered the general principles underlying all wireless systems (and incidentally quite a number of other things such as deaf aids and industrial r.f. heating), together with sufficient examples of their application to provide at least the outlines of a complete picture of the broadcasting and reception of sound programmes. There remains one device which is so important for such purposes as television and radar that this book would be incomplete without some account of it—the cathode-ray tube.

In many respects it resembles the valve; the differences arise from the different use made of the stream of electrons attracted by the anode. Both devices consist of a vacuum tube containing a cathode for emitting electrons, an anode for attracting them, and (leaving diodes out of account) a grid for controlling their flow. But whereas the valve is designed for making use of its anode current outside the tube, the cathode-ray-tube anode current is utilized

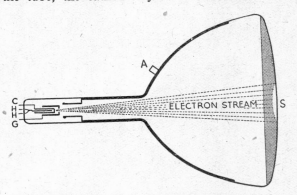

Fig. 220—Section of typical cathode-ray tube of a type in which focusing and deflection are by means of coils round the outside of the neck. H = heater; C = cathode; G = grid; A = anode; S = fluorescent screen

inside the tube by directing the stream of electrons against a fluorescent coating at one end, where its effects can be seen. This stream was originally known as a cathode ray—hence the name of the tube.

Fig. 220 shows a section of a typical c.r. tube. The collection of electrodes at the narrow end is termed the *gun*, because its purpose is to produce the stream of high-speed electrons. There is the cathode with its heater, and close to it the grid. Although the names of these electrodes follow valve practice, their shapes are modified; the emitting part of the cathode is confined to a spot at its tip, and the " grid " is actually more like a small cup with a hole in the bottom. Provided that the grid is not so negative with respect to the cathode as to turn back all the emitted electrons, a narrow stream emerges from this hole, attracted by the positive anode voltage, which for television is usually between 4 and 10 kV. Many different shapes of anode have been favoured, almost the only feature common to all being a hole in the middle for allowing the electrons, greatly accelerated by such a high voltage, to pass on to the enlarged end of the tube, which is lined with a material that glows under the impact. Although the lining is generally called the screen, the name has nothing to do with screening as we considered it in connection with valves. Since it is translucent its glow can be seen through it, from the outside. After striking the screen the electrons are collected by the anode, which is usually extended in the form of a coating of carbon inside the tube, as shown in Fig. 220.

The only thing that can be done with the tube as described so far is to vary the brightness of the large patch of light on the screen by varying the grid bias. To make it useful, two more things are needed: a means of *focusing* the beam of electrons so that the patch of light on the screen can be concentrated into a small spot; and a means of *deflecting* the beam so that the spot can be made to trace out any desired path or pattern. Both of these results are obtained through the influence of electric or magnetic fields. The fact that electrons are so infinitesimally light that they respond practically instantaneously, so that the trace of the spot on the screen faithfully portrays field variations corresponding to frequencies up to millions per second, is the reason for the great value of the cathode-ray tube, not only in television but also in almost every branch of scientific and technical research.

In television tubes both focusing and deflection are almost invariably done by magnetic fields, but as the electric methods are rather easier to understand we shall consider them first.

ELECTRIC FOCUSING

When considering electric fields we visualized them by imagining lines of force mapping out the paths along which small charges such as electrons would move under the influence of the field forces (p. 58). For example, if two parallel circular plates, A and B in Fig. 221a, were maintained at a difference of potential, the lines would be somewhat as marked—parallel and uniformly distributed except near the edges. As an electron moves from, say, A to B, its potential at first is that of A and at the end is that of B; on the journey it passes through every intermediate potential; and the voltages could be marked, like milestones, along the way. If this were done for every line of force, we could join up all the points

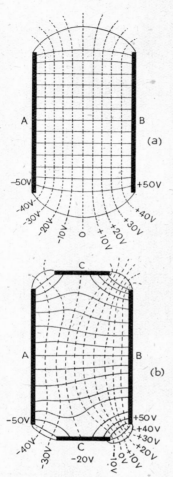

marked with the same voltage, and the result would be what is called an equipotential line. If potential is analogous to height above sea level (p. 50) equipotential lines are analogous to contour lines.

In Fig. 221a the equipotential lines (dotted) are labelled with their voltages, on the assumption that the total p.d. is 100V. An important relationship between the lines of force and the equipotential lines is that they must cross at right angles to one another.

Now introduce a third electrode, C in Fig. 221b, consisting of a cylindrical ring maintained at − 20 V. As C is a conductor, the whole of it must be at this voltage; so the equipotential lines between C and B must be very crowded. Along the axis between A and B, where C's influence is more remote, they open out almost as they were in a. When the lines of force are drawn it is seen that in order to be at right angles to the equipotential lines they must bend inwards towards the centre of B.

This is the principle employed in electric focusing. At least one extra anode (corresponding to C) is adjusted to such a voltage as to make the convergence bring all the electrons to the same spot on the screen. The process is analogous to the focusing of rays of light by a lens, and in fact the subject in general is called electron optics. Just as a lens has to be made up of more than one piece of glass if it is to give a really fine focus, so a good electron lens generally contains at least three anodes at progressively higher voltages. The focus is usually adjusted by varying the potential of the middle anode.

Fig. 221—Diagrams to illustrate electrostatic focusing, by showing how the nearly parallel lines of force between two plates maintained at opposite potential (a) are bent and made to converge by means of a third electrode C, held at a suitable intermediate potential (b). The dotted lines are equipotential lines

DEFLECTION

Electric deflection is a simpler business. If two small parallel plates are placed, one above and the other below the beam as it emerges from the gun (Y_1Y_2 in Fig. 222), and there is a difference of potential between the plates, the electric field between them will tend to make the electrons move from the negative to the positive plate. This tendency, combined with the original axial motion, will deflect the beam upwards or downwards, depending on which

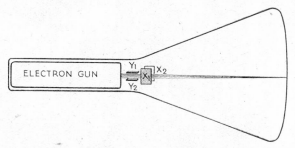

Fig. 222—Arrangement of deflector plates in a cathode-ray tube

plate is positive. A second pair of plates, X_1X_2, is placed on each side of the beam for deflecting it sideways. By applying suitable voltages between Y_1 and Y_2 and between X_1 and X_2 the spot of light can be deflected to any point on the screen.

Magnetic deflection depends on the force which acts on an electric current flowing through a magnetic field (p. 67). In this case the current consists of the electron beam, and the field is produced by coils close to the neck of the tube. The force acts at right angles to the directions of both the current and the field, so if the coils are placed at the sides of the beam as in Fig. 223, so as to set up a magnetic field in the same direction as the electric field between the X plates in Fig. 222, the beam is deflected, not sideways, but up or down. A second pair of coils, above and below, provides sideways deflection.

With electric deflection, the angle through which the beam is deflected is inversely proportional to the final anode voltage. So if, say, 100 V between the plates is sufficient to deflect the spot to the edge of the screen when the voltage on the final anode is 1,000, raising

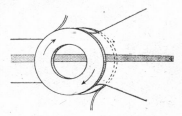

Fig. 223—Arrangement of deflector coils in a cathode-ray tube

the anode voltage to 2,000 makes it necessary to raise the deflecting voltage to 200. With magnetic deflection, the angle is inversely proportional to the square root of the anode voltage; so if, say, 20 mA in the deflecting coils was sufficient in the first case, it would only have to be raised to 28·3 mA in the second.

Raising the anode voltage brightens the glow on the screen, and generally improves the focus.

295

MAGNETIC FOCUSING

For focusing magnetically, a coil is wound around the neck of the tube so as to produce a field along the tube's axis. Electrons travelling exactly along the axis are therefore parallel to the field and experience no force. Those that stray from this narrow path find themselves cutting across the field and being deflected by it. That much is fairly obvious, but it is not at all easy to predict from first principles the final result of such deflection. Actually, by suitably adjusting the field strength, the electrons can be made to converge to a focus, but instead of doing so in the same plane as the divergence (as they would in electric focusing) the path is a spiral one. As with electric focusing, the beam is subjected to the focusing field before being deflected. It is not necessary for the focusing magnet to be an electromagnet; a permanent magnet will do, provided that there is some device such as a movable yoke for adjusting the focus.

OPERATION OF CATHODE-RAY TUBE

Although the final anode voltage is high, by receiver valve standards, the current in the electron beam is small—of the order of microamps—so a low-power rectifier and simple resistance-capacitance smoother is usually sufficient. As with valves, the grid is normally kept negative and takes negligible current. A variable bias voltage is used for adjusting brightness. The focus is adjusted as already described, according to the type of tube. Sometimes there are shift controls, for adjusting the initial position of the spot on the screen by applying bias voltages between the plates.

It is obvious that an electrically-deflected c.r. tube with these auxiliaries can be used as a voltmeter, by applying the voltage to be measured between a pair of deflection plates. It has the advantage of being a true voltmeter, since negligible current is drawn; but, of course, the anode voltage must be accurately maintained or the reading will be affected. If the deflector voltage alternates at any frequency above a few cycles per second, the movement of the spot cannot be followed by eye; what one sees is a straight line of light, the length of which is proportional to the peak voltage. But the possibilities of the c.r. tube are more fully realized when voltages are simultaneously applied to both pairs of plates. For example, if a source of test input voltage to an amplifier is applied to one pair and the output is applied to the other, the appearance of the line or trace on the screen is very informative. If the amplifier is linear and free from phase shift, it is a diagonal straight line. Non-linearity shows up as curvature of the line, and phase shift as an opening out into an ellipse.

A particularly useful range of tests can be performed if to the horizontally-deflecting (or X) pair of plates is applied a voltage that increases at a steady rate. The c.r. tube then draws a time graph of any voltage applied to the other pair, and in this way the waveform can be seen. The usual procedure is to arrange that when the

" time " voltage has moved the spot right across the screen it returns it very rapidly to the starting point and begins all over again. If the time of traverse is made equal to that of one or any other small whole number of cycles of the waveform to be examined, the separate graphs coincide and appear to the eye as a steady " picture ".

A c.r. tube unit designed for test purposes, and especially for examining waveforms, is called an *oscilloscope*. The apparatus for producing the deflection proportional to time is a *time base generator*, and is so important both for oscilloscopes and television that it deserves further consideration.

Time Bases

For depicting a waveform graph with a linear time scale, it is necessary for the deflecting voltage (or current, if magnetic deflection is used) to increase at a uniform rate; then, to avoid losing part of the waveform to be observed, its return should be as nearly as possible instantaneous. Another reason for a quick flyback is that the faster the spot moves the briefer the time any particle of the screen is being bombarded and the less visible is the resulting glow.

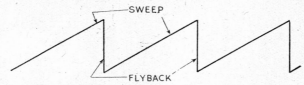

Fig. 224—Sawtooth waveform used for c.r. tube time-base deflection

So the ideal waveform of the X deflecting voltage is as in Fig. 224; which explains why a time base generator is often called a sawtooth generator.

The subject of time bases is a very large one, and hundreds of circuits have been devised. The two main problems are to obtain a linear working stroke and a rapid flyback. The basis of many of the methods is to charge a capacitor at a controllable rate through a resistor, and then discharge it quickly by short-circuiting it. With an ordinary resistor the charging is not linear; it follows the exponential curve shown in Fig. 34*b*, the reason being that as the voltage across the capacitor rises the charging voltage falls off and so (with an ordinary resistor) does the current. But if we look at the characteristic curves of a pentode (Fig. 204) we see that over a wide range of anode voltage the anode current changes very little. So if the capacitor is charged through a pentode, the voltage across it increases at a nearly constant rate, which can be adjusted by controlling the grid bias or screen voltage of the pentode.

One effective form of discharger consists of an elaboration of the soft diode described on page 284. If it is made into a triode by adding a grid, held at a suitable negative bias, the anode has to be

K

raised to a much higher voltage before sufficient current passes to start ionization. When once it does start, however, the negative grid is blanketed with the suddenly created swarm of positive ions, and loses control of the anode current, which attains a very high value and quickly discharges the capacitor. At the end of the discharge there is nothing left to maintain the ionization, so that the valve resumes its original state and its grid regains control, holding

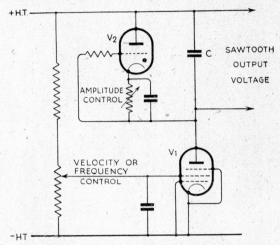

Fig. 225—Outline circuit of sawtooth generator

back the discharge until the capacitor is charged to a certain voltage. This kind of soft valve is called a *gas-filled triode* or *thyratron*. Fig. 225 shows the essentials of a simple time base generator along the lines just described; V_1 is the charging valve, V_2 the discharging valve, and C the capacitor.

APPLICATION TO TELEVISION

In cinematography the appearance of motion is produced by showing successive still pictures at a sufficiently high rate to deceive the eye—say 25 per second. Each picture can be regarded as made up of a great number of small areas of light and shade; the greater the number of these *picture elements*, the better the definition. For entertainment, hardly less than 200,000 is acceptable. Now it is obviously impracticable to communicate as many as 200,000 radio signals, indicating degrees of light and shade, simultaneously; the only way is to send them in succession. If the whole lot has to be transmitted 25 times per second, the total picture element frequency is $25 \times 200,000 = 5,000,000$ per second. If light and dark picture elements alternate, each pair necessitates one cycle of signal; so the signal frequency is 2·5 Mc/s. In practice this calculation has to

298

be slightly modified to take account of other things, but it does give a fair idea of the problem.

These picture-element or *vision-frequency* (v.f.) signals must not be directly radiated, because they are liable to have any frequency from 2·5 Mc/s down to almost zero; so they must be used to modulate a carrier wave just like a.f. signals. But for reasons discussed in Chapter 16 it is necessary for the carrier-wave frequency to be a good many times higher than the highest modulation frequency. That is why television cannot be satisfactorily broadcast on frequencies less than about 40 Mc/s, and the bandwidth is not a mere 20 kc/s or so as in sound broadcasting but extends to about 5,000 kc/s (or half of this if one sideband is suppressed).

To deal with picture elements successively, it is necessary to scan the scene in such a way as to include them all. The usual method is like that of the eye in reading a page of printed matter; it moves in lines from left to right, with rapid flyback between lines; and this horizontal movement is combined with a much slower vertical movement down the page. It should be clear that scanning of this kind can be achieved in a cathode-ray tube by means of a high-frequency time base connected to the horizontally-deflecting plates or coils, and a low-frequency vertical time base. The spot then traces out a succession of lines, and if its brightness is meanwhile being controlled by the v.f. signals in proportion to the brightness of the corresponding point in the scene being broadcast, a picture will be produced on the screen of the c.r. tube.

To cover all the picture elements, the scene has to be scanned in some hundreds of lines—in the British system 405—and as a complete picture is covered 25 times per second the line frequency is $25 \times 405 = 10,125$ c/s. The picture frequency, 25 c/s, is low enough to cause noticeable flicker, so to avoid this the picture is scanned 50 times per second, odd and even lines being covered in alternate sweeps or " frames ". The frequency of the vertical (frame) time base is therefore 50 c/s, and its flyback occurs after every $202\frac{1}{2}$ lines. This subdivision of the scanning is called *interlacing*.

At the sending end an image of the scene is focused as in a photographic camera; but in place of the film the television camera contains a plate inside a special form of cathode-ray tube. This plate is covered with a vast number of spots which become electrically charged in proportion to the amount of light reaching them from the scene. The electron beam is caused to scan the plate in the manner already described, and picks off the charges; their voltages are amplified, and used to modulate the carrier wave of the sender.

An essential addition to the system is some means for ensuring that all the receiving scanners work in exact synchronism with the scanner in the camera; otherwise the picture would be all muddled up. Synchronizing signals are transmitted during the flyback periods of the camera scanner, and the receivers separate these from the picture signals and apply them to the time base generators to control their exact moments of flyback.

APPLICATION TO RADAR

If one makes a sound and hears an echo *t* seconds later, one knows that the object reflecting the wave back is 550*t* feet distant, for sound travels through air at about 1,100 feet per second and in this case it does a double journey. Radar is based on the fact that radio waves also are reflected by such objects as aeroplanes, ships, buildings and coastlines, so that if the time taken for the echo to return to the point of origin is measured the distance of the reflecting object is known to be 93,141*t* miles away, the speed of radio waves through space being 186,282 miles per second. Since the distances which it is useful to measure are seldom more than one or two hundred miles, and may be less than one mile, it is obvious that one has to have means for measuring very small fractions of a second. In radar, time is measured in microseconds (μsec).

This is where the cathode-ray tube again comes in useful. With a time base of even such a moderate frequency as 10 kc/s one has a scale that can be read to less than 1 μsec, and a much faster time base can easily be used if necessary. The time between sending out a wave and receiving its echo can be measured by making both events produce a deflection at right angles to the time base line. This can best be understood by considering a typical sequence of operations.

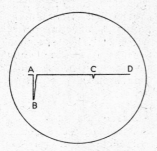

Fig. 226—Appearance of trace on cathode-ray tube in one type of radar receiver

We start with the spot at A in Fig. 226, just starting off on a stroke of the time base. Simultaneously a powerful sender is caused to radiate a burst or *pulse* of waves. This is picked up by a receiver on the same site, connected to the Y plates so that the spot is deflected, say to B. The pulse must be very short, so that echoes from the nearest objects to be detected do not arrive while it is still going on. In practice it may have to be a fraction of a microsecond, and as it has to consist of a reasonable number of r.f. cycles, their frequency obviously has to be many Mc/s.

The time base voltage continues to move the spot across the screen, and if the receiver picks up one or more echoes they are made visible by deflections such as C. When the spot reaches the end of its track, at D, it flies back to the start; then, either at once or after a short interval, begins another stroke. The sender, being synchronized, registers another deflection at A, and the echo is again received at C. The repetition frequency is normally high enough for the trace of the spot to be seen steadily as a whole.

The time for an echo to return from a distance of one mile being 1/93,141 second, it is equal to the time occupied by one cycle of a 93,141 c/s oscillation. So by switching the Y plates over to a 93,141 c/s oscillator, so that the cycles are seen as a wavy line, the time base can be marked off in distances corresponding to miles.

This is only a mere outline of one of many ways in which the c.r. tube is used in radar. In one of the most-used, the time base begins at the centre and moves radially outwards like spokes of a wheel. Normally it is suppressed by negative bias on the c.r. tube grid; echoes reduce this bias, bringing up the glow on the tube at the appropriate radial distance and at an angle which indicates the angle at which the outgoing waves were being radiated.

NOISE

The amount of power reflected by a distant object is an extremely small fraction of the power radiated by a radar sender, and the power received as an echo is a far smaller fraction still. So a very large amount of amplification is needed to bring it up to a level capable of showing a visible deflection. There is no great difficulty in making apparatus to give enough amplification; what really sets the limit to the smallness of echo that can be detected—or in fact the limit to any kind of wireless reception—is the competition which the desired signal has to face. If there are other senders radiating on the same frequency, the desired signal may have to be quite strong to be heard or seen above it. Interference can also be caused by many kinds of electrical appliances. Anything that switches current suddenly on and off can do so, because radiation is proportional to the rate at which current varies, and a sudden switch-off may cause it to do so at an enormous number of amps per second.

Looking at it another way, we find the analysis of a series of square waves with sharp corners (p. 76) gives hundreds of detectable harmonics, covering a very wide range of frequency.

But even when all interference coming in from outside is suppressed or tuned out, there is still an unavoidable limit to the amount of amplification that can be usefully employed. An electric current is not a continuous flow; it is made up of individual electrons, and even when there is no net current in one direction or another the electrons in, say, a resistor are in a continuous state of agitation. Their random movements, like the aimless jostling of a crowd which, as a whole, remains stationary, are equivalent to tiny random currents, and they give rise to small voltages across the resistor. Quite a moderate amount of amplification, such as can be obtained with three or four stages, is enough to enable them to be heard as a rushing or hissing sound, or seen on the cathode-ray tube rather like animated grass on the base line.

The electron agitation increases with temperature, and can only be quelled altogether by reducing the temperature to absolute zero (—273° C) which is not a practical proposition. It is known variously as *thermal agitation, circuit noise,* and *Johnson effect.* Although these voltages occur in a completely random fashion, their r.m.s. value over a period of time is practically constant; rather as the occurrence of individual deaths in a country fluctuates widely but the death-rate taken over a period of months changes very little from year to year. Since the frequency of the jostlings is completely random, the power represented by it is distributed uniformly over the whole frequency band. So if the amplifier is selective, accepting only part of the frequency band, the noise is reduced. The actual formula is

$$E = 2\sqrt{kTRf_w}$$

where E is the r.m.s. value of noise voltage, k is what is called Boltzmann's constant and is equal to $1\cdot37 \times 10^{-23}$, T is the temperature in degrees Kelvin (Centigrade $+ 273°$), R is the resistance in ohms, and f_w is the frequency bandwidth in c/s.

For example, suppose the input resistance of an amplifier is $0\cdot1$ MΩ, and it is tuned to accept a band 20 kc/s wide. Room temperature is usually about 290° K. So the r.m.s. noise voltage would be $2\sqrt{1\cdot37 \times 10^{-23} \times 290 \times 10^5 \times 2 \times 10^4} = 5\cdot6$ μV. If the total voltage gain up to the grid of the output valve were, say, one million, this noise would be very disturbing. Note that the $0\cdot1$ MΩ might be the dynamic resistance of a tuned circuit; but if so the noise voltage across it would be less than that across a $0\cdot1$ MΩ resistor because its resistance is less than $0\cdot1$ MΩ at all except the resonant frequency.

A somewhat similar source of noise, usually called *shot effect*, is due to the anode current in a valve being made up of individual electrons. Obviously the first valve in a set is the one that has to be considered, because it is followed by the greatest amplification. The noise due to the valve is sometimes expressed in terms of the resistance which would set up the same amount of noise by thermal agitation if connected across the input of an otherwise noiseless valve. Johnson noise and shot noise are lumped together under the name *set noise* or *amplifier noise*.

CHAPTER 21

Transmission Lines

FEEDERS

IN DEALING WITH circuit make-up we have for the most part assumed that resistance, inductance and capacitance are concentrated separately in particular components, such as resistors, inductors and capacitors. True, any actual inductor (for example) has some of all three of these features, but it can be imitated fairly accurately by an imaginary circuit consisting of separate L, C and R (p. 114). One exception we have come across is the aerial (p. 159), in which L, C and R are all mixed up and distributed over a considerable length. The calculation of aerials is therefore generally much more difficult than anything we have attempted, especially as they can take so many different forms.

But one example of distributed-circuit impedance does lend itself to rather simpler treatment, and makes a good introduction to the subject, as well as being quite important from a practical point of view. It is the *transmission line*. The most familiar example is the cable connecting the television aerial on the roof to the set indoors. For reasons already noted (p. 299) television uses signals of very high frequency, which are best received on aerials of a definite length (p. 160). It is desirable that the wires connecting aerial to receiver should not themselves radiate or respond to radiation, nor should they weaken the

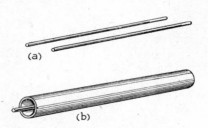

Fig. 227—The two main types of r.f. transmission line or feeder cable: (a) parallel-wire, and (b) coaxial

v.h.f. signals. The corresponding problem at the sending end is even more important, because a large amount of power has to be conveyed from the sender on the ground to an aerial hundreds of feet up in the air. A transmission line for such purposes is usually called a *feeder*.

To reduce radiation and pick-up to a minimum, its two conductors must be run very close together (p. 157). One form is the parallel-wire feeder (Fig. 227a); still better is the coaxial feeder, in which one of the conductors is totally enclosed by the other (b).

ELECTRICAL EQUIVALENT OF A LINE

With either type, and especially the coaxial, the closeness of the two leads causes a high capacitance between them; and at very

303

high frequencies that means a low impedance, which, it might be supposed, would more or less short-circuit a long feeder, so that very little of the power put in at one end would reach the other. But it must be remembered that every inch of the feeder not only has a certain amount of capacitance in parallel, but also, by virtue of the magnetic flux set up by any current flowing through it, a certain amount of inductance in series. Electrically, therefore, a piece of transmission line can be represented with standard circuit

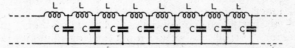

Fig. 228—Approximate electrical analysis of a short length of transmission line

symbols as in Fig. 228, in which L and C are respectively the inductance and capacitance of an extremely short length, and so are extremely small quantities. Each inductance is, of course, contributed to by both wires, but it makes no difference to our argument if for simplicity the symbol for the total is shown in one wire; it is in series either way. As we shall only be considering lines that are uniform throughout their length, every L is accompanied by the same amount of C; in other words, the ratio L/C is constant.

Having analysed the line in this way, let us consider the load at the receiving end; assuming first that its impedance is a simple resistance, R (Fig. 229a). If we were to measure the voltage across its terminals and the amperage going into it, the ratio of the two readings would indicate the value R in ohms.

Next, suppose this load to be elaborated by the addition of a

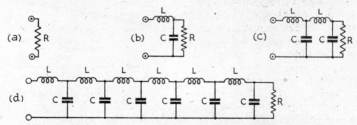

Fig. 229—Synthesis of transmission line from basic circuit elements

small inductance in series and a small capacitance in parallel, as at b. Provided that the capacitance really is small, its reactance, X_C, will be much greater than R. By an adaptation of the method used on page 115 a relatively large reactance in parallel with a resistance can, with negligible error, be replaced by an equivalent circuit consisting of the same resistance in series with a relatively small reactance. Calling this equivalent series capacitive reactance X_C', we have $X_C'/R = R/X_C$, or $X_C' = R^2/X_C$. And if we make this

304

X_C' equal to X_L, it will cancel out the effect of L (p. 103), so that the whole of Fig. 229b will give the same readings on our measuring instruments as R alone. X_L is, of course, $2\pi fL$, and X_C is $1/2\pi fC$; so the condition for X_C' and X_L cancelling one another out is

$$2\pi fL = R^2 \times 2\pi fC$$
$$\text{or,} \quad L = R^2C$$
$$\text{or,} \quad R = \sqrt{\frac{L}{C}}.$$

Notice that frequency does not come into this at all, except that if it is very high then L and C may have to be very small indeed in order to fulfil the condition that X_C is much larger than R.

Assuming, then, that in our case $\sqrt{L/C}$ does happen to be equal to R, so that R in Fig. 229a can be replaced by the combination LCR in b, it will still make no difference to the instrument readings if R in b is in turn replaced by an identical LCR combination, as at c. R in this load can be replaced by another LCR unit, and so on indefinitely (d). Every time, meters connected at the terminals will show the same readings, just as if the load were R only.

The smaller L and C are, the more exactly the above argument is true at all practical frequencies. This is very interesting, because by making each L and C smaller and smaller and increasing their number we can approximate as closely as we like to the electrical equivalent of a parallel or coaxial transmission line in which inductance and capacitance are uniformly distributed along its length. In such a line the ratio of inductance to capacitance is the same for a foot or a mile as for each one of the infinitesimal " units ", so we reach the conclusion that provided the far end of the line is terminated by a resistance R equal to $\sqrt{L/C}$ ohms the length of the line makes no difference; to the signal-source or generator it is just the same as if the load R were connected directly to its terminals.

That, of course, is exactly what we want as a feeder for a load which has to be located at a distance from the generator. But there is admittedly one difference between a real feeder and the synthetic one shown in Fig. 229d; its conductors are bound to have a certain amount of resistance. Assuming that this resistance is uniformly distributed, every 100 feet of line will absorb a certain percentage of the power put into it; for example, if the power put into a 100-foot length has to be 25·9% greater than that coming out at the far end, the loss is said to be 1 db per 100 feet (p. 250); and we then know that a 20-foot length of the same line will cause a 0·2-db loss. Obviously, a line made of a very thin wire, of comparatively high resistance, will cause greater loss than one made of low-resistance wire. So, too, will a pair separated by poor insulating material (p. 114). Although the loss due to resistance is an important property of a line, it is generally allowable to neglect the resistance itself in calculations such as that at the top of this page.

CHARACTERISTIC RESISTANCE

The next thing to consider is how to make the feeder fit the load, so as to fulfil the necessary condition, $\sqrt{L/C} = R$. $\sqrt{L/C}$ is obviously a characteristic of the line itself, and to instruments connected to one end the line appears to be a resistance; so for any particular line it is called its *characteristic resistance*, denoted by R_0*.

If you feel that the resistance in question really belongs to the terminating load and not the line, then it should be remembered that the load resistance can always be replaced by another length of

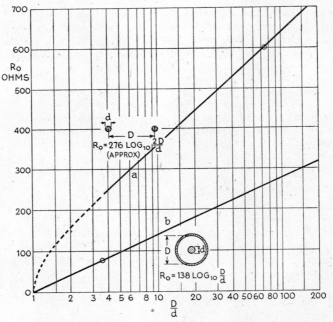

Fig. 230—Graphs showing characteristic resistance (R_0) of (*a*) parallel-wire and (*b*) coaxial transmission lines in terms of dimensions

line, so that ultimately R_0 can be defined as the input resistance of an infinitely long line. Alternatively (and more practically) it is a resistance equal to whatever load resistance can be fed through any length of the line without making any difference to the generator.

In any case, L and C depend entirely on the spacing and diameters of the wires or tubes of which the line consists, and on the permittivity and permeability of the spacing materials. So far as

* If loss resistance is taken into account the expression is slightly more complicated than $\sqrt{L/C}$, and includes reactance; so the more comprehensive and strictly accurate term is characteristic (or surge) impedance, Z_0. With reasonably low-loss lines there is not much difference.

306

possible, to avoid losses, feeders are air-spaced. The closer the spacing, the higher is C (as one would expect) and the smaller is L (because the magnetic field set up by the current in one wire is nearly cancelled by the field of the returning current in the other). So a closely-spaced line has a small R_0, suitable for feeding low-resistance loads. Other things being equal, one would expect a coaxial line to have a greater C, and therefore lower R_0, than a parallel-wire line. Formulae have been worked out for calculating R_0; for a parallel-wire line (Fig 230a) it is practically 276 $\log_{10}(2D/d)$ (so long as D is at least 4 or 5 times d), and for a coaxial line (Fig. 230b) 138 $\log_{10}(D/d)$. Graphs such as these can be used to find the correct dimensions for a feeder to fit a load of any resistance, within the limits of practicable construction. It has been found that the feeder dimensions causing least loss make R_0 equal to about 600 Ω for parallel-wire and 80 Ω for coaxial types; but a reasonably efficient feeder of practical dimensions can be made to have an R_0 of anything from, say 200 to 650 and 40 to 140 ohms respectively. We shall see later what to do if the load resistance cannot be matched by any available feeder.

In the meantime, what if the load is not a pure resistance? Whatever it is, it can be reckoned as a resistance in parallel with a reactance. And this reactance can always be neutralized or tuned out by connecting in parallel with it an equal reactance of the opposite kind (p. 108). So that little problem is soon solved.

WAVES ALONG A LINE

Although interposing a loss-free line (having the correct R_0) between a generator and its load does not affect the voltage and

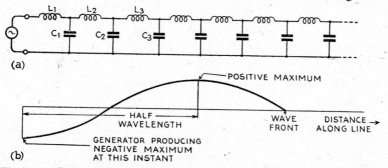

Fig. 231—(a) Electrical representation of the generator end of a transmission line, and (b) instantaneous voltage (and current) diagram ¾ of a cycle from the start of generating a sine wave

current at the load terminals—they are still the same as at the generator—it does affect their phase. The mere fact that the voltage across R in Fig. 229b is equal to the voltage across the terminals makes that inevitable, as one can soon see by drawing the vector diagram. There is a small phase lag due to L. In

307

a line, the phase lags adds up steadily as one moves along it. If we consider what happens in a line when the generator starts generating (Fig. 231) we can see that what the gradual phase lag along it really means is that the power takes time to travel from generator to load.

During the first half-cycle (positive, say) current starts flowing into C_1, charging it up. The inductance L_1 prevents the voltage across C_1 rising to its maximum until a little later than the generator voltage maximum. The inertia of L_2 to the growth of current through it allows the charge to build up in C_1 a little before C_2, and so on. Gradually the charge builds up on each bit of the line in turn. Meanwhile, the generator has gone on to the negative half-cycle, and this follows its predecessor down the line. At its first negative maximum, the voltage distribution will be as shown at b. With a little imagination one can picture the voltage wave flashing down the line, rather like the wave motion of a long rope waggled up and down at one end.

Our theory showed that the current is everywhere in phase with the voltage, so the wave diagram also represents power flowing along the line. In an air-spaced line it travels at the same speed as electromagnetic waves in open space (p. 31)—nearly 300 million metres per second. So the time needed to reach the far end of any actual line is bound to be very short—a small fraction of a second. But however short, there must be some interval between the power first going into the line from the generator and its coming out of the line into the load. During this interval the generator is not in touch with the load at all; the current pushed into the line by a given generator voltage is determined by R_0 alone, no matter what may be connected at the far end—which is further evidence that R_0 is a characteristic of the line and not of the load.

During this brief interval, when the generator does not " know " the resistance of the load it will soon be required to feed, the R_0 of the line controls the rate of power flow tentatively. In accordance with the usual law (p. 128), the maximum power goes into the line during this transient state if R_0 is equal to r, the generator resistance.

Neglecting line loss, the voltage and current reaching the load end will be the same as at the generator. So if the load turns out to be a resistance equal to R_0, it will satisfy Ohm's Law, and the whole of the power will be absorbed just as fast as it arrives. For example, if a piece of line having an R_0 of 500 Ω is connected to a 1,000-V generator having an r or 500 Ω, the terminal voltage is bound to be 500 V and the current 1 A until the wave reaches the far end, no matter what may be there. If there is a load resistance of 500 Ω, the r.m.s. current will, of course, continue at 1 A everywhere.

WAVE REFLECTION

But suppose that the load resistance is, say, 2,000 Ω. According to Ohm's Law it is impossible for 500 V applied across 2,000 Ω

to cause a current of 1 A to flow. Yet 1 A is arriving. What does it do? Part of it, having nowhere to go, starts back for home. More scientifically, it is *reflected* by the mismatch. The reflected current, travelling in the opposite direction, can be regarded as opposite in phase to that arriving, giving a total which is less than 1 A. The comparatively high resistance causes the voltage across it to build up above 500; this increase can be regarded as a reflected voltage driving the reflected current. If half the current were reflected, leaving 0·5 A to go into the load resistance, the voltage would be increased by a half, making it 750. A voltage of 750 and current 0·5 A would fit a 1,500 Ω load, but not 2,000 Ω, so the reflected proportion has to be greater—actually 60%, giving 800 V and 0·4 A at the load.

We now have 1 A, driven by 500 V, travelling from generator to load, and 0·6 A, driven by 300 V, returning to the generator. (The ratio of the reflected voltage to the reflected current must, of course, equal R_0.) The combination of these two at the terminals of the load gives, as we have seen, $1 - 0·6 = 0·4$ A, at $500 + 300 = 800$ V. But at other points on the line we have to take account of the phase lag. At a distance from the load end equal to quarter of a wavelength ($\lambda/4$) the arriving and returning waves differ in phase by half a wavelength ($\lambda/2$) or 180° as compared with their relative phases at the load (because a return journey has to be made over the $\lambda/4$ distance). So at this point the current is $1 + 0·6 = 1·6$ A at $500 - 300 = 200$ V. At a point $\lambda/8$ from the load end the phase separation is $\lambda/4$ or 90°, giving 1·16 A at 582 V. At intervals of $\lambda/2$, the two waves come into step again.

STANDING WAVES

Calculating the current and voltage point by point in this way and plotting them, we get the curves in Fig. 232. It is important to realize that these are not, as it were, flashlight photographs of the waves travelling along the line; these are r.m.s. values set up continuously at the points shown, and would be indicated by meters connected in or across the lines at those points (assuming the meters did not appreciably affect the R_0 of the line where connected). Because this wavelike distribution of current and voltage, resulting from the addition of the arriving and reflected waves travelling in opposite directions, is stationary, it is called a *standing wave*. For comparison, the uniform distribution of current and voltage when the load resistance is equal to R_0 is shown dotted.

The ratio of maximum to minimum current or voltage is called the *standing wave ratio*; in our example it is 800/200 (or 1·6/0·4) = 4.

In due course the reflected wave reaches the generator. It is in this indirect way that the load makes itself felt by the generator. If the 2,000-Ω load had been directly connected to the generator terminals, the current would have been $1,000/(500 + 2,000) = 0·4$ A, and the terminal voltage $0·4 \times 2,000 = 800$ V, and the power $800 \times 0·4 = 320$ W. This, as we have seen, is exactly what the

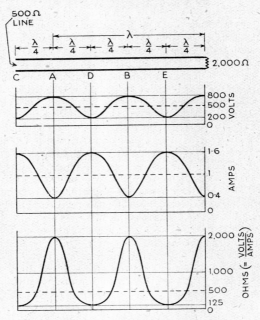

Fig. 232—Diagrams of voltage, current, and (as a
result) impedance at the load end of an unmatched
transmission line, showing standing waves

load at the end of the line is actually getting. But the power that
originally went out from the generator, being determined by R_0,
was $500 \times 1 = 500$ W. The reflected power is $300 \times 0.6 = 180$ W,
so the net outgoing power is $500 - 180 = 320$ W, just as it would
have been with the load directly connected.

Line Impedance Variations

So the power adjustment is (in this case) quite simple. But the
current and voltage situation at the generator is complicated by the
time lag, and is not necessarily the same as at the load. Unless the
length of the line is an exact multiple of $\lambda/2$, the phase relationships
are different. Suppose, for example, it is an odd multiple of $\lambda/4$;
say, $5\lambda/4$, as in Fig. 232. Then the current and voltage at the
generator end will be 1.6 A and 200 V respectively. That makes
320 W all right—but compare the power loss in the generator.
1.6 A flowing through $r = 500$ Ω is $1.6^2 \times 500 = 1,280$ W, whereas
at an 800-V point the current would be only 0.4 A and the loss in
the generator only $0.4^2 \times 500 = 80$ W! So when there are standing
waves, the exact length of the line (in wavelengths) is obviously
very important. If there are no standing waves, it does not matter
if the line is a little longer or shorter or the wavelength is altered

310

slightly; and that is one very good reason for matching the load to the line. The usual way of making sure that the load is right is by running a voltmeter or other indicator along the line and seeing that the reading is the same everywhere, except perhaps for a slight gradual change due to line loss.

Connecting the generator to a point on the line where the voltage and current are 200 V and 1·6 A respectively is equivalent to connecting it to a load of $200/1·6 = 125 \ \Omega$. The impedance of the line at all points can easily be derived from the voltage and current curves, as at the foot of Fig. 232. This curve indicates the impedance measured at any point when all the line to the left of that point is removed. The impedance depends, of course, not only on the distance along the line to the load but also on R_0 and the load impedance. From a consideration of the travelling waves it can be seen that at $\lambda/4$ intervals the phases of the currents and voltages are exactly the same as at the load, or exactly opposite; so that if the load is resistive the input resistance of the line is also resistive. At all other points the phases are such as to be equivalent to introducing reactance.

In our example we made the generator resistance, r, equal to R_0. If it were not, the situation would be more complicated still, because the reflected wave would not be completely absorbed by the generator, so part would be reflected back to the load, and so on, the reflected power being smaller on each successive journey, until finally becoming negligible. The standing waves would be the resultant of all these travelling waves. Even quite a long line settles down to a steady state in a fraction of a second, but it is a state that is generally undesirable because it means that much of the power is being dissipated in the line instead of being delivered to the load.

It should be noted that mismatching at the generator end does not affect the standing-wave ratio, but does affect the values of current and voltage attained.

Another result of making $r = R_0$ is that any reflection from the load or elsewhere inevitably impairs the generator-to-line matching. That is so even if the generator is connected to a point where the impedance curve coincides with the 500-Ω line in Fig. 232, because then the impedance is reactive. But if r were, say, 2,000 Ω, so that it would be mismatched to the 500-Ω line during the brief moment following the start, there would be a chance that when the reflected wave arrived it would actually improve the matching, even to making it perfect (e.g., if connected at A or B in Fig. 232); but on the other hand it might make it still worse (if connected at C, D, or E).

It should be remembered that " perfect " matching is that which enables maximum power to be transferred; but in practice, as we have seen in other connections (pp. 152 and 262) there may be good reasons for deliberately mismatching at the generator. To take figures we have already had, it may be considered better to deliver

311

320 W with a loss of 80 W than the maximum (500 W) with a loss of 500 W.

THE QUARTER-WAVE TRANSFORMER

An interesting result of the principles exemplified in Fig. 232 is that a generator of one impedance can be perfectly matched to a load of another by suitably choosing the points of connection. For instance, a generator with an internal resistance of 125 Ω would be matched to the 2,000 Ω load if connected at C, D or E. The line then behaves as a 1 : 4 transformer. Points can be selected giving (in this case) any ratio between 1 : 4 and 4 : 1, but except at the lettered points there is reactance to be tuned out.

It is not necessary to use the whole of a long line as a matching transformer; in fact, owing to the standing waves by which it operates, it is generally undesirable to do so. We can see from Fig. 232 that the maximum ratio of transformation, combined with non-reactive impedance at both ends, is given by a section of line only quarter of a wavelength long. We also see that the mismatch ratio to the line is the same at both ends; in this particular case it is 1 : 4 (125 Ω to 500 Ω at the generator end and 500 Ω to 2,000 Ω at the load end), which, incidentally, is equal to the voltage ratio of the whole transformer. In general terms, if R_1 denotes the input resistance of the line (with load connected), R_1 is to R_0 as R_0 is to R; which means $R_1/R_0 = R_0/R$, or $R_0 = \sqrt{R_1 R}$.

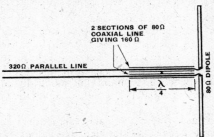

This formula enables us to find the characteristic resistance of the quarter-wave line needed to match two unequal impedances,

Fig. 233—Example of a quarter-wave length of line being used as a matching transformer

R_1 and R. Suppose we wished to connect a centre-fed dipole aerial (say 80 Ω) to a 320-Ω parallel-wire feeder without reflection at the junction. They could be matched by interposing a section of line λ/4 in length, spaced to give a R_0 of $\sqrt{80 \times 320} = 160$ Ω. Parallel wires would have to be excessively close (Fig. 230a), but the problem could be solved by using a length of 80-Ω coaxial cable for each limb and joining the metal sheaths together as in Fig. 233, putting the 80-Ω impedances in series across the ends of the 320-Ω line.

FULLY RESONANT LINES

Going now to extremes of mismatch, it is of interest to inquire what happens when the " load " resistance is either infinite or zero; in other words, when the end of the line is open-circuited or short-circuited. Take the open circuit first. If this were done to our

312

original 500-Ω example, the current at the end would obviously be nil, and the voltage would rise to 1,000—double its amount across the matched load. This condition would be duplicated by the standing waves at points A and B in Fig. 232; while at C, D, and E the voltage would be nil and the current 2 A. The impedance curve would consequently fluctuate between zero and infinity.

With a short-circuited line, there could be no volts across the end, but the current would be 2 A; in fact, exactly as at E with the open line. A shorted line, then, is the same as an open line shifted quarter of a wavelength along. Reflection in both cases is complete, because there is no load resistance to absorb any of the power.

If the generator resistance is very large or very small, *nearly* all the reflected wave will itself be reflected back, and so on, so that if the line is of such a length that the voltage and current maximum points coincide with every reflection, the voltages and currents will build up to high values at those maximum points—dangerously high with a powerful sender. This reminds us of the behaviour of a high-Q resonant circuit (p. 103). The maximum current or voltage points are called *antinodes*, and the points where there is *no* current or voltage are *nodes*.

When the length of a short-circuited or open-circuited line is a whole number of quarter-wavelengths, the input impedance is approximately zero or infinity. An *odd* number of quarter-wave-lengths gives opposites at the ends—infinite resistance if the other end is shorted, and vice versa. An *even* number of quarter-wave-lengths gives the same at each end.

In between, as there is now no load resistance, the impedance is a pure reactance. At each side of a node or antinode there are

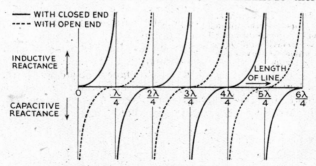

Fig. 234—Showing how the reactances of short-circuited and open-circuited lines vary with their length

opposite reactances—inductive and capacitive. If it is a current node, the reactance at a short distance each side is very large; if a voltage node, very low. Fig. 234 shows how it varies. It is clear from this that a short length of line—less than quarter of a wavelength—can be used to provide any value of inductance or capacitance. For very short wavelengths, this form is generally more convenient than the usual inductor or capacitor, and, under the name of a *stub* is often used for balancing out undesired reactance.

LINES AS TUNED CIRCUITS

A quarter-wave line shorted at one end is, as we have just seen, a high—almost infinite—resistance. But only at the frequency that

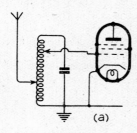

makes it quarter of a wavelength (or an odd multiple of $\lambda/4$). This resistance is closely analogous to the dynamic resistance of a parallel resonant circuit; and in fact a line can be used as a tuned circuit. At wavelengths less than about 2 metres it is generally more efficient and easily constructed than the conventional sort.

The lower the loss resistance of the wire, the higher the dynamic resistance across the open ends; and to match lower impedances all that is necessary is to tap it down, just as if it were any other sort of tuned circuit.

The parallel wire or bar type lends itself to push-pull connection, and the coaxial type to single-ended circuits. Fig. 235*a* is an example of a conventional tuning circuit, such as might be used in a receiver, and *b* is the coaxial equivalent. A coaxial feeder is also used to connect the aerial, and being normally about 80 Ω, is tapped low down, near the earthed end. The impedance at the top end is normally many thousands of ohms, and may be too high for the input of a valve, which is quite low at very high frequencies.

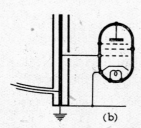

Fig. 235—(*a*) Conventional aerial input circuit using "lumped" components, and (*b*) distributed equivalent using a quarter-wave coaxial line

At still higher frequencies, with waves only a few centimetres long, the inner conductor becomes unnecessary, and power can be transmitted along hollow pipes (called waveguides) and tuned by cavities. But that is a subject in itself.

Appendix 1

ALTERNATIVE TECHNICAL TERMS

The reader of books and articles on radio is liable to be confused by the use of different terms to mean the same thing. The following list has therefore been compiled. In most cases the first alternative to be mentioned is the one preferred in this book. The associated terms are not necessarily *exact* equivalents. Terms distinctively American are printed in italics. The numbers refer to the pages in this book where the terms are defined or explained.

	Page
Accumulator—Secondary battery	280
Aerial—*Antenna*	31–2
Amplification—Gain	125
Anode—*Plate*	118
Anode a.c. resistance—Anode incremental resistance—Valve impedance—*Plate impedance*	119
Anode battery—H.T.—" *B* " *battery*	118
Atmospherics—Strays—X's—*Static*	165
Audio frequency (a.f.)—Low frequency (l.f.)—Speech frequency—Voice frequency	75
Auto-bias—Self bias	291
Automatic gain control (a.g.c.)—Automatic volume control (a.v.c.)	218
Capacitance—Capacity	57
Capacitor—Condenser	60
Characteristic resistance—Characteristic impedance—Surge impedance	306
Coaxial—Concentric	303
Detection — Rectification — *Demodulation* (British usage originally reserved this term for a different phenomenon)	169
Dielectric—Insulating material	59
Dynamic resistance—*Antiresonant impedance*	110
Earth—*Ground*	50
Filament battery—L.T.—" *A* " *battery*	118
Frame aerial—*Loop antenna*	157
Frequency—Periodicity	27
Frequency changer—Mixer—First detector	230
Grid battery—Bias battery—G.B.—" *C* " *battery*	129
Hard—High-vacuum	284
Harmonic—Overtone—Partial	252
Heptode—Pentagrid	236
Image interference—Second-channel interference	239
Inductor—Coil	70
Interference—Jamming	221
Intermediate frequency (i.f.)—Supersonic frequency	230
Lead—Connecting wire	43
Loss—Attenuation	249
Moving coil (of loudspeaker)—Speech coil—*Voice coil*	277
Moving-coil loudspeaker—*Dynamic loudspeaker*	277
Mutual conductance—Slope—*Transconductance*	122
Negative feedback—*Degeneration*	270
Noise—Machine interference—*Man-made static*	301
Parallel—Shunt	43
Peak value—Crest value—Maximum value	78
Permittivity—Dielectric constant—Specific inductive capacity (s.i.c.)	59

315

APPENDIX 1

	Page
Picofarad—Micromicrofarad	60
Q—Q factor—Magnification—Storage factor	104
Quality (of reproduced sound)—Fidelity	249
Radar—Radiolocation	300
Radio—Wireless	9
Radio frequency (r.f.)—High frequency (h.f.)	75
Reaction—Retroaction—Positive feedback—*Regeneration*	135
Reaction coil—*Tickler*	135
Root-mean-square (r.m.s.)—Effective—Virtual	78
Screen—*Shield*	204
Sender—Transmitter	28
Soft—Low-vacuum—Gas-filled	284
Telephones—Phones—Earphones—Headphones—Headset	29
Tetrode—Screen-grid valve (but not all tetrodes are screen-grid valves)	206
Time base—*Sweep*	297
Tuned circuit—LC circuit—Resonant circuit—*Tank circuit*	105
Valve—*Vacuum tube*—Tube	117
Variable-mu valve—*Supercontrol tube*—*Remote cut-off tube*	217
Vision frequency (v.f.)—Video frequency	299

Appendix 2

General Abbreviations

a.c.	alternating current	i.f.	intermediate frequency
a.f.	audio frequency	l.f.	low frequency
a.g.c.	automatic gain control	m.m.f.	magnetomotive force
c.r.	cathode ray	p.d.	potential difference
d.c.	direct current	r.f.	radio frequency
e.h.t.	extra-high tension	r.m.s.	root-mean-square
e.m.f.	electromotive force	v.f.	vision frequency
h.f.	high frequency	v.h.f.	very high frequency
h.t.	high tension	z.f.	zero frequency

Greek Letters

Letter	Name	Usual Meaning
θ	theta	an angle
κ	kappa	permittivity
λ	lambda	wavelength
μ	mu	(1) permeability
		(2) valve amplification factor
		(3) one millionth of (as a prefix to a unit symbol)
π	pi	$\dfrac{\text{circumference}}{\text{diameter}}$ of circle ($= 3\cdot14159\ldots\ldots$)
ρ	rho	resistivity
ϕ	phi (small)	angle of phase difference
Φ	(capital)	magnetic flux
ω	omega (small)	$2\pi f$
Ω	(capital)	ohm

Quantities and Units

Quantity	Symbol	Unit	Abbreviation for unit
Time	t	second	s or sec
Frequency	f	cycle per second	c/s
Time period of one cycle	T		
Wavelength	λ	metre	m
Electromotive force	E	volt	V
Potential difference	V	volt	V
Current	I	ampere	A
Power	P	watt	W
Capacitance	C	farad	F
Self inductance	L	henry	H
Mutual inductance	M	henry	H
Resistance	R	ohm	Ω
Reactance $\begin{cases} \text{Capacitive} \\ \text{Inductive} \end{cases}$	$X \begin{cases} X_c \\ X_L \end{cases}$	ohm	Ω
Impedance	Z	ohm	Ω
Conductance	C	mho	
Quantity of electricity, or charge	Q	coulomb	

317

Quantity	Symbol	Unit	Abbreviation for unit
Magnetic flux	Φ	weber	
Q factor, X/R	Q		
Signal gain or loss		decibel	db

Note.—Small letters (e, v, i, etc.) are used to indicate instantaneous values.

Unit Multiple and Submultiple Prefixes

Symbol	Read as	Means
M	mega-	one million ($\times 10^6$)
k	kilo-	one thousand ($\times 10^3$)
m	milli-	one thousandth ($\times 10^{-3}$)
μ	micro-	one millionth ($\times 10^{-6}$)
p (or $\mu\mu$)	pico- (or micromicro-)	one billionth ($\times 10^{-12}$)

Examples:
$1 \text{ Mc/s} = 1,000,000 \text{ c/s}$
$1 \text{ k}\Omega = 1,000 \text{ }\Omega$
$1 \text{ mA} = 0\cdot001 \text{ A}$
$1 \text{ }\mu\text{H} = 0\cdot000001 \text{ H}$
$1 \text{ pF} = 0\cdot000000000001 \text{ F}$

Valve Abbreviations

μ	amplification factor
r_a	anode a.c. resistance
g_m	mutual conductance
g_c	conversion conductance (of frequency changer)
k	cathode
g	grid
g_1	first grid (nearest cathode)
g_2	second grid; and so on
a	anode

Note.—Symbols are frequently combined, thus—

I_a = Anode current
V_{g2} = Voltage at second grid
R_a = Resistance connected externally to anode
c_{gk} = Internal capacitance from grid to cathode

Capital letters are used for associated items outside the valve; small letters for items inside the valve itself.

Special Abbreviations Used in this Book

f_r	frequency of resonance
f_o	frequency of oscillation
f'	frequency off-tune
A	voltage amplification
B	feedback factor

Appendix 3

CIRCUIT SYMBOLS

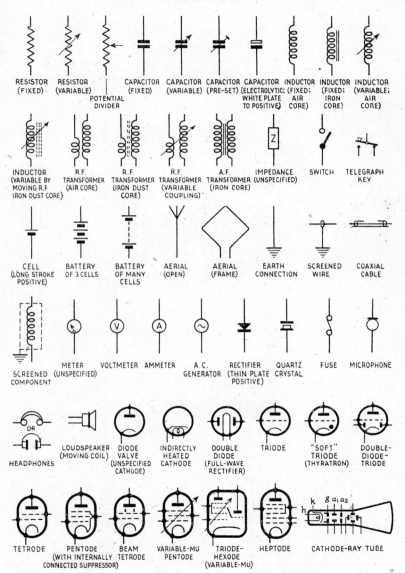

RESISTOR (FIXED) · RESISTOR (VARIABLE) · POTENTIAL DIVIDER · CAPACITOR (FIXED) · CAPACITOR (VARIABLE) · CAPACITOR (PRE-SET) · CAPACITOR (ELECTROLYTIC; WHITE PLATE TO POSITIVE) · INDUCTOR (FIXED; AIR CORE) · INDUCTOR (FIXED; IRON CORE) · INDUCTOR (VARIABLE; AIR CORE)

INDUCTOR (VARIABLE BY MOVING R.F IRON DUST CORE) · R.F. TRANSFORMER (AIR CORE) · R.F. TRANSFORMER (IRON DUST CORE) · R.F. TRANSFORMER (VARIABLE COUPLING) · A.F. TRANSFORMER (IRON CORE) · IMPEDANCE (UNSPECIFIED) · SWITCH · TELEGRAPH KEY

CELL (LONG STROKE POSITIVE) · BATTERY OF 3 CELLS · BATTERY OF MANY CELLS · AERIAL (OPEN) · AERIAL (FRAME) · EARTH CONNECTION · SCREENED WIRE · COAXIAL CABLE

SCREENED COMPONENT · METER (UNSPECIFIED) · VOLTMETER · AMMETER · A.C. GENERATOR · RECTIFIER (THIN PLATE POSITIVE) · QUARTZ CRYSTAL · FUSE · MICROPHONE

HEADPHONES · LOUDSPEAKER (MOVING COIL) · DIODE VALVE (UNSPECIFIED CATHODE) · INDIRECTLY HEATED CATHODE · DOUBLE DIODE (FULL-WAVE RECTIFIER) · TRIODE · "SOFT" TRIODE (THYRATRON) · DOUBLE-DIODE-TRIODE

TETRODE · PENTODE (WITH INTERNALLY CONNECTED SUPPRESSOR) · BEAM TETRODE · VARIABLE-MU PENTODE · TRIODE-HEXODE (VARIABLE-MU) · HEPTODE · CATHODE-RAY TUBE

319

Appendix 4

Decibel Table

The decibel figures are in the centre column: figures to the left represent decibel loss, and those to the right decibel gain. The voltage and current figures are given on the assumption that there is no change in impedance.

Voltage or current ratio	Power ratio	← — db + →	Voltage or current ratio	Power ratio
1·000	1·000	0	1·000	1·000
0·989	0·977	0·1	1·012	1·023
0·977	0·955	0·2	1·023	1·047
0·966	0·933	0·3	1·035	1·072
0·955	0·912	0·4	1·047	1·096
0·944	0·891	0·5	1·059	1·122
0·933	0·871	0·6	1·072	1·148
0·912	0·832	0·8	1·096	1·202
0·891	0·794	1·0	1·122	1·259
0·841	0·708	1·5	1·189	1·413
0·794	0·631	2·0	1·259	1·585
0·750	0·562	2·5	1·334	1·778
0·708	0·501	3·0	1·413	1·995
0·668	0·447	3·5	1·496	2·239
0·631	0·398	4·0	1·585	2·512
0·596	0·355	4·5	1·679	2·818
0·562	0·316	5·0	1·778	3·162
0·501	0·251	6·0	1·995	3·981
0·447	0·200	7·0	2·239	5·012
0·398	0·159	8·0	2·512	6·310
0·355	0·126	9·0	2·818	7·943
0·316	0·100	10	3·162	10·00
0·282	0·0794	11	3·55	12·6
0·251	0·0631	12	3·98	15·9
0·224	0·0501	13	4·47	20·0
0·200	0·0398	14	5·01	25·1
0·178	0·0316	15	5·62	31·6
0·159	0·0251	16	6·31	39·8
0·126	0·0159	18	7·94	63·1
0·100	0·0100	20	10·00	100·0
$3·16 \times 10^{-2}$	10^{-3}	30	$3·16 \times 10$	10^3
10^{-2}	10^{-4}	40	10^2	10^4
$3·16 \times 10^{-3}$	10^{-5}	50	$3·16 \times 10^2$	10^5
10^{-3}	10^{-6}	60	10^3	10^6
$3·16 \times 10^{-4}$	10^{-7}	70	$3·16 \times 10^3$	10^7
10^{-4}	10^{-8}	80	10^4	10^8
$3·16 \times 10^{-5}$	10^{-9}	90	$3·16 \times 10^4$	10^9
10^{-5}	10^{-10}	100	10^5	10^{10}
$3·16 \times 10^{-6}$	10^{-11}	110	$3·16 \times 10^5$	10^{11}
10^{-6}	10^{-12}	120	10^6	10^{12}

Index

This index, besides having an exceptionally large number of references to help the reader find what he wants quickly, is unusual because it includes not only the technical terms actually used in the book but also the equivalents listed in Appendix I. So it is also, in effect, a glossary of terms, American as well as British, and can be consulted to find the meanings of terms encountered elsewhere. If the index reference is to page 315 or 316, the subject should be looked up again under the first alternative given there

" A " BATTERY, 315
Acceptor circuit, 112
Accumulator, 280
Adjacent-channel interference, 221
— - — selectivity, 221, 227, 245
Aerial, 31
— arrays, 167
—, Coupling to, 144, 152, 161, 188
—, Dipole or half-wave, 160, 166
—, Directional, 166
—, Frame, 168
—, Inverted L and T, 162
—, Marconi or quarter-wave, 161
— resistance, 168
—, Short-wave, 163, 166
— tuning, 161
Alternating current (a.c.), 74, 75
— —, Generation of, 131
— — meters, 79
— — in various types of circuit.
    See Circuit, A.c.
Ammeter, 40, 51
Ampere, 40, 53
Amplification, 124, 125
—, Calculation of, 127, 203, 210,
    258, 270
— factor, 13, 21
—, Limit to, 301
Amplifier, 34
—, A.f., 248
—, I.f., 242, 247
—, Instability of, 204, 211, 213, 271
—, Power, 145, 261
—, R.f., 201
—, Resistance-coupled, 124, 201
—, — - —, Distortion in, 257
— screening, 212
—, Transformer-coupled, 259
—, Tuned-anode, 202

Amplifier, V.f., 259
— noise, 302
—, Voltage, 124
Amplitude, 25
— modulation (a.m.), 150
— of oscillation, 137
Anode (of cathode-ray tube), 292
— (of valve), 118
— a.c. resistance, 119
— d.c. resistance, 119, 120
— by-pass, 193
Anode-bend detector, 185
Antenna, 315
Antinode (on transmission line), 313
Antiresonant impedance, 315
Atmospherics, 165
Atoms, 36
Attenuation, 315
Audio frequency (a.f.), 75
Auto-bias, 291
Auto-transformer, 100, 153
Automatic gain control (a.g.c.),
    218, 235
Average value (of a.c.), 78

" B " BATTERY, 315
Baffle, 278
Band (of frequencies), 27
Band-pass filter, 246
Battery, 39, 42, 279
Beat frequency (b.f.), 231
Bias. See Grid bias
Blocking capacitor, 136, 180
Boltzmann's constant, 302
Bottom bend, 139, 172
Bridge rectifier, 287
Brightness control, 296
Broadcasting frequencies, 75, 106,
    150, 165, 221

By-pass capacitor, 193, 290

" C " BATTERY, 315
Carrier wave, 146, 175, 299
Camera, Television, 299
Capacitance, 57, 84
—, Amount of, for resonance, 107, 191
—, Calculation of, 60
—, Interelectrode, 136, 191, 202, 205, 273
—, Measurement of, 192
—, Stray, 107, 114, 116, 202, 257
Capacitances in parallel and series, 87
Capacitive circuits. See Circuit, A.c.
Capacitor, By-pass, 193, 290
—, Electrolytic, 60, 288
—, Frequency-stabilizing, 140
—, Neutralizing, 204
—, Padding, 238
— radiator, 159
—, Reservoir, 173, 283
—, Smoothing, 288
—, Trimming, 238
—, Tuning, 61, 107
—, Variable, 61
Capacitors, 59–61
Capacity, 315
Cathode (of cathode-ray tube), 292
— (of valve), 117, 279
— follower, 272
Cathode-ray tube, 292
Ceramic capacitors, 140
Channels, Frequency, 221
Characteristic curves, 41, 118, 121, 138, 207, 217, 268
— —, Circuit for, 120
— resistance, 306
Charge and discharge of capacitor, 61, 84, 297
—, Electric, 37, 56, 63
Charging of accumulators, 51, 64, 280
Choke modulation, 149
—, R.f., 149
—, Smoothing, 288
Circuit, 39
—, A.c., Capacitance only, 84
—, —, Inductance only, 93
—, —, Inductance and capacitance (in series), 101
—, —, — — — — (in parallel), 108

Circuit, A.c., Resistance only, 76, 83
—, —, — and capacitance (in series), 89
—, —, — — — — (in parallel), 91
—, —, — inductance (in series), 96
—, —, — — — — (in parallel), 97
—, —, —, capacitance and inductance (in series), 102
—, —, —, — — — — (in parallel), 108
— diagrams, 20, 42
—, Equivalent. See Equivalent circuit
— noise, 301
—, Tuned. See Tuned circuit
Class A (oscillator), 141
— B (oscillator), 142
— C (oscillator), 143
Coaxial line, 303
Coil. See Inductor
Colpitts circuit, 136, 146
Concentric, 315
" Concertina " circuit, 276
Condenser, 59
Conductance, 48
—, Mutual, 122, 215, 218, 237
Conductor, 38, 119
Conversion conductance, 236, 247
— gain, 237
Coulomb, 57, 63
Counterpoise, 161
Coupling, Magnetic, 73, 212
— to aerial, 144, 152, 161, 188
Crest value, 315
Critical coupling, 244
— damping, 134
Cross-modulation, 216
Crystal control, 145
— microphone, 152
— receiver, 170
Current, Electric, 38, 117
—, —, Direction of, 38
Cycle (of oscillation), 132
— (of wave), 27, 80

DAMPING (of oscillation), 133, 194
— (of tuned circuit), 175, 178, 190, 193, 202, 209
Decibel, 250, 320
Decoupler, 289
Deflection (of cathode ray), 293, 295
Degeneration, 315

Demodulation, 315
Depolarizer, 280
Depth of modulation, 148, 186
Detection, 169
Detector, 32, 169
—, Anode-bend, 185
—, A.f. output of, 170, 176, 179
— characteristics, 182
— circuit, Typical, 181
—, Crystal, 170, 234
— damping, 175, 178
—, Diode, 176
— distortion, 179, 184, 186
— filter, 180
—, Grid, 178, 188
—, R.f. output of, 170, 176, 179
—, Z.f. output of, 170, 176, 179, 180, 218
Dielectric, 59
— constant, 59
— loss, 114
— strength, 61
Difference of potential, 37, 48, 56
Diode rectifier, 172, 283
— valve, 118
Dipole, 160, 166
Direct current, 74, 77
Directional aerials, 166
Distortion due to detector, 179, 184, 186
— due to wave interference, 164
—, Frequency, 196, 199, 221, 227, 249, 251, 257, 270
—, Harmonic, 252, 270, 276
—, —, Calculation of, 264
— in a.f. amplifier, 248
— in r.f. amplifier, 215
—, Intermodulation, 253
— of modulation, 148, 176, 196, 215
—, Non-linearity, 249, 251, 267
— of oscillation, 139
—, Phase, 256
Drive, Grid, 137, 271
Dry battery, 280
Dynamic characteristic, 265
— loudspeaker, 315
— resistance, 110, 211, 213, 229

Earphones, 315
Earth, 50, 160
— connection, 161
—, Effect of, on radiation, 167
Echo, Wireless, 300

Eddy currents, 113
Effective height, 168
— value, 315
Efficiency of amplifier, 267
— of detector, 183
— of valve oscillator, 141, 152
Electric charge, 37, 56
— current, 38, 117
— field, 37, 58, 64, 155, 293
Electricity, Nature of, 36
Electrification by rubbing, 37
Electrode voltages (of valve), how reckoned, 120
Electrodes, 118
—, Nomenclature of valve, 206
Electrolyte, 279
Electrolytic capacitor, 60, 288
Electromagnet, 65, 277
Electromagnetic microphone, 152
Electromotive force (e.m.f.), 39, 48, 51, 53, 56, 67
Electron drift, Speed of, 38
— optics, 294
Electrons, 36, 56, 117, 206, 283, 292
Electrostatic microphone, 152
— voltmeter, 51, 61, 79
Emission, 117
—, Secondary, 207, 283
Energy, 54
— stored in capacitance, 64, 132
— stored in inductance, 72, 131
Envelope (of waveform), 26, 147, 215
Equations, 13
Equipotential lines, 294
Equivalent circuit, 102, 103, 110, 114, 115, 261, 304
— — (of a valve), 125
Excitation, Grid, 137
Exponential curve, 63, 72

Fading (of signals), 164
Farad, 57
Faraday, Michael, 57
Feed current (to valve), 127
— — — —, Parallel, 136
— — — —, Series, 136
Feedback, Negative, 270
—, Positive, 135
Feeder, 303
Fidelity, 316
Field. See Electric and Magnetic
Filament, 117
Filter, 179, 283, 288

Filter, Band-pass, 246
—, Detector, 180
Fluorescent screen, 292
Flux, Leakage, 69
—, Magnetic, 66, 98
Focusing (in cathode-ray tube), 293
Fourier, 253
Frame aerial, 158
Frequencies, Tables of, 75, 165
Frequency, 26, 27, 31, 75
—, Audio (a.f.), 75
—, Beat (b.f.), 231
— of carrier wave, 33, 221
— characteristic, 249
—, Choice of, for wireless communication, 35, 163
— distortion, 196, 199, 221, 227, 249, 251, 257, 270
—, Intermediate (i.f.), 230, 241
— of light waves, 30
— modulation (f.m.), 150
—, Modulation (m.f.), 175, 221, 299
— of oscillation, 133
—, Radio (r.f.), 35, 75
— of resonance (parallel), 111
— — — (series), 106
— stability, 140, 144
—, Vision (v.f.), 259, 299
Frequency-changer, 230
Full-wave rectifier, 287
Fundamental (of waveform), 252
Fuse, 51

Gain, 125, 229, 249. *See also* Amplification
— control, 181, 214
— —, Automatic, 218, 235
—, Conversion, 237
Ganged tuning, 190, 237
Gas-filled triode, 298
Generator, Electrical, 39, 51, 68, 76, 126, 131
—, R.f., 141
Germanium rectifier, 170
Graphs, 15, 41
Grid bias, 129, 181, 236, 274, 290
— of cathode-ray tube, 292
— current, 129
— detector, 178, 188
— drive or excitation, 137, 271
—, Suppressor, 209
— (of valve), 120, 217
Gridleak, 188, 291

Ground, 315
— wave, 163
Gun, Electron, 292

Half-wave aerial, 160
— - — rectifier, 285
Harmonics, 240, 252, 264
Hartley circuit, 136
Headphones, 188
Heater (of valve), 117, 281
Heating effect of electricity, 50, 54, 64, 72, 79, 142
Height, Effective, of aerial, 168
Henry, 68, 74
Heptode valve, 236
Hertz, 30, 33
High-note loss, 196, 199, 221, 226, 251, 258, 260, 262, 274
Horsepower (h.p.), 54
Hughes, 151
Hum, 271, 283
Hysteresis, 113

Image, 239
Impedance, 91
— matching, 311
— transformation, 100
Incremental resistance, 315
Indices, 15
Inductance, Amount of, for resonance, 107, 191
—, Mutual, 73, 95
—, Self, 68, 94
—, —, Calculation of, 69
Inductances in series and parallel, 95
Induction, Magnetic, 67
Inductive circuit, Growth of current in, 70
— circuits. *See* Circuit, A.c.
Inductor, 70
—, Design of, 228
— radiator, 157
—, Resistance of, 96, 113, 228
Instability of amplifier, 204, 211, 213
Instantaneous value, 78
Insulator, 39, 59
Interelectrode capacitance, 136, 191, 202, 205, 273
Interference, Electrical, 301
—, Harmonic, 240
—, I.f., 239
—, Radiation, 242

Interference, Second-channel, 239
—, Station, 165, 216, 221, 241
—, Wave, 164
Interlacing, 299
Intermediate frequency (i.f.), 230, 241
Intermodulation, 253
Ionization, 284, 298
Iron core, 98, 113, 228, 261

JAMMING, 315
Johnson effect, 301

KEY, Morse, 32, 146
Keying (a sender), 146
Kinetic energy, 54
Kinkless tetrode, 210, 267
Kirchhoff's Laws, 48, 57, 83

LEADS, 43
Linear (meaning of term), 41
Linearity of rectification, 172, 182
Lines as tuned circuits, 314
— of force, Electric, 58, 293
— — —, Magnetic, 65
Load current (in transformer), 99
—, Electrical, 76, 304
— line, 123, 138, 183, 262
— matching, 129, 153, 311
— resistance, Effect of, on amplification, 127
— — for detector, 175, 180
— —, Optimum, 152, 263
Logarithmic scales, 19, 223, 249
Loop antenna, 315
Loss, Dielectric, 114
—, Inductor, 96, 113
—, Line, 305
—, Transformer, 100
Loudspeaker, 261, 272, 277
Low-note loss, 251, 259, 260, 261, 278

MAGNET, 65
Magnetic field, 65, 72, 155, 295
— flux. See Flux
— saturation, 261, 276
Magnetizing current, 98
— effect of electricity, 29, 51, 65
Magnification, Circuit, 104
Man-made static, 315
Marconi aerial, 161
—, Transatlantic signals by, 32
Master-oscillator system, 145

Matching load or impedance, 129, 153, 189, 311
Maximum-power Law, 128, 152, 262, 308
Maxwell, Clerk, 30
Mean value (of a.c.), 78
Measuring instruments, Electrical, 51, 79
Metal rectifier, 284
Mho, 48, 122
Microfarad, 60
Microhenry, 70
Microphone, 29, 150
—, Types of, 152
Miller effect, 191, 202, 273
Milliammeter, 52
Mixer, 233
Modulation, 146
—, Amplitude (a.m.), 150
—, Depth of, 148, 186
—, Frequency (f.m.), 150
— frequency (m.f.), 175, 221, 299
—, Methods of, 149
Modulators, 33, 149, 233
Morse code, 33
Moving-coil loudspeaker, 277
— - — meter, 51, 67, 79
— - — microphone, 152
Moving-iron meter, 51, 79
Multiplier (for voltmeter), 52
Mutual conductance, 122, 215, 218, 237
— inductance, 73, 95
— reactance, 243

NEGATIVE feedback, 270
Neutralizing capacitor, 204
Node (on transmission line), 313
Noise, 214, 301
Non-linearity (of resistance), 171, 182
— - — distortion, 249, 251, 267
Nucleus, Atomic, 36

OHM, 40
Ohmmeter, 53
Ohm's Law, 40, 77, 86, 94, 119, 171, 308
— —; application to resistance networks, 45
Optimum load resistance, 152, 263
Oscillation, 133
— in amplifier, 204, 211
—, Amplitude of, 137

Oscillation, Distortion of, 139
—, Frequency of, 133
Oscillator, 134, 141
—, Circuit for superhet, 238
—, Class A, 141
—, — B, 142
—, — C. 143
—, Colpitts, 136, 146
— harmonics, 240
—, Hartley, 136
—, Reaction-coil, 135, 212
—, T.A.T.G., 137, 192, 204
Oscillatory circuit, 131, 144
Oscilloscope, 297
Output stage, 261
— transformer, 261
Overtone, 315

PADDING capacitor, 238
Parallel connection, 43
— feed, 136, 261, 290
Parallel-wire line, 303
Parameters, 123, 211
Partial, 315
Peak value, 78
Pentagrid, 315
Pentode valve, 209, 266
Period (of cycle), 27
Periodicity, 315
Permeability, 13, 66, 69
Permittivity, 59
Phase, 80, 91
— distortion, 256
— splitter, 276
Picofarad, 60
Picture elements, 298
— frequency, 299
Piezo-electric microphone, 152
Pitch (of sound), 26, 28, 249
Plate, 315
Polar diagrams, 166
Polarization of waves, 156
Positive electricity, 37, 284
— feedback, 135
Potential difference (p.d.), 37, 48, 56
— —, Measurement of, 51
— divider, 47
— energy, 54
— transfer by capacitor, 63
Potentiometer, 47
Power amplifier, 145, 261
— in capacitive circuit, 88
—, Electrical, 53, 64, 72, 77
— in grid circuit, 129, 137, 143

Power, Law of maximum, 128, 152, 262, 308
— output of valve, Calculation of, 142, 263
— supplies, 279
Preselector, 239, 241
Primary winding, 73, 98, 188
Propagation of wireless waves, 163
Pulse, 300
Push-pull connection of valves, 275
Pythagoras, Theorem of, 91

Q (OF CIRCUIT), 104, 195, 220
— — —, Calculation of, 112, 115
Quality of reproduction, 221, 227
Quantity of electricity, 57, 84
Quarter-wave aerial, 161
— - — transformer, 312

RADAR, 300
Radian, 82
Radiation resistance, 167
— of waves, 31, 155, 242
Radio frequency (r.f.), 35, 75
Radiolocation, 316
Random movements of electrons, 38, 135, 301
Reactance, Capacitive, 87, 103, 258
—, Inductive, 95, 103
— of lines, 313
—, Mutual, 243
Reaction, 135, 194
Receiver, 29
—, Single-valve, 188
—, Superheterodyne, 230
Reciprocal, 15
Rectification, 170
— efficiency, 172
— linearity, 172
Rectifier, 79, 234, 283
— circuits, 285
—, Copper-oxide, 170, 284
—, Diode, 118, 172, 283
—, Germanium, 170
—, Half-wave, 285
—, Selenium, 170, 285
—, Vibrator, 170
Reflection, Line, 309
Reflector (aerial), 166
Regeneration, 316
Rejector circuit, 112, 240, 260
Remote cut-off tube, 316
Reservoir capacitor, 173, 283
Resistance, 14, 40, 54

Resistance of aerial, 168
—, Calculation of, 47, 112, 115
— coupling, 124, 201
—, Dynamic, 110, 211, 213, 229
— of inductor, 96, 113
—, Non-linear, 171
— in parallel tuned circuit, 108
—, R.f., 114, 189
—, Radiation, 167
— of valve, 119, 208, 272, 273
Resistances in series and parallel, 44
Resistivity, 47
Resistor, 43
Resonance of aerial, 168
— curve, Generalized, 223
— of lines, 312
—, Mechanical, 151, 272, 278
— (series), 105, 112
— (parallel), 111, 112
Resultant, 82
Retroaction, 135
Rheostat, 117
Root-mean-square (r.m.s.) value, 78

SATURATION, Magnetic, 261, 276
— (of valve), 119
Sawtooth generator, 297
Scanning, 299
Screened valve, 205
Screening of amplifier, 212
—, Theory of, 204
Swing (of voltage), 123, 141, 252
Second-channel interference, 239
Secondary battery, 315
— emission, 207, 283
— winding, 73, 98, 188
Selectivity, 105, 220
—, Adjacent-channel, 221, 227, 245
— and cross modulation, 216
— — gain, 225
— — number of tuned circuits, 225
— — reaction, 195
—, Effect of aerial coupling on, 189
— factor, 222
— in i.f. amplifier, 242
Self bias, 315
— inductance. See Inductance
Sender, 28, 141
Sensitivity, 220, 267
Series connection, 43
— feed, 136
Set noise, 302
— —, Effect on reproduction of, 196, 199, 221, 225

Shield, 316
Shift controls, 296
Short circuit, 49
Shot effect, 302
Shunt connection, 43. See also Parallel
— (for current meter), 52
Sidebands, Theory of, 197, 221
Signal current (in valve), 127
Sine wave, 76, 81
Sinusoidal, 76
Skin effect, 114
Skip distance, 163
Sky wave, 163
Slope (of valve characteristic), 122, 207, 215
Smoothing circuit, 283, 288
Soft valve, 284, 297
Sound waves, 23
— —, Characteristics of, 25
— —, Speed of, 24, 28
Space charge, 118, 283
Specific inductive capacity, 315
Speech coil, 315
— frequency, 315
Speed of light. See Velocity
Squegging, 291
Stability of amplifier, 211, 271
— — frequency, 140, 144
Stage gain, 258, 270. See also Amplification
Stagger tuning, 246
Standing waves, 309
Static, 315
Storage factor, 316
Striking voltage, 284
Stub, Matching, 314
Supercontrol tube, 316
Superheterodyne receiver, 230
Supersonic frequency, 315
Suppressor grid, 209
Surge impedance, 306
Sweep, 316
Switch, 43
Symbols, 11, 206, 317
Synchronizing signals, 299

TANK circuit, 144
Telegraph, 29
Telephone, 30
Television, 9, 165, 201, 221, 246, 257, 259, 273, 293, 298, 303
—, Valves for, 211
Temperature compensation, 140

Tetrode, Kinkless, 210
— valve, 206
Thermal agitation, 301
Thermionic valve. *See* Valve
Thermocouple (or thermojunction)
   meter, 79
Thyratron, 298
Tickler, 316
Time base, 297
— constant, 63, 72
— — of detector, 174
Tone control, 251
Tracking (of superhet tuning), 238
Transconductance, 315
Transformer, 73, 98
—, Microphone, 151
—, Output, 261
—, Power, 288
—, Quarter-wave, 312
—, R.f., 189
Transformer-coupled amplifier, 259
Transit-time effect, 193
Transmitter. *See* Sender
Transmission line, 303
Trimming capacitor, 238
Triode valve, 120
Triode-heptode valve, 236
Triode-hexode valve, 235
Tube, 316
Tuned circuit, Effect of aerial
   coupling on, 189
— —, Effect of reaction on, 195
— — (parallel), 111
— — (series), 103
— circuits, Selectivity of, 220, 230,
   242
Tuned-anode coupling, 202
— — tuned-grid oscillator, 137,
   192, 204
Tuning, 29, 33, 107. *See also*
   Resonance
— circuits, Coupled, 242
— ratio (or tuning range), 107, 191
Turns ratio, Choice of, 100, 189

Units, Electrical, 40, 53, 317
—, Prefixes to, 42, 318

Vacuum tube, 316
Valve, 117
—, Diode, 118
— equivalent generator, 126, 152
—, Frequency-changer, 235
—, Heptode, 236

Valve, Hexode, 235
— oscillator, 135
—, Pentode, 209, 266
—, Screened, 205
—, Sending, 141
—, Soft, 284, 297
—, Tetrode, 206
—, Triode, 120
—, Triode-heptode, 236
—, Triode-hexode, 235
—, Variable-mu, 216, 236
Variable-mu valve, 216, 236
Vector diagram, 81
Velocity of light and wireless waves,
   31, 155, 300
— — sound, 24, 28
Very-high-frequency effects, 129,
   136, 193, 211, 236
Vibrator rectifier, 170
Video frequency, 316
Vision frequency (v.f.), 259, 299
Voice coil, 315
— frequency, 315
Volt, 40
Voltage doubler, 287
— quadrupler, 288
Voltmeter, Electrostatic, 51, 61,
   79, 296
—, Moving-coil, 52
Volume control, 181, 214

Watt, 53
Wattmeter, 79
Waveform, 26, 252
— analysis, 76, 253, 301
Waveguides, 314
Wavelength, 27, 31, 222
— of resonance, 107
Waves, Characteristics of, 25
—, Electromagnetic (or wireless),
   30, 155
—, Propagation along line, 307
—, — of wireless, 163
—, Reflection of wireless, 163, 300
—, Sine, 76
—. Standing, 309
Whistles (in superhet), 239
Wire communication, 29
Wireless telegraph, 32, 146
— telephone, 33, 146
Work, 53

X's, 315

FOUNDATIONS OF WIRELESS

"WIRELESS WORLD" BOOKS